CHEMTRAILS CONFIRMED

WILLIAM THOMAS

ISBN 1-893157-10-5

Published by
BRIDGER HOUSE PUBLISHERS, INC
P.O. Box 2208, Carson City, NV 89702, 1-800-729-4131

Cover design and layout by The Right Type
Printed in the United States of America
10 9 8 7 6 5 4 3 2 1

CONTENTS

William Thomas

For the chemtrails contributors to this story...

TOP CHEMTRAILS WEBSITES

www.willthomas.net/
www.holmestead.ca/
www.rense.com/politics6/chemdatapage.html
www.geocities.com/canadianchemtrails/
www.chemtrailcentral.com/
www.groups.yahoo.com/group/chemtrailtrackingusa/

HIGHLIGHTS:

Latest scientific findings on contrail formation.

Latest findings on natural and artificial cloud cover impacts:
climate and weather.

What Air Traffic Controllers are seeing at America's biggest airports.

Why NASA says contrails have significantly decreased in recent years.

Close up photos of aircraft spray nozzles,

USAF C-130 spray plane hit Colombia and USA communities.

Troubled tankers: more on JP-8 illness, tanker shortage, aircrew exodus.

Night spraying explained.

Spraying over cities and croplands instead of oceans explained.

Spraying chemclouds above natural clouds explained.

Lab tests from Espanola, Edmonton, Michigan.

Airline and tanker pilots speak out.

"Chembusters" – do they work?

William Thomas

Chapter 1

CONTRAILS, CHEMTRAILS

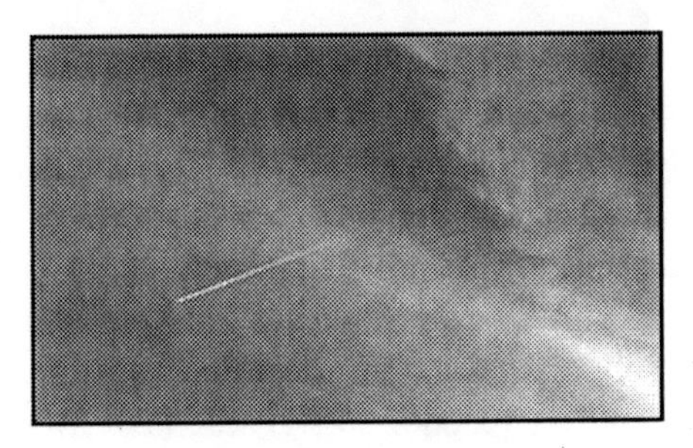

It was nearly noon when S.T. Brendt awoke and entered the kitchen of her country home in Parsonsfield, Maine. As she poured her first cup of coffee, the late night reporter for WMWV radio could not guess that her life was minutes away from drastic change.

Her partner Lou Aubuchont was already up, puzzling over what he had seen in the sky a half hour before. The fat puffy plumes arching up over the horizon were unlike any contrail he had ever seen, even during his hitch in the Navy.

Like breath exhaled on a winter day, the contrails he was used to seeing flare briefly in the stratosphere as hot moist engine exhaust flash-freezes into a stream of ice-crystals. These pencil-thin condensation trails are pretty to watch but short-lived, subliming into invisibility as exhaust gases cool quickly to the surrounding air temperature.

But in late 1997 Aubuchont started observing thicker 'trails extending from horizon to horizon. Hanging in the sky long after their creators had flown from view, these expanding white ribbons would be invariably interwoven by more thick lines left by unmarked jets, air force white or silver in color.

On this March 12 morning 2001, Lou did not mention his sighting as S.T. indulged in caffeine. Sipping gratefully, she glanced out the window. It looked like another gorgeous, cloudless day.

But not quite. Brendt balked at several chalk marks scrawled across the crystalline blue sky. "Contrails or chemtrails?" she jokingly remarked.

Lou got up and looked. *What kind of clouds run exactly side-by-side in a straight line?* he wondered. *It's just too perfect to happen naturally.* When he said he wasn't sure, S.T. stopped smiling and went outside.

Looking up towards the southeast over West Pond, she spotted the first jet. A second jet was laying billowing white banners to the north. Both aircraft appeared to be over 30,000 ft. Turning her gaze due west, Brendt saw two more lines extending over the horizon. She called Lou. Within 45 minutes the couple counted 30 jets.

This isn't right, S.T. thought. *We just don't have that kind of air traffic here.* While Lou kept counting, she went inside and started calling airports. One official she reached was guarded but friendly. He had relatives in West Pond.

The Air Traffic Control manager told Brendt her sighting was "unusual". His radars showed nine commercial jets during the same 45-minute span. From her location, he said, she should have been able to see one plane.

And the other 29? The FAA official confided off the record that he had been ordered "by higher civil authority" to re-route inbound European airliners away from a "military exercise" in the area. "Of course they wouldn't give me any of the particulars and I don't ask," he explained. "I just do my job."

Excited and puzzled by this information, S.T. and Lou got into their car and headed down Route 160. Looking in any direction they could see five or six jets flying over 30,000 ft. Never in the dozen years they'd lived in rural Maine, had they seen so much aerial activity. As a former U.S. Navy intelligence courier, Aubuchont was used to large-scale military exercises. But he told S.T. he had never seen anything this big.

"It looked like an invasion," he later recounted. Another driver almost went off the road as he leaned over his dashboard trying to look up. As they passed, he acknowledged them with a nod.

As far as they could see stretched line after line. Two giant grids were especially blatant. Instead of dissipating like normal contrails, these sky trails grew wider and wider and began to merge. Looking towards the sun, Aubuchont saw what looked like "an oil and water mixture" reflecting a prismatic band of colors.

He couldn't call it a rainbow. Rainbows aren't sinister.

As Lou and S.T. completed their errands, the jets kept them company, leaving lines and even circles that resembled smoke rings. Even living near Kennedy, LaGuardia and Newark jetports, Aubuchont had never seen so many big jets performing identical maneuvers in the same sky. When they returned to Parsonsfield around four, the lines were starting to merge into a dingy haze.

Richard Dean called back. After receiving S.T.'s message, the assistant WMWV news director had gone outside with other news staff and counted 370 lines in skies usually devoid of aerial activity.

Brendt put in another call to the FAA official. He had never heard of chemtrails. But similar military activities were ongoing in other regions. His radars showed the aircraft – which he identified as U.S. Air Force tankers – flying north into Canada.

BLUE SKY DAYS

Blue skies seem to bring them out. Silent, silver or white with red bands matching official USAF markings, formations of three-and four-engine U.S. Air Force KC-10 and KC-135 tanker planes trail broad white ribbons that instead of quickly dissipating like normal contrails, linger for hours in overlapping lines that gradually coalesce, until the sun is obscured behind milky haze.

Once you have watched two, six, eight or more unmarked tanker planes weaving broad white plumes into cross-hatched tic-tac-toe grids, giants X's or furrows of expanding parallel lines – you will never look at the sky the same way again.

Someone is stealing our skies.

And sickening us, as well. As the temperature drops and the wind begins to rise, you might smell petrochemicals. Or taste something metallic on your tongue.

Depending on your age, general health and immunity, the congestion and dry hacking cough, fierce headache and gushing nosebleeds, suffocating asthma attacks, stiff neck and aching joints, twitching eyelids, dizziness and inability to concentrate or remember simple errands could begin within 24 to 48 hours. It is not the flu. There is no fever. But the ensuing onslaught of "flu-like" symptoms is more drastic than any illness you have ever endured. Pneumonia, heart problems, even death may follow.

And still they come.

In the words of eyewitnesses across 48 states:

— "I've lived here for 26 years never seeing this number of contrails at once."

— "They look like they're playing tic-tac-toe up there. You know darn well it's not passenger planes."

— "I watched a clear blue sky become criss-crossed with the white trails from many jets. The sky then became overcast, in spite of the forecast calling for sunny weather. I felt stunned as I witnessed this event."

— "I remember sitting on my porch and telling my husband that the trails from jets were different now days, they stayed longer in the sky and looked different. He laughed at me."

— "One morning I saw so many I almost had a car accident. They were X'ing, probably 50, 100 of them, as far as I could see. Lots of X's and parallel lines. Definitely not normal air traffic."

— "These contrails do indeed behave differently from the usual contrails made by jets. They don't dissipate right away. They like linger, hang there. But they were so heavily concentrated that I just about fell over."

— "I am under the understanding that we have regular flight patterns. This however, broke all the rules, as these patterns criss-crossed one another over a dozen times."

— "About the contrails in Montana. The first time I noticed the different types of contrails was about five years ago. I was in the Air Force. So I know the difference."

— "I was southbound on Interstate 65 from Indianapolis toward Camp Atterbury. I had just heard of chemtrails on Coast to Coast earlier in the week and thought it was a bit of a kooky theory. I noticed the sky in front of me had 27 separate contrails. I then noticed a large jet at altitude, also southbound parallel to the highway, was not leaving any contrails. I wondered, *Why?* This jet began to turn. As it settled up on 090 (due east), it immediately began to leave a classic chemtrail. That was when I knew it is being done on purpose."

— "We are a society that doesn't look up. But these chemtrails were so out of place one couldn't help but notice them. We never see planes in that area of the sky at that time of day, for one thing. And for another, their trajectories were all weird. I had already mentioned chemtrails to one of my co-workers months ago, and when she came in on Tuesday morning I asked, "Did you see them?" She said she had noticed, and said they were 'all over the place.'"

— "Everywhere from horizon to horizon, as far as I could see above the trees and buildings, perfectly parallel streaks or stripes of clouds."

— "The band in question was about 30 to 40 miles wide. I started by seeing them about three miles west of Crawford notch, and as we got onto I 93 I counted 18 aircraft. It is incredibly strange to see so many jet aircraft in this type of formation. It gives me the shivers because it looks like a high density bombing run, and you know what? Maybe that's just what it is. I checked myself this morning to see if I had morphed into a different sex or something, but things seemed OK so far."

Crawford, Texas Jan. 4, 2002

— "The day starts out clear, and then they come, from the east, in a fan-shaped spread, laying down the trails. By noon, or early afternoon, the sky is solidly overcast. Sometimes they just go back and forth down south, over Yuma. Sometimes it's to the north, over Las Vegas. Our two senators, Kyl and McCain, think I'm nuts for pointing this out to them, as does our representative, Bob Stump. I'm not. I know too many people who've been sickened by the chemtrails. I'm a retired airline pilot. I know a chemtrail from a contrail!"

— "I am a private pilot and have a penchant for watching everything that moves in the skies above me. On Thursday, beginning around mid-morning, high altitude jets began 'painting' the sky with *non-dissipating contrails.* I am familiar with the physics involved in the production of 'normal' contrails. The fact that these contrails do not dissipate leads me to suspect that something of a chemical nature was being emitted."

— "I am a veteran of eight years active duty in the Navy and still serve in the reserves. I was a qualified lookout while stationed aboard ship and was trained to observe the sea and sky and identify targets. I am also an aviation buff and also interested in weather. I have therefore spent a lot of time flying and also observing the sky from the ground. I jog every morning at a park near my apartment in the DFW metroplex.

— "I am a police officer and have been one for 15 years. I was driving to a doctor's appointment in Beachwood, Ohio, a suburb of Cleveland. My attention was drawn to an unusually thick contrail traveling from the southeast to the northwest. I saw a large four-engine jet, silver in color. There was not a cloud in the sky and no other contrails. Unusual for Cleveland weather in February – basically a beautiful day. The plane was unusual because it was so big and lower than most jets that leave a contrail. Also it seemed to take a very long time to travel its path. I got a good look at it at a stoplight and from what I could make out it was silver and was reflecting the sunlight. It had four engines, two on each side and was making two large contrails that did not dissipate."

"I am ex-Air Force myself and not even around major airbases had I witnessed a sky full of contrails like this."

— "On the morning of 10 March, 1999, as I looked to the sky I saw something I have never seen before. The sky was covered as far I could see with a criss-cross pattern of evenly spaced thick contrails. I counted at most three aircraft still spraying trails. This day had begun sunny with a brilliant blue sky just as forecast by weather channel and local forecasters, but they did not seem bothered by this unexpected 'haze.'"

Daylesford, Australia Aug. 3, 2000

— "Our skies [in Australia] are being sprayed almost daily since April. Planes with red tanks underneath, spraying from 7 am till 8 pm at night. People getting sick everywhere, and no one gets answers. Why?"

— "I am under the understanding that we have regular flight patterns. This however, broke all the rules, as these patterns criss-crossed one another over a dozen times."

— "Real jet trails are not as low as these."

— "I work out on the runway at Sea-Tac Airport and I have been observing these all summer. Quite amazing! I have asked pilots about them just to get a reaction. What always tickles me how fast intelligent people 'dummy-up' when I look up in fake amazement and say 'wow, what are those'?"

> *"I have been in aviation for thirty years and was in the U.S. Air Force for sixteen. Never have I observed a pattern of contrails like that one."*

CONTRAILS OR CHEMTRAILS?

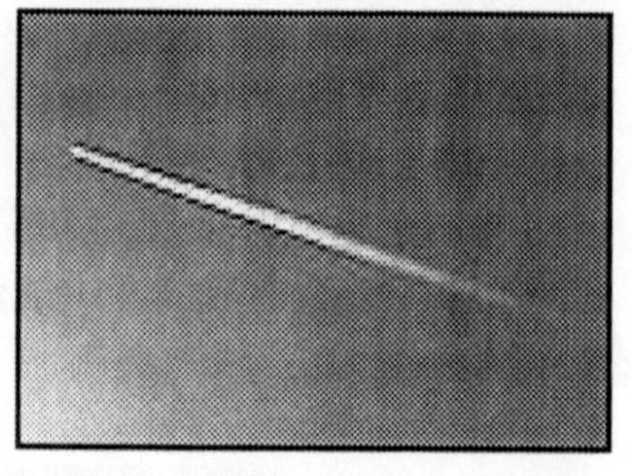

Contrails are formed when hot, moist engine exhausts momentarily condense stratospheric ice crystals into wispy trails, like breath exhaled on a cold day.

But contrails are anything but harmless.

Cloud cover has increased by 5% nationwide – and as much as 20% in some U.S. air corridors – since the jet age took off just three decades ago. If contrails are the culprit, "normal" jet contrails comprised mostly of "harmless" water vapor could in fact have already added during those 30 years of jet plane metastasis *one-third to two-thirds as more* warming than we would have gotten from pigging out on gas, coal and oil during the past century.

During the 1970s, governments started throwing airplane loads of money, scientists and technology at atmospheric and cloud physics.

An early Airbus study on the atmospheric impacts of multi-engine jetliners flying nearly nose-to-tail in the most heavily traveled oceanic and continental air corridors jolted government and industry. As our increasingly carbon-driven Chaos Climate spasms in ever more erratic Extreme Weather Events, the added effects of contrails on local weather and regional climate are of increasing concern to governments and the industries they supposedly regulate.

Atmospheric studies such as SUCCESS, TARFOX and more recent offshoots have employed a variety of aircraft, from airliner-size jets to the executive Cessna Citations sighted dispensing chemtrails over Arizona and Ohio, to spray small amounts of atmospheric "tracers" that can be tracked by satellite, LIDAR (laser radar) and other sophisticated sensors to measure atmospheric responses to pollutants produced by us.

The SONEX project looked at the interactions of ozone and nitrogen oxide. NASA also cooperated with the EU's POLINAT project, which flew research aircraft in the North Atlantic Flight Corridor to correlate actual measurements of aircraft pollution with computer models.

Scientists now say that artificial cloud cover formed around jet pollution affects the heat interchanges that drive weather and climate. Too high to trap heat like lower level clouds, "normal contrails" left by jetliners and military aircraft high in the stratosphere are increasing Earth's albedo – reflecting more sunlight back into space and possibly

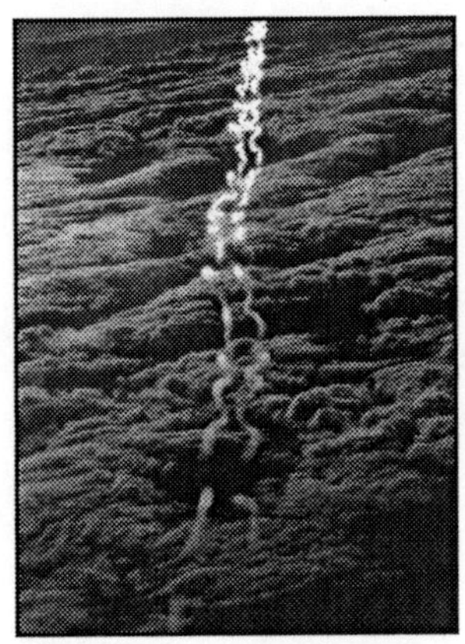

NASA vortex experiment

cooling climate change before we join the many species around us going extinct.

Computer models show that using aircraft to lay down microscopic sunlight-scattering particles of very high reflectivity can make natural clouds even more sunlight-reflective. In clear blue skies, these same chemicals added to the fuel and sprayed through the exhaust of many jet engines can create "made-to-order" overcasts over entire regions for days and weeks at a time.

Observations with a sunlight-measuring photometer by Clifford Carnicom in October 2003 show sunlight transmission dropping from 97% on a clear New Mexico day to about 80% under a thin chemtrail layer. The purpose of my five year investigation was to discover and document who was giving those orders. And why.

THE CONTRAIL CONNECTION

Let's start with contrails. In 1996, NASA began launching specially instrumented jets into the wild blue yonder with some SUCCESS. The Subsonic Aircraft Contrail and Cloud Effects Study used satellite tracking developed by NASA's Patrick Minnis to study clouds, while vectoring chase planes to sniff a DC-8's four-engine exhaust. Richard Miake-Lye's chemistry team at Aerodyne Research in Cambridge, Mass. expected soot from all that combusted carbon to dominate. Instead, they found proliferating particles of sulfuric acid. *[Christian Science Monitor July 29/97]*

Meanwhile, the well-funded drive to understand and control contrails continues, driven by the Pentagon's need to stop drawing arrows to very expensive "stealth" aircraft - and the imperative of airlines to avoid government-imposed fines or crippling regulations as climate change really starts to really gallop beneath the Sixth Great Extinction Event.

TOO HOT FOR CONTRAILS?

Contrails cannot form behind aircraft unless the atmosphere is very cold. As NASA explains, "*Contrails only form at very high altitudes (usually above 8 km) where the air is extremely cold (less than -40°C / -70°F).*

NASA, NOAA and other scientific cloud-gazers also agree that a relative humidity of 70% or higher is necessary for cloud and contrail formation. *If the air is very dry, contrails do not form behind airplanes," states the National Oceanic and Atmospheric Administration.*

Taking NASA's expertise as contrail catechism, chemtrail investigator Clifford Carnicom correlating atmospheric readings by NASA's Climate Diagnostics Center of with 21 days of heavy "chemtrail" gridding over Santa Fe from Jan. 1999 to Aug. 1999. At altitudes where persistent white plumes criss-crossed the usually cloudless New Mexico sky.

Carnicom found *30% humidity or less*

Santa Fe Jan. 15, 2002

In a region known for big blue skies 360 days of the year, most desert days began with typically clear skies. But as "USAF Weather Force" tanker planes were photographed laying chemical tails in extensive grid patterns and characteristic satellite-marking X's, Carnicom and other New Mexico skywatchers saw the planes create artificial cirrus cloud layers - turning clear skies into a milky haze. "One would have expected these days to be generally clear at that altitude," Carnicom commented. "But that was not the case."

CLOUD RECIPE

Vincent Schaefer, a Naval postgraduate who invented iodine cloud-seeding techniques in 1946, and Joseph Moran's contemporary textbook, *Meteorology* agree that clouds form when water vapor accretes around particles of grit acting as attracting nuclei. Recent NOAA and NASA atmospheric studies such as TARFOX, ACE-Asia, ACE-I and II, INDOEX and Project SUCCESS have confirmed that the only way to form artificial clouds under conditions of low humidity and less than ideal temperatures is *by dispensing additional particles from aircraft.*

In other words, when atmospheric conditions prevent the moisture-attracting nuclei from aircraft engine exhausts from forming contrails, chemicals added to the fuel can leave enough extra particles exhausted behind three- and four-engine planes to *create clouds when relative humidity is less than 70%.*

In fact, among the principle variables of cirrus cloud development modeled by Paul Demott at Colorado State University's Department of Atmospheric Science are temperature, relative humidity, and aerosol size. The last variable is of primary importance, and may be supplied inadvertently or deliberately by aircraft. The smaller the size of each additional nuclei, the greater the rate of cirrus cloud formation.

When confronted with their own weather data showing the impossibility of normal contrail formation during heavy "spray days", officials grow silent.

MAKING CLOUDS AND RAIN

Al Cooper studies the tiny particles that form the nuclei of condensing clouds and raindrops at the National Center for Atmospheric Research (NCAR) in Boulder. Burning tropical forests and grasslands may be the largest source of these cloud-forming particles, Cooper says. Other cloud condensation nuclei are dust, sea salt, the nitrogen and sulphur compounds released by aircraft engines – as well as very fine particulates released by specially equipped aircraft. Spread a few extra nuclei like silver iodide into highly humid air and rainfall results.

Here's the catch: In air that is not already swollen with moisture – especially in near-drought conditions – introducing too many particulates into the atmosphere to compete for a small amount of moisture can act like a sponge, *resulting in decreased rainfall.*

"ROUTINE OPERATIONS"

North American officials insist that nothing unusual is going on – that precisely spaced grid patterns and perfectly intersected X's are "normal flight operations". But when confronted with their own data showing the impossibility of normal contrail formation during heavy "spray days" they grow silent.

Meanwhile, a growing number of pilots, police officers, former military personnel, air traffic controllers and thousands of other observers report that they have never seen so many jet trails at once - *often at altitudes below which commercial jetliners are simultaneously seen leaving no contrails at all.*

As this eyewitness explains:

> Sunday between the hours of 12:30 and 1:30 in Mesa, AZ while standing outside Borders bookstore at Alma School Road and Southern conversing in the parking lot, I looked up and saw broad low hanging contrails running at angles mainly east-west across the sky and spreading apart north and south. High above were normal contrails coming from commercial flights, which dissipated within minutes behind the aircraft. I counted five or six low broad contrails slowly spreading out but not dissipating like the ones high above. Being involved with science it was very strange that these were above and not below the contrail.

Aviation authorities have also failed to explain the sudden appearance of formations of grid-weaving jets over communities unused to seeing any air traffic at all. Why are so many people who have lived near airbases and airports for most of their lives – and who would not normally give contrails a second glance – stopping their cars or hauling family members and neighbors outside their homes to point cameras and camcorders at unprecedented concentrations of jet spoor they instinctively recognize are not normal contrails?

Nanaimo, Canada Jan. 22/03

NOW YOU SEE 'EM, THEN YOU DON'T, THEN THEY'RE BACK

Since when does "scheduled air traffic" suddenly appear, saturating rural skies for weeks, only to abruptly cease – before starting up again weeks later?

> *How can lingering "contrails" form below aircraft leaving no contrails at all?*

Most sightings take place far from navigation beacons and established air routes. Nor do airliners obsessed with point A to B efficiency spend hours criss-crossing the same patch of sky in close formation. To do so would violate many air safety regulations mandating minimum commercial aircraft separation.

TAKING A FLIER

Scientists warn that at the rate our planet's life-support systems are being poisoned and dismantled, we're looking at major life-support systems failures within 50 years – just when the oil runs out. We can buy time to deal with this peril by practicing conservation and efficiency energy use in our personal and business lives.

Yet, millions of people still drive to the airport to jump on jets without the faintest concern for the growing hazards of high-altitude flight, or the havoc they are wreaking aloft.

Somewhere on Earth, every minute of every day and night, dozens of commercial airlines commence their take-off runs. With the runway speeding past and four huge jet engines howling at take-off thrust, a 747 gulps a gallon of fuel every second, generating enough power to light the city of Belize. Just five minutes into an eight-hour flight, the jumbo jetliner will have burned the day's oxygen production of a 44,000-acre rainforest.

Creatures of another ocean, jets prefer to cruise in the cold, airless reaches of the stratosphere about 11 kilometers above the Earth. Pollutants linger here. By the time a New York-departed 747 descends into Ireland, some 239,000 pounds of "jet A" will have been spewed out its exhaust pipes as soot, Greenhouse gases and ozone-destroying chemicals.

Jets fly in the ozone layer. By converting their annual fuel loads into 774 million tons of atmosphere-altering gases – and injecting them directly into the upper atmosphere – these commonplace conveyances are having a drastic impact on Earth's climate and ultraviolet radiation levels. Jet emissions linger long in the clear, cold, calm of the stratosphere, modifying Earth's atmosphere about 100-times longer than when released near the ground.

The assault of air traffic on Earth's atmosphere is relentless. More than five million civil and military flights *each year* continue to significantly affect an atmosphere already severely impacted by dangerously outmoded internal combustion engines and "smokestack" industries. According to Dr. Robert Egli, jet-induced cloud cover, along with their high-altitude carbon dioxide and nitrogen oxide emissions, account more than 10% of global warming.

USAF radar-surveillance jet attacking ozone layer

NOX-IOUS JETS

Jets emit four principle pollutants: smoke, carbon dioxide (CO2), unburned hydrocarbons, and a combination of carbon monoxide and nitrogen oxides called nitrous oxide or NOx. In their "Environmental Protection" report, Airbus warns that nitrogen oxides are the most worrisome of jet engine emissions.

They are also jets' biggest pollutant. Dr. Colin Johnson of the UK Atomic Energy Authority has found that the NOx exhaled by high-flying jets cause 30-times more atmospheric warming than nitrogen oxides emitted on the ground. Even though aircraft account for only three-percent of all human-produced NOx emissions, Dr. Johnson claims they contribute as much to global warming as all car emissions worldwide.

NOx released by aircraft in the lower atmosphere forms a photochemical smog, which traps heat and attacks human respiratory systems.

As jets climb higher into the stratosphere, their nitrogen oxide emissions begin consuming ozone. As the ozone layer shreds, more solar radiation streams through, attacking the immune systems of trees, crops, people and animals.

The disintegrating ozone layer also stops retaining heat, causing stratospheric temperatures to plunge. In 1993, clouds of ice crystals formed high over the tropical Caribbean. The resulting concentrations of ozone-damaging chemicals locked in those stratospheric ice clouds dramatically thinned solar radiation shielding over beaches there.

Unfortunately, Airbus Industries notes, "there is no alternative to our atmosphere." This major European manufacturer of commercial jets warns that the international economy could erode as drastically as the atmosphere when its present carbon overloading doubles and the climate warms drastically over the next few decades.

Airbus says the resulting "irreversible" climatic modification "would weaken the world economy enough to seriously jeopardize...the international competitiveness of industrial firms."

Still, stratospheric freeways remain packed with gas guzzling jets. In 1991, 57 of the world's biggest airlines were annually flying nearly 82 million people to destinations of their choice. Despite the events of 9/11, by 2006 demand for air transportation is expected to *double.*

By 1999, NASA's "Atmospheric Effects of Aviation Project" estimated that aircraft produce up to 4% of the annual global CO2 emissions from fossil fuels near the Earth's surface – in addition to emissions at higher altitudes above 25,000 feet.

This is not good news for North Americans and Europeans already experiencing successive years of record-breaking temperatures. Air traffic contrails are unevenly distributed around the globe. Besides blocking sunlight and depressing people who might otherwise be enraged under incessant artificial overcasts, contrails also undergo a "photo-chemical" reaction as photons from the sun catalyze chemicals in jet exhaust – and eat the ozone layer.

> *"There is no alternative to our atmosphere."*
> *-Airbus Industries*

HOT AND COLD

Tinkering with cloud cover could trigger unintended consequences. Acting as a complex planetary thermostat, clouds cool the Earth by reflecting sunlight. But clouds also heat the atmosphere by trapping outgoing heat.

"The net effect is a very delicate balance of cooling and warming," a NASA scientist told the *Rocky Mountain News*. "A small tip in one direction or another can eliminate global warming or greatly enhance it."

Both natural and aircraft-induced cloud decks can reflect sunlight that would otherwise warm the Earth's surface. Or they can act like an atmospheric blanket, trapping heat radiating up from the ground, instead of allowing it to escape.

The big question is whether contrails, chemtrails and clouds heat or cool the Earth. For the past 10 years NASA has held a conference on The Atmospheric Effects of Aviation Project (AEAP). Several hundred researchers from around the world attend annually.

It turns out that contrails are concentrated over parts of the United States and Europe, where local warming is already *35-times higher than the global average. [Christian Science Monitor July 29/97]*

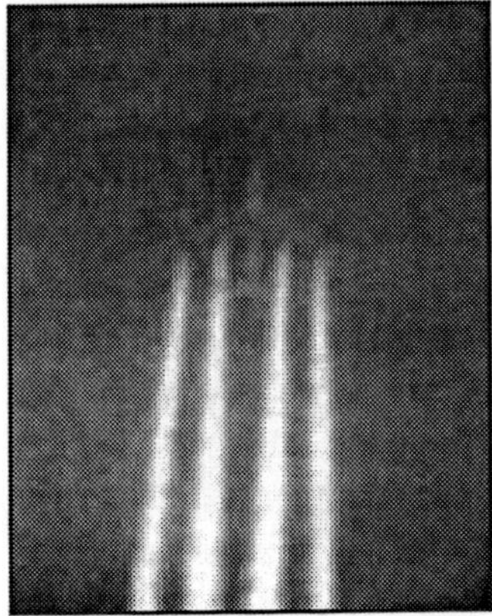

Nightspray Orlando, FL 2003

In 1997 researchers from NASA's Langley Research Center showed that contrails are contributing to global warming, while disrupting local weather in areas seeing heavy air traffic.

They argued that the sharp increase in air traffic for the last 20 years was responsible for the most significant warming detected over North America – which occurs at night. So any efforts to mitigate global warming should include the night sky.

The Intergovernmental Panel on Climate Change (IPCC) has calculated that supposedly "harmless" contrails spread across the world's skies by 12,000 civil airliners contribute as much to global warming as the carbon burnt in their jet engines.

Even worse, a research team of American and German scientists, headed by NASA atmospheric scientist Dr. Patrick Minnis "conservatively" predicted that contrails would increases by up to 600% over the next 50 years.

SHARK PLANES

The quickest way to cut pollution and make airlines more competitive in a cutthroat industry is to cut fuel consumption. Engineers are copying the roughened skin, that allows sharks to "fly" underwater with remarkable swiftness. Overlaying wings with shark-like "riblets" has substantially reduced drag, saving three million tons of fuel per year. By boosting fuel economy 50% since the early 1970s, jet engine manufacturers have cut emissions of unburned hydrocarbons and carbon monoxide by about 80% and 60% respectively.

Research to reduce contrails and fuel consumption continues. In April 2000, NASA's Glenn Research Center for aeropropulsion began developing quieter, more fuel-efficient engines with fewer harmful emissions. Hotter running engines have already slashed 70% of airborne carbon emissions from 1976 levels.

The hotter the temperature inside the combustor, the more miles can be flown on the same amount of fuel. But the higher temperatures needed to boost fuel combustion and efficiency, the more noxious NOx emissions are produced – further munching an already tattered ozone layer protecting all life from increasingly fierce nuclear reactions on the sun.

It's not a happy tradeoff. Nevertheless, the airline industry's reduction in fuel consumption over the previous 20 years has been so dramatic, total nitrogen oxide emissions have actually declined by 12%. By 2005, manufacturers like Airbus anticipate that fresh advances in aerodynamics, propulsion, structure and materials will see another 50% energy savings for long-range aircraft. This is an impressive performance.

But fuel consumption and pollution by commercial aircraft continued to rise as forecast fuel savings are offset by almost half-a million additional passengers taking to the skies every year. Despite stunning gains in fuel efficiency from 1977 to 1988, passenger volumes fueled a 37% increase in fuel consumption.

GET DOWN

Swiss atmospheric scientist Robert Egli was one of the first scientists to study the impacts of high-altitude jet traffic on global warming. He's all for getting jets out of the stratosphere. "The best cruising altitude depends on the geographical latitude and the season," Egli says. "For the main traffic routes, it is probably about nine kilometers above sea level."

Connecting jet turbines to propellers makes them much more fuel-efficient at these lower altitudes. Experiments with "ducted fan" engines, which enclose multi-bladed propellers in high-efficiency ducts, and the use of weight-saving "composite" plastics and ceramics also promise much better fuel economy at lower altitudes.

Contrails could be eliminated if aircraft reduced their altitude from about 33,000 feet to between 24,000 feet and 31,000 feet.

But current turbo-prop planes fly at least 150 miles per hour slower than stratospheric jets. Slogging through the troposphere, "propjets" also encounter much more weather than their higher-flying pure-jet sisters. Advances in onboard sensors and "hands off" landing systems will allow these planes to contend with turbulence, thunderstorms, icing and other meteorological hazards with much greater aplomb than their forerunners

The simplest solution will help save our space colony from cracking up, while sparing you exposure to X-rays and gamma rays streaming unimpeded through aircraft aluminum and human tissues exposed to this solar radiation high within the thinnest layers of a depleted ozone shield. This solution will also save you tons of money: Stay on, or close to the ground.

At least that's what a British Royal Commission on Environmental Pollution recommends. In a report released in the winter of 2003, the commission urged Whitehall to "discourage short-haul passenger flights, such as UK and European journeys, that pollute disproportionately compared to rail journeys made over similar distances."

Air freight "should be restricted to high value and perishable goods" the Commission said, where carbon dioxide emissions and fuel use are up to 200 times higher for air than rail transport.

Expressing disappointment that international aviation emissions were omitted from the Kyoto Protocol, the royal study also recommended introducing "climate protection charges" for take-off and landings – as well as restricting the number of take-off slots.

GLOBAL DIMMING

Airline executives suffering acute indigestion over royal findings predicting that continuing growth in post-911 air travel will easily outstrip advances in aircraft and engine technology clutched their hearts on Dec. 18, 2003.

That's when the London Guardian reported levels of sunlight reaching the Earth's surface have declined by more than 10% in the three decades since air traffic took off. If left unchecked this new crisis called "Global Dimming" could crank up climate change – and kill sunlight starved crops. Sunshine in Ireland is on the wane. Ditto Japan, where the Land of the Rising Sun has become the land of rising smog. The Arctic and the Antarctic are also getting darker. Levels of solar radiation reaching parts of the former Soviet Union have gloomily darkened almost 20% between 1960 and 1987!

The phenomenon - which most likely relates to increasing atmospheric pollution and resulting cloud formation – explains the lack of increased evaporation as Earth warms. Despite the heat, less sunlight means less evaporation.

COUNTING CONTRAILS OVER CONUS

While you're waiting for the train, here is a chemtrail koan straight from NASA and the Pentagon:

Conundrum: *How can contrails be increasing when they are declining?*
Answer: *When they are really chemtrails and not contrails at all.*

NASA scientists say that despite a steady increase in commercial air traffic over the Continental United States (CONUS) in recent decades, contrails are *decreasing* over the USA. The aeronautical agency's 2002 study, "An Estimation of CONUS Contrail Frequency", was conjured after correlating rapid meteorological updates called RUCs with near "real time" flight data supplied by FlyteTrax of Silicon Valley.

During November 2001, FlyteTrax provided up-to-the-minute specs on all commercial air traffic over the continental US. This included readouts on commercial aircraft type, latitude, longitude and altitude every five minutes around the clock.

Air traffic densities were then charted on grids encompassing 10,000 square kilometers each, and extending from 20°N to 50°N and 135°W to 60°W. Within each grid at 40-kilometer intervals, detailed atmospheric profiles of height, temperature, humidity and horizontal and vertical wind speeds were derived from one-hourly Rapid Update Cycle analyses.

When the flight data for an aircraft transiting an area matched atmospheric requirements for contrail formation, the computer made predictions concerning contrail formation and persistence over CONUS. Minnis, an ardent foe of "chemtrail conspiratorialists" helped calculate the computer algorithms used to estimate "CONUS contrail frequency".

> *As contrails declined over the USA, sightings of long lingering plumes left by jet aircraft increased.*

WHERE HAVE ALL THE CONTRAILS GONE?

"According to the classical contrail formation theory, contrails can persist when the ambient air is super-saturated," says this latest NASA contrail study. Which isn't often. Even when NASA's meteorological model was re-jiggered with software instructions to predict more contrails under less than ideal contrail conditions – the number of contrails was found to be declining two months after the endlessly replayed images of two jetliners impacting New York City's two tallest buildings dampened public enthusiasm for commercial flying.

The "Potential Persistent Contrail Frequency" shows the month of Thanksgiving to be typically the heaviest air traffic month in the U.S. – where the region with the highest potential occurrence of contrails continues to be the Pacific Northwest. Other regions of high contrail frequency occurred in central Canada and the eastern Midwestern US. These areas can see twice the number of contrails as the continental average.

But in December 2001 the distribution and magnitude of potential contrails "changed dramatically" said NASA – not because of Sept. 11, but as a result of radical, unexpected changes in weather patterns between November and December. Even in the contrail congested Portland and Seattle regions, contrail frequency *dropped well below continental averages.*

Presented to the "10th Conference on Aviation, Range, and Aerospace Meteorology" in Portland, Oregon in May 2002, NASA's newest findings show that contrail coverage over the North Atlantic and central Europe remains "significantly smaller than those given" in 1994. Ditto the Pacific Northwest.

Gambling with the sky over Las Vegas 1999

UNHAPPY TRAILS TO YOU

Try telling Leslie that jet plumes are decreasing.

That same November – with far fewer contrails showing up than predicted and photographs and eyewitness reports of persistent white plumes left by high-flying jets flooding the Internet – this school teacher took a trip from Las Vegas "up to Reno, over to Sacramento, up to Portland, Oregon, and then over through Idaho and down through Wyoming into Denver and back to Las Vegas. And every bit of the way, they were spraying. The range of the spraying was just phenomenal. We covered six states in four days and saw them everywhere."

Leslie became "very, very sick". It took almost two months for her lungs to clear from something "almost exactly like a whooping cough I got ten or so years ago that turned out to be a lung fungal infection."

Ice crystal condensation trails do not cause fungal infections in the lungs. But airborne colonies of mutated molds and fungi *brought down from the irradiated upper atmosphere by chemtrails* could certainly cause symptoms experienced by Leslie and tens of thousands of North Americans following chemtrail exposure.

Chapter 2

POISONS AND PATHOGENS

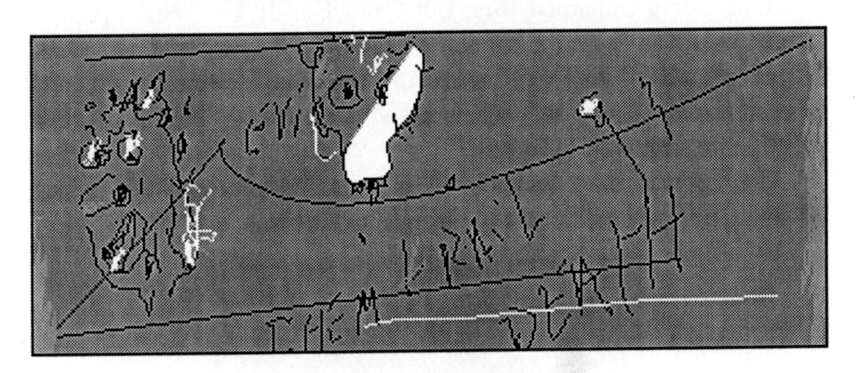

Contrails may cloud the sky. But flash-frozen water vapor doesn't make people sick. Yet many observers become ill within hours of watching chemtrails form. In a correlation that defies coincidence, hospital admissions following heavy "spray days" across the U.S. have jumped to *nearly double* normal peak flu-season rates, even in states reporting a "mild" flu season.

PANDEMIC '98-99

On January 7, 1999 – just as I went on Art Bell's "Coast to Coast" radio show for the first of seven shows with news of chemtrails, the *Philadelphia Daily News* was reporting that Emergency Room (ER) patients were overflowing into the hallways at West Jersey Hospital in Berlin, New Jersey yesterday "as a wave of respiratory illnesses swept the area."

New York State hospital was so full of patients suffering with the "flu" there was a 24-hour waiting period to get in. The following day, local San Francisco TV stations reported that paramedics were being diverted to help handle swamped ERs.

Two days later, a person in Portland "heard on the radio that the hospitals in Portland are jammed up with people coming in. Plus in

Eugene it seems like everyone is coming down with something. And my wife and I saw some rainbow-colored clouds yesterday. We are calling them chem-clouds." The Oregon Health Science Building, which takes overflow from hospitals, was "overloaded with people with upper respiratory problems."

On January 31, Lake Havasu's *Today's News Herald* reported: "Victims Curse Unnamed Bug, But Can't Call It The 'Flu'". A local family physician "said Friday that a nameless virus is bringing at least 10 patients a day into her office and driving some into the hospital, but laboratory tests show only a few are suffering from Type A or other identifiable strains of influenza."

After cobweb-like filaments fell in Santa Cruz, one resident collected some, only to see the strange strands disintegrate in a jar.

Lake Havasu April 21/02

"Hospitals full here in Santa Cruz, and also in Salinas," she reported.

A HAM radio operator in contact with a Richmond resident learned that "a lot of planes flew very low over his home one night which was very unusual and very quickly he and his wife got very ill. When they went to the hospital they "couldn't get in 'cause it was filled up with people. The MD he saw there hadn't seen anything like it and was rather upset."

> *"Laboratory tests show only a few are suffering from influenza."*

In Castle Rock, Colorado: "The emergency room was filled with people and the prescription line was out the front door; all the cold medicine was on a table in the lobby instead of behind the counter. The woman doctor who was new to the USA told my wife, 'You don't have to say anything, everyone here has the same thing.' And she told my wife it was a new bacteria that they can't fight. She said 'your sickness will last for up to three months.'"

On February 9, one month after I was assigned by the Environment News Service to cover the strange sky patterning, seven Kentucky counties closed all the schools because of sick children. All with flu-type symptoms.

In Colorado following a day of heavy spraying: "Right now, the news is showing that hospitals in our area are turning away patients with flu, asthma, etc. Greeley, Fort Collins hospital is 95% full. Operations are being postponed for lack of beds."

In Youngstown, Ohio, a doctor told a patient "the hospitals were filled with patients having severe problems."

In Akron on February 15, 1999 a resident reported:

> The trails above our home are lower and wider. *How long has this been going on*? Our kids are coming up with throat, lung, and upper respiratory ailments that no one can figure out. My husband started with the sore throat last week. Also, my elderly neighbor across the street is now in a hospital on a ventilator. She came down with what they thought was pneumonia, then decided it wasn't that. It's a thick lining growing in her lungs, and they do not know how to get rid of it or what it is. A local hospital is leasing an entire floor and it's growing into a hospital company who specializes in upper-respiratory diseases.

Another morning in late March, observers in Spokane counted 33 chemtrails in a two and half hour period. "We have a police scanner, and we are hearing so many rescue calls for people with breathing difficulties."

> *"We know there's a lot of sickness, but our diagnosis shows that it's not the flu."*

In Everett, Washington about the same time:

> I've been noticing the chemtrails for a while now. My 8-year old daughter has been sick this week with a bad upper respiratory infection and her asthma has flared up. My 18-year old son came home sick about three weeks ago with fever, bronchitis and incredible dizziness. Took him to the doctor a couple of days later and all the staff were out very sick with the same thing.
>
> One of the office girls fell over from dizziness at the office, nearly hitting her head on the filing cabinet! They had to drive her home because she was too sick to drive. They had to hire outside temporary help just to run the office! They were extremely busy with patients coming in all week very sick with the same symptoms.
>
> Same thing with my son. His girlfriend had to drive him home because he was too dizzy and sick. Also – and this really scares me – one of my son's friend's sister who is about 22-years old showed up at her parent's house sprawled out on their couch very sick with 104 fever. The next day she had open sores all inside her mouth with bleeding gums! *What awful things are they spraying on us and why?*

"We are hearing so many rescue calls for people with breathing difficulties."

In Chandler, Arizona that spring, one resident reports that after heavy chemtrail activity, "the doctor's offices and hospitals were totally packed the next week and one of the nurses I spoke to said they didn't know what was wrong with everyone." In Norfolk, Virginia, "schools were closed and everyone was sick."

WHAT DOCTORS SAID

Often degenerating into serious, even fatal pneumonia, chronic bronchitis, and/or acute asthma attacks, the resulting severe "flu-like" symptoms lingered for months. By the week ending February 13, 1999, the CDC reported "Deaths from influenza and pneumonia in a sampling of 122 cities were at epidemic levels for the third consecutive week." The CDC's definition of influenza includes "*influenza-like illness* and/or culture-confirmed influenza."

But lab tests for influenza kept coming up negative. Robert Page, director of the Chemung County Health Department in Elmira, New York, told reporters "We know there's a lot of sickness, but our diagnosis shows that it's not the flu."

MDs across America told the *New York Times* and other newspapers:

— "This is the worst crisis I have seen."
— "We have people double- and triple-parked in the ER on stretchers."
— "Respiratory and gastrointestinal illnesses are filling up the beds."
— "It was surprising to me how sick they got and how quickly it happened."
— "The increase in respiratory infections may not be due to the flu."
— "We know there's a lot of sickness, but our diagnosis shows that it's not the flu."
— "We've seen a lot of cases that you can't typically classify as flu."

WHAT REGISTERED NURSES SAID

After serving two hitches in the Navy, a Registered Nurse for nearly 20 years claimed that Americans "were being used as Guinea pigs for man-made pathogens, quite probably viral, which were designed to produce different symptoms by casting off a series of shells or layers." Crop-dusters, she noticed, "were spraying at the wrong time of year and over populated areas instead of over the fields."

Another RN spoke up in the winter of '99, worried that "Omaha announced there was very few cases of flu this winter, and then just a few weeks ago we had an outbreak of flu-like symptoms in the hospitals and where I work."

In Austin, Texas, a resident reported:

> My wife is a nurse. The local hospitals are begging the nurses to work extra shifts and there are no empty beds in town. About two weeks ago, on a beautiful clear-blue day I made a trip to

> the store with my six-year-old daughter. In the parking lot when we got out, she pointed to the sky overhead and said, "Look daddy, it's tic-tac-toe." I looked up and saw the giant pattern of huge contrails – four of them crossed in a perfect tic-tac-toe.

In Pierce County, Washington:

> When I went to St. Francis Hospital's emergency room for treatment, the number of severely coughing patients there was overwhelming. Nurses and doctors kept saying it was the flu and bronchitis. But when I told my mother about the chemtrail reports over the Internet, a doctor who was treating another woman in the same room with my mother, he suddenly stopped talking to his patient and turned round and looked at me for several seconds rather sternly, then began talking to his patient. I don't know what that was about really, but I feel like we were both poisoned by something.

In Blaine, Washington, a couple of sky watchers were noticing short contrails that quickly dissipated. "The next thing we see blows our minds. Out of the north comes one humongous, huge jet. This thing was as big as a C5A and it was leaving a contrail miles long. It was painted white all over. Our neighbor, who is a Med Tech at Saint Francis Hospital, says they are jammed packed with people with upper respiratory problems."

Another registered nurse travels extensively working for a home health care service:

> Approximately December 16th or the 17th, while traveling north, I could see 'stripes' in the sky. It appeared as if someone took white paint on their fingers and from north to south ran their fingers through the sky. These contrails were evenly spaced and covered the *whole* sky! They covered it completely! When I was finished with the next visit, approximately 45 minutes, I came out of the house and found the whole sky was white. There was no definition in cloud pattern.
>
> Within the 24 hours I became very weak, feverish, and my

> asthma began to act up. I didn't think too much about it, until my boyfriend told me that many in his family started coming down with the same complaints. I also started noticing a lot of my patients and their family members were coming down with these symptoms at the same time. In our area we have one main hospital which I was the Supervisor of for four years. I worked there a total of six years. I stay in close contact with the nurses and physicians and am planning on investigating into this more. At that time, they complained of being extremely busy with respiratory diagnoses.

In Russell Springs, Kentucky, in a case of sudden fatal illness repeated throughout the USA: "My uncle who has always been healthy, had to go to the hospital because he couldn't breathe. Well, he died in the hospital. He wasn't even sick!"

Another report among many similar incidents:

> Mrs. Betty Marlin and Mrs. Pricilla Cisneros – suddenly deceased. Both died suddenly of pneumonia, which overtook them so fast that family members did not even have time to get their families together. Mrs. Marlin was admitted to the hospital on Friday afternoon. Her lips were already blue and her lungs were full of fluid. By Sunday morning, she was gone.

And this from Utah:

> We've had an unusually mild winter here in Utah. Warm sunny days, dry climate. Not the sort of weather you would associate with such a widespread pneumonia epidemic. Within weeks of each other, the mothers of two of my closest friends passed away. Both died of a pneumonia that overtook them so quickly that there was no time to even prepare family members. On one of the local news channels, there was a special report about the hospitals in Provo, Utah being filled to capacity with cases of pneumonia.

In Jefferson City, Missouri, after a "co-worker helped me count 25 various size contrails which lingered until it was too dark to see," this correspondent "Received call from nurse at Carroll County Memorial

Hospital. She said that a child in ER was being seen for severe respiratory distress, but I didn't think much of it until later because the nurse was coughing almost uncontrollably during the call."

"We don't know what this is or where it came from."

That spring, in another state:

> My nurse contact...states emphatically that a number of people have died, and are dying this very day, having displayed symptoms of Sarin gas poisoning. All ages, all economic groups, all ethnicities. She was amazed that I, a non-med type, was aware of the "mysterious" symptoms that are killing people. She also stated that it is not one or two a week or month who are dying, but that several people die *each day* from "flu-like" symptoms just in her hospitals alone, when, in fact, no known flu strains are present. She is an RN who serves at several local hospitals, not just one place.
>
> My contact RN is scared of this and isn't really telling me much more. I believe many meds know exactly what is happening but have been told to keep it quiet. My wife's eye doctor says, "It is some strange allergy that we don't know about," when she went to have blisters checked on her eyelids. Me too. Very painful burning, itching, watering. Horrible headaches, dried blood in noses upon waking in am, muscle weakness and lethargy. I'm ready to move away.

Sore necks and meningitis have followed after chemtrail spraying. In January, February and March 1999, outbreaks of rare meningitis were reported in Bakersfield, California; Putnam County, Florida; Belle River, Ontario; Atlanta and other U.S. cities. On January 21, 1999, *The Lancet* reported that meningitis cases in Britain reached a 50-year high, with 440 notifications in the first 3 weeks of January, compared with 255 for the same period in 1998. Lupus outbreaks also followed heavy spraying at high and low altitudes over Sallisaw, Oklahoma and other cities. In Kansas City, one resident reported: "Lots of Lupus here. Doctors are telling people to 'go home and die.'"

PANDEMIC '99-'2000

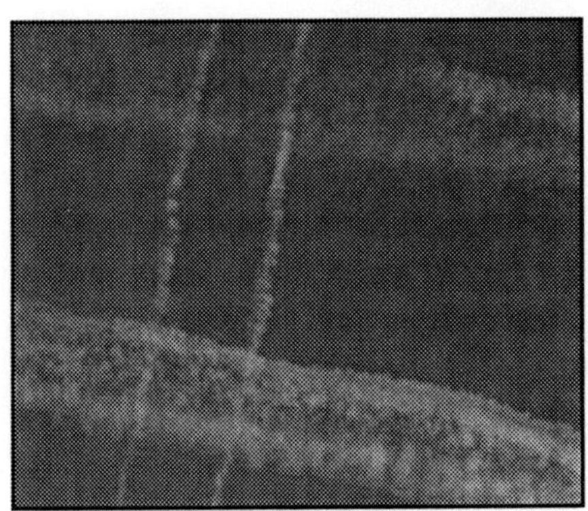

"Look daddy. It's tic-tac-toe."

1999's deadly epidemic of Influenza-Like Illness (ILI) was a virtual repeat of last winter's toll. Only this season, the number of acute care patients actually testing positive for the flu was even lower.

On January 8, 2000 the London *Telegraph* reported: "Refrigerated lorries are once again being used by the National Health Service as temporary morgues in a grim repetition of scenes outside hospitals last winter."

Hospitals on Britain's south coast were forced to store bodies in trailers after nearly *40%* of elderly victims of pneumonia contracted from an Influenza-Like Illness died.

A spokesman at the Conquest Hospital in Hastings explained why a refrigerated container was brought into use on New Year's Eve: "We can't stack bodies up in the corridor."

"I don't think anybody really knows what's causing it," said Silvia Mieure, nursing supervisor at Northridge Hospital Medical Center northwest of Los Angeles. After reporting outbreaks in 17 Minnesota schools and nine nursing homes, Channel 4000 TV News in St. Paul told viewers that the mystery ailment could be "possibly a viral infection masking itself as influenza."

OH OH, CANADA

Nauseous, aching, coughing Canadians also flooded clinics and hospital Emergency Rooms that winter. But this onslaught of fevers were not symptoms of chemtrail poisoning – which results in a *lowering* of body temperatures. Not flu-like fevers.

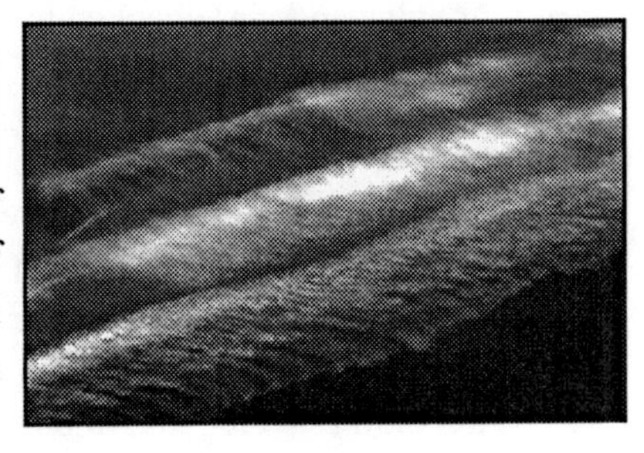

CALIFORNIA'S WINTER "FLU"

On December 18, 1999 the Associated Press (AP) reported, "A nasty strain of the flu is flooding Southern California hospitals with haggard patients, straining emergency rooms and forcing some medical centers to send the sick elsewhere."

At a hospital northwest of Los Angeles, patients suffering acute upper respiratory distress rocketed the emergency admissions count by 30 to 40 patients *per day* for 18 consecutive days. "I don't think anybody really knows what's causing it. Maybe it's a new strain," said Silvia Mieure, nursing supervisor at Northridge Hospital Medical Center.

According to one eyewitness, "Unbelievable chemtrail sprayings" took place December 4th and 5th, (1999) over Los Angeles and Orange County involving "dozens of trails sprayed" from approximately 9:00 am to noon – "until the entire sky was covered." John Quinn corroborated many California chemtrail reports. The News Hawk noted that "Full-on inundation of California skies with a tremendous number of jet contrails occurred both prior to and during the outbreak of this unknown, horrendous 'flu.'"

In nearby Nevada, more reports came in from "Coast-To-Coast" host Art Bell's hometown of Pahrump during December 1999:

> Contrails have been extremely heavy over Pahrump, NV for weeks also. I have been too ill as has my family to do much more than stay alive. Husband is barely making it to work, falling asleep immediately upon getting home. Kids have been sick. Doctor tested me last Thursday for some 'immune compromise'. I had thrush in mouth real bad, so much pain in joints I have not been able to work over one year. Found a photo of my girls, maybe three years old, playing on the beach in Santa Monica and was shocked to notice the sky was filled with contrails."

Texas turned toxic, too:

> Christmas Day in Houston was most remarkable for the massive chemical spraying that begin near dawn over the outer western suburbs. We drove through an area that revealed a great view of the sky for about 25 miles in all directions. A little math revealed that in only five hours or so, the three or four

aerial tankers working that morning had managed to saturate an area of about 1,500 square miles!

Worse was driving by so many homes with children outside, playing with new Christmas toys and never looking up to notice the bizarre appearance of the sky above them. I wondered how many had recently been diagnosed with asthma.

About two weeks ago I was the guest of a radio program in Asheville, NC, where spraying has been heavy all year. As luck would have it, three or four aircraft were engaged in spray operations that very morning, and listeners were calling in frequently to tell their neighbors to get their lazy butts outside to see what everyone was talking about. After about 25 minutes of this, callers reported that all three aircraft had turned off their pumps and were "high-tailin' it outta here."

On the second day of Year 2000, a Long Island woman was coughing blood:

Still sick here. Even my houseguest and his friend took ill. Steve is not well yet. I have a patchy rash and feel very weak. Trouble breathing and I am experiencing a lack of balance. I packed a suitcase just in case I have to go to the hospital. I cannot eat, as all food tastes very odd to me. I do not even feel like drinking, but am forcing water and juice. My animals are ill. Two of my cats got sick today. One of my goats looks bad, too. Emergency rooms are filling up quickly here. When Steve was taken to the hospital last week, patients were lying in stretchers in the aisles.

As this coughing correspondent correlates:

If I had any doubt that there was such a thing as "chemtrails" and that they were poisoning the public, it was removed after returning from our recent road trip to Las Vegas. Upon our return from the town that never sleeps, my email "in" box had an unsolicited message from somebody with a report from December 4, 1999.

The email report stated that on the Las Vegas Channel 8

evening news every emergency room in the area was overcrowded with people suffering from upper respiratory infections. The story was rather in-depth for a TV news segment – a little over a minute long. The anonymous Las Vegas resident stated that he has witnessed many chemtrails over Las Vegas over the last month and that many others have also witnessed the phenomenon.

The news story was eerily consistent with what we experienced in our travels through Nevada with our eventual arrival in Las Vegas. [We] entered Nevada in the early morning of December 2. We traveled south all day long through the sparsely populated Nevada high country of Interstate 93. Having seen contrails in the skies above north Idaho almost daily since last spring, we were habitually looking up as we drove toward Las Vegas. We had noticed that the sparsely populated areas in Nevada had brilliantly clear blue skies and that occasional airplanes left vapor trails that dissipated normally.

But as soon as we neared Las Vegas, the skies directly above the city recorded a smoky brownish gray grid pattern of airplane traffic. We watched what appeared to be a military C-135 transport spraying something over the populated areas over Las Vegas and then shut off whatever was being sprayed. When the plane was no longer directly over Las Vegas it continued flying, leaving a vapor trail that dissipated normally.

As heavy spraying continued over Sedona, residents felt as if they were under sustained aerial attack. Diane wrote:

The skies are so saturated here lately it's becoming hard to understand where the real air might be. I've never seen such a thick stew and frequent spew. Lately I am detectably succumbing to whatever this is: definite and rather alarming periods of mental confusion, muscle weakness, inflamed lymph system, and the primary ongoing problem of super- (un) natural fatigue. Before, I was more impersonally outraged than personally affected. Now my deteriorating personal condition is adding a whole new fear and loathing to the equation.

She passed out and was rushed to hospital:

> I don't know what happened to me yesterday, but I ended up in the emergency room. On the way to lunch with a friend, not feeling well anyway, I was suddenly overcome with intense nausea and began to black out. Three people tried six times to find a vein for intravenous rehydration with no success. I heard them say, "Huh, I never saw this before." This was not comforting. You and I know that *this is not the flu* in the ordinary sense.
>
> I've had degrees of fever and chills for a very long time, but the last two weeks of heavy heavy spraying here have finally knocked me over. I'm taking some sort of (Yeah I know) powerful antibiotic which I am assured will do nothing whatsoever for getting rid of the virus, but will prevent me from sliding into pneumonia and exiting this lunatic asylum prematurely. I never thought I would be a victim of this, but here we are. What is to be done? Spraying here is intense again today.

"I don't think anybody really knows what's causing it."

"CHEMTRAIL ELBOW"

I experienced severe pain in my left elbow after heavy chemtrail spraying over my remote hillside home following my first appearance on Art Bell's radio show. Another writer was "very excited to see the 'tennis elbow' and wrist pain symptoms, which I noticed personally but did not really think of as a flu symptom."

Sore joints and skin inflammations appear to be characteristic of the '99-2000 epidemic:

> A massage therapist had the flu and one of the symptoms was with the acute wrist pain, like glass broken in the joint. I also had the flu and briefly had the same symptom of the wrist and also tendonitis pain in the tennis and golfer elbow area, infections on the skin, red inflamed, wounds on the hands, and two boil-like pimples on the face next to the mouth, and a boil-like pimple on the chest red and itchy, all right-sided.

Another correspondent encountered symptoms felt by many North Americans:

> Depression, hopelessness, overwhelm, frustration, unable to find a remedy that fit. Chill would drive me to bed and then would sleep for three hours and then had to force myself to wake up. Periodic, the symptoms would all get better and 24 or so hours later it was all back. Felt not myself for weeks, vision slightly skewed, head slightly dizzy, mind not clear.
>
> And this is spooky because I am experiencing this, and a significant percentage of chemtrail sufferers are also reporting this unusual symptom…
>
> Both me and my wife, my left eye has been twitching disturbingly, hard to look at something at times, never had this or the pimple on the face symptom before. Wife's left eye twitching in the same area. Her lower lid almost spasms to the point of having to hold it.

TOXIC TWITCH

I experienced an annoying and worrisome twitching left eyelid following heavy chemtrail spraying over my relocated residence on Gabriola Island off Canada's west coast. Like the pain in my elbow, this symptom of neurotoxin exposure eventually went away. Thank God. But handling artificial "cobwebs" can be hazardous to your health. As this correspondent writes:

> In Feb. '99 I was waiting for my daughter at her school and got out of the car to stretch my legs. As I leaned back I saw three large Xs in the sky. Then I noticed a web-like strand clinging to my radio antenna. Foolishly, I touched it and it dissolved unlike a spider web.
>
> Within 24 hours I was sick with all the flu-like symptoms I had read about. I tried to tough it out and go to work. The sickness seemed to recede (causing me to think it was going away) only to come back stronger. I was out of work for 4 days but the effects lasted a couple weeks. Before that I hadn't missed a day

of work due to illness in probably 15 years. I practically never get sick. During that time period, supermarkets sounded like TB wards and a friend of mine came down with the same symptoms.

I hadn't thought much about my experience until I saw this on your website: "A twitching left eyelid nearly drove me nuts before finally abating". For the last 6 months or so I've had this twitch. I find myself trying to 'rub it out' frequently. It started with twitching in both eyelids but settled in the left one. It seems to me that it may have something to do with the right side of the brain because it controls the left side.

BLOODY NOSES

Gushing nosebleeds are a common chemtrail symptom. In mid-January, 2000, Vicki posted this account on her Oklahoma website:

On Monday of this week, the chemfog rolled in. I had lots of errands to do and was outside for about 3-4 hours. I had sneezed 2 or 3 times but no big deal. About 10 minutes after I got home, both sides of my nose started *gushing* blood. I don't get nosebleeds, and this wasn't the minor kind. This was the posterior kind – no matter if I was leaning forward, or standing, blood was gushing down my throat.

I would put a tissue to my nose with my left hand, and by the time I reached for another tissue with my right hand, the tissue in my left hand was completely soaked with blood. I had to use a towel. If you've ever had a bad head cold where you feel the mucous bubbling around in your head and in your ears, this is what it felt like, only it wasn't mucous, it was blood.

I'm not squeamish and am usually very calm when there's an injury. But I must admit, this freaked me out. When the bleeding finally stopped after about 20 minutes, we noticed that my ears were bright red and they felt like they were on fire.

All day yesterday it felt like every sinus passage in my head was on fire and my eyeballs ached. Every joint in my body was

> sore and I was extremely cranky. Every footfall resounded in my head. Suffice it to say, I now believe there is something going on here more sinister than weather modification.

"Supermarkets sounded like TB wards."

In another incident in the fall of 2000, while driving to the radio station, a talk show host suddenly started gushing blood from his nose. At the radio station, he discovered that two office workers also had nosebleeds. So the talk jockey asked his listeners to call in with their most notorious nosebleed stories.

A listener described what happened next:

> Most of the calls were, surprisingly, about people who had nosebleeds that afternoon. A lot of them had never had one before and were wondering what could have caused it. Some of them, including the talk show host, also had flu-like symptoms. The host usually tries to make a joke out of everything, but he had a difficult time trying to lighten up the show on this particular afternoon.

SICK IN SALLISAW

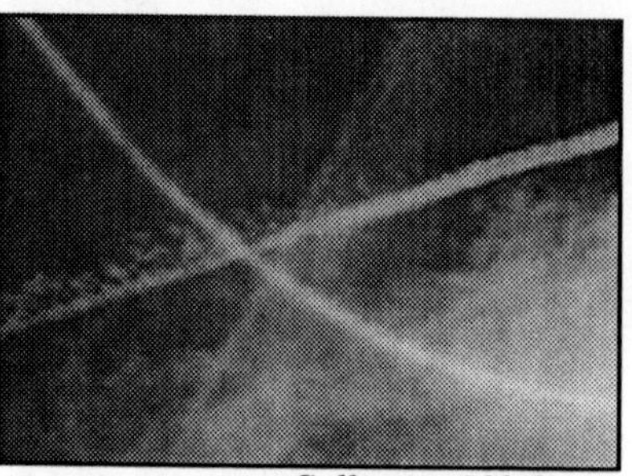

Sallisaw, Oklahoma

In Sallisaw, Oklahoma, restaurant owner Pat Edgar has watched "cobwebbing stuff coming down" from the zigzagging jets flying "all day long, line after line, back-and-forth, like furrows in a farm field."

An exasperated Edgar now says, "I wish more people would pay attention. There must've been 30 contrails in the sky on a sunny day last October."

"You and I know that this is not the flu."

Before Edgar sold his restaurant, customers came in complaining of airplanes "flyin' around all night" over this remote area of Oklahoma. In the morning, they could see "stuff comin' out of their wings."

Edgar knows four-dozen witnesses who have "come down violently ill, coughin' up blood for two weeks, or real bad nosebleeds."

As William Wallace relates, after being sprayed by a low-flying Intruder-type jet while plowing a field in Washington state: "They are spraying something deliberately. I must've had 15 nosebleeds last summer. I'd blow my nose and it would bleed. And I never had that before. I'd bend over planting and it would bleed."

BREAKING PLATELETS

Wallace was not tested. But blood from his wife Ann was later lab-tested and found to have dangerously low blood platelet counts. According to one medical lab: "When platelets are low, microscopic vessels become weak and rupture easily. Patients can have spontaneous nosebleeds."

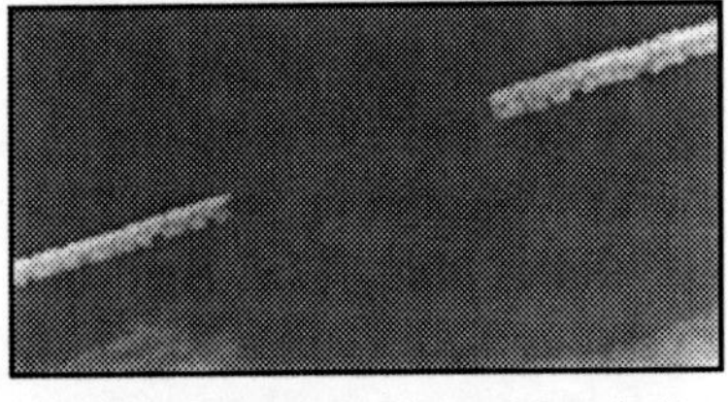

Platelets are produced in the bone marrow by large cells called megakaryocytes. A normal platelet count is 130,000 to 400,000. The bone marrow is capable of increasing the production of platelets up to 6 to 8 times normal, if necessary.

Platelet production can plunge when antibodies are triggered, destroying platelets in the marrow before they can be released into the blood. When the immune system attacks the body's platelets, bright purple and red bruise-like spots can appear on the skin. Some chemtrail sickness sufferers will immediately recognize this symptom. Low platelet counts are associated with lupus and mononucleosis (Epstein-Barr) – often reported in the wake of heavy spraying.

"Everybody in this town is sick right now – sicker than a damn dog."

MISSION STATEMENT

Pat Edgar is convinced. "They have a mission. They go back and forth all day. Hey man, I'm talkin' hundreds of contrails in a day! It's unbelievable."

On January 24, 1999 Edgar reported that on "Monday, Tuesday and Wednesday and Thursday of last week, we were really hit hard with the contrails. I mean real bad. Everybody in this town is sick right now – sicker than a damn dog. It's all in their head and their sinuses, and it hangs in the throat, [sore necks], ears ringing."

Edgar added: "Some customers that frequent our business have stated that they have been to the doctor and the offices have been full of sick people. Same thing at the Indian clinic.

People have to wait for hours because the waiting room is full. Some people have reported being on their third and fourth round of antibiotics and they are still ill. We noticed excessive contrails Thursday Feb. 11th."

Edgar became ill the following day, and visited a doctor. From a friend he learned that "Sparks regional hospital had over 500 people seeking medical attention at the emergency room for flu, or flu-like symptoms."

In nearby Gore, Oklahoma, Mary Young was watching TV on January 20, 1999 "about 2:30, quarter to three in the morning," when she heard a prop plane in the distance, "going around and around."

Ignoring the television, she listened as the plane "kept getting closer and closer and closer." Finally it went right over the house – so low "the windows rattled, and everything shook. It sounded like sand was hitting the windows."

About 1:30 that afternoon, Young went outside to rake leaves with her cousin. But when she began burning them, "an odor like the smoke bombs kids play with" made them put it out. "The smell was so nasty and so bad it scared me. I told my cousin let's put it out because it's hurting my eyes and burning my throat bad."

The full-blooded Cherokee has had a bad cold ever since. She says she "Keeps coughing phlegm that tastes bad. My eyes hurt, my joints hurt. I'm not catchin' my breath right. I can't get rid of this cold."

Even worse, Young says, "I've had this bad headache. It's not just a headache. My eyeballs hurt so bad – way in the back – I just wish they would fall out. I've got a neighbor lady down the road who keeps talking about headaches all the time. This person had never complained of headaches before."

> *"My eyeballs hurt so bad – way in the back –*
> *I just wish they would fall out."*

THE EYES HAVE IT

Gastrointestinal problems are also linked with chemtrails. And in December 1999 a chemtrail watcher from San Francisco Bay described a new symptom:

> The last two weeks of non-stop spraying is and has been affecting my eyes. People of all ages around here are having eye problems – from pink eye to blurred and deteriorating vision. I'm trying to compensate with herbs, vitamin C eye drops and other nutritional nervous system support supplements, but it is not enough to evade the effects entirely. I hope they are reversible.

Two years later, a Floridian was also experiencing chemtrail-related eye problems. In November 2001, Barbara wrote:

> Well, they are spraying today across Tallahassee. I went to walk the dogs around 10:30 and, our beautiful sunny day was already being marked by 'contrails' – the kind that spread out and become a haze.
>
> These are different from the original chemtrails we had last year in that they don't appear greasy. When they sprayed several weeks back with what appears to be the same stuff, my eyes began itching and burning like mad and my nose became very irritated and runny. Well, now the same thing is happening. Now, there are rain clouds threatening and my head is

killing me – all in three hours. This really, really sucks! It's not nice to fool Mother Nature. I fear we will pay a terrible price for their interference – one day soon.

A CANCER CONNECTION?

Like many inhabitants of Sedona, Donna has observed chemtrail spraying for years –including sticky "angel hair" which she and others found on rocks on at least one occasion. Donna became very ill herself from the spraying and finally moved away.

Another Sedona resident takes up the story: "Here's the interesting part. Back then, the spraying occurred on an infrequent basis. Maybe every couple of weeks, or maybe not even that often. So, most people went on with life as normal and ignored it. However," Elora goes on to explain, "after a few years of this, Donna said that many, many people began to get liver cancer. Donna, who lived in Sedona for many years, said that once they got it, they died within six months. Pretty much across the board."

In early 2001, Pat Edgar sent a Sallisaw update:

> I'm not fairing well myself. Last Thanksgiving I was sick again and my throat was sore. I noticed a lesion that popped up beside my tongue in the back of my throat. My father and I were in the town of Rochelle, Illinois back in September. Dad had a seizure and ended up in the community hospital. I was telling all the nurses about the contrails and all the Lupus in our area, as they were spraying the hell outside overhead. Complete with the cobwebs coming down. They were all most interested. The one nurse told me they are at epidemic stage in their town with people being diagnosed with Non-Hodgkin's Lymphoma.

This writer has experienced purple bruising on my upper arms, as well as intense vertigo and sudden extreme exhaustion following heavy chemtrail spraying over Canada's west coast. I am not alone. As Edgar relates:

> A few months back, Julie and a few others with Lupus had a major flare. It looked like they were beat up with *major bruis-*

ing on the arms and legs. The one lady started having problems breathing and they did a CAT scan on her. They discovered a huge blood clot lodged in her abdomen and removed it. It took several months for her to recover. And yes, there was major spraying a few days before this all occurred. Will, I am afraid I may have been right about calling all this a population cull of some kind. Presently all our hospitals in Ft. Smith are filled again."

DO YOU MIND?

Other symptoms now associated with chemtrails include disorientation, depression, inexplicable anxiety, and an inability to concentrate. The Wallaces have been sick and lethargic ever since being sprayed by aircraft flying at high and extremely low altitudes. Echoing many other reports across the USA, William Wallace reports that residents of Coleville, Washington and the surrounding heavily sprayed area have been experiencing headaches so excruciating "your eyeballs hurt."

Chicago Aug 6/01

Despite their isolation in a remote mountainous area of eastern Washington, Wallace's wife Ann has been newly diagnosed with Epstein-Barr. "Her heart is bothering her," a worried William says, "and her white blood cell count is very low, and she remains in terrible pain, almost too weak to move."

Is something else is going on?

"Whatever they're dumping on us does something to your mind," Wallace insists. Like the veterans of a distant desert war, some chemtrail-contaminated people like Wallace –who have never served in the military – now forget simple errands. When I asked William Wallace for directions, he couldn't even remember the name of the town closest to his own.

"Whatever they're dumping on us does something to your mind."

Mental muddling is a common chemtrail complaint. After a heavy spray week in Santa Fe this fall, a waitress and her co-workers found it "hard to think, hard to put two thoughts together."

Everyone, she said, felt "spaced out, wavy, woozy – like coming ashore after being on a boat." It felt like the onset of flu. But the spraying stopped and the strange symptoms went away the next day.

SOL POWER

As unprecedented solar storms wash electromagnetically-sensitive humans with waves of invisible energy – and Earth's shrinking magnetic field is felt by beings acutely attuned to its subtly shifting frequencies – chemicals sprayed into air already charged with nerve-jangling electronic "smog" may be triggering emotional storms.

In Glenwood Springs, Colorado where another despondent correspondent reported relentless spraying, the correlation between chemtrails and consciousness is not encouraging. "People are acting weird," wrote this waitress after work. "People are acting strange. People don't have really good mental health. Everybody's sick. More people are down. Things are just not right. Erratic behavior. It's not like life used to be."

In mid-September, 1999, a chemtrailed Californian wrote:

> Will, they are really doing their job in a big way – chemtrail overlords, that is. My IQ has been rated at 180 IQ. I feel as if I'm functioning like a 12 yr. old. Also feel close to physical exhaustion. The feeling down here is rather scary. Cats nervous, ducks nervous. I'm on guard. That's the best way I can describe it. Cats sticking very close. We sit up at night, outside, and wonder.

One mother whose white blood (platelet) counts is down by half reports:

> I live in a rural community and most of these people work outside and have their whole lives and have never experienced these kind of symptoms till the contrails started showing up last fall. We live in no flight area, yet it is not uncommon for us to see up to 50 contrails a day, flying the multiple line pattern and the X pattern.

Referring to the resulting illness, she added:

> Not just the usual sicknesses, ones that doctors have no idea what is causing them and have no cure for. We had two children die here from totally unexplained illnesses when the contrails were flying all the time. We have dead birds in our yards, we have dead animals. The livestock are sick. Suddenly last winter my nine year-old daughter came down with an asthma problem out of the blue. My uncle died of respiratory problems, again, out of the blue.
>
> Then just a couple of weeks ago my sixteen-year-old daughter started having panic attacks, just sitting at the computer it started and went on for a week till I took her to the doctor and he gave her Xanax.

Yes, indeed. Take this pill. All the symptoms you are suffering are really all in your head.

Mindy from Arkansas might be describing a chemical attack:

> I am a preschool teacher in Birmingham and we are experiencing a "flu" outbreak like I haven't seen before. Many of our children have been out sick And many, many parents of children in our school were sick over this past weekend.

> What caught my attention was that Monday of this week I saw (for the first time) a white airplane flying high in the sky (approx. 7:45 a.m.) with a thick white trail behind it. It was flying up in the sky and had a line that stretched as far behind it as I could see. I called to my six-year-old son to come out and look (we had just arrived at school) and he said, "Cool! A rocket!"
>
> As I was walking to the other building, I noticed other trails

pointing in different directions. (After the fact, I realize it was probably an X or criss-cross.) Later that same afternoon, I began coughing with a bronchitis type cough. The next morning I remember joking with a parent about it because I've never gotten a cough that just started in full-force like that before – usually I get "sick" first. The cough just seemed to appear. I was feeling great before.

THE ABC'S OF CHEMTRAILS

On March 21, Jane reported:

> Several of my teacher colleagues and I have been observing the trails here in central Virginia since 1997. They have grown more numerous and occur more often. I personally have been out of school, sick with flu-like symptoms, three times this school year.
>
> As I think back over the past few years, I have noted a huge increase in the numbers of students and staff who are absent for illness; respiratory problems are far and away the most frequent. Almost daily on my drive to work from Madison Heights to Nelson County I can count anywhere from six to 26 trails fanning out over our skies. The science teacher next door and I have even gotten students into going out back to count the trails. White aircraft can be seen making patterns...

Chapter 3

FALLOUT

Ice-crystal contrails do not rain cobwebs and "goo" over porches, power lines and police cruisers. Yet, cobwebs or "angel hair" have been observed in Tennessee; New Jersey, Ohio, Colorado, Washington and New York states, Oklahoma, Oregon, Illinois, California, Nevada, Arizona, Pennsylvania, New Mexico and Quirindi, Australia – to name a few locations.

Alighting from a helicopter to effect repairs on five different rigs in the Gulf of Mexico in 1998, an oil worker was stunned to see a "*white web* or *angel hair* type stuff," draping each platform.

Also that year, while backpacking up in the mountains of California near Yosemite, William Wallace was startled to see "this stuff comin' out of the sky at 8 to 9,000 feet. High up in a forest, it was just hanging all over, just like cobwebs falling out of the sky – long strands of it, 20 foot long, [for] hundreds of feet."

When Wallace wadded some of the lightweight substance into a marble-size ball, "it just disintegrated after a while."

In November of 1998, an MD from Sedona says that he and his wife, "observed hundreds, thousands perhaps of these filaments seemingly drifting in the wind and landing on the ground, covering all the plants with their shiny structures. The filaments appear to be several

feet long, perhaps over 10-foot and relatively thick, like large spiders will make. We both became sick a month later coming back to California with running noses, cough, extreme fatigue and I am still experiencing pain in my arm. Coincidence? Maybe."

Near Jonesboro, Arkansas that same month, a wife and husband traveling to his mother's for Thanksgiving dinner…

> began noticing what appeared to be spider webs suspended up in the air or attached to trees and high-line electric wires. The webs continued on for several miles towards Jonesboro. We noticed some people rolling their windows down and trying to catch the webs or strands as they drove.
>
> As we approached Walnut Ridge, we began to see more of the fiber. It would be in big floating streams hundreds of feet long tens to hundreds of feet in the air and also gathered along the highway in bushes and trees and hi-line poles like so many very large cobwebs. As we were driving westward home with light high clouds allowing some sun to shine through the webs gathered along the highway looked like ice frozen in webs.

Another eyewitness driving nearby also saw gossamer strands "like a blanket 300 to 400 feet-long, blanketing power lines over the highway, hanging in trees, blowing in the air."

Also that November, this policeman wrote in his journal:

> I have been a police officer for nearly 24 years, and the last three years of my career has been spent working at Denver International Airport. Some of my work there includes directing traffic – most often at passenger drop-off on United Airlines side of the terminal (what we call 'Six-West').

> A couple weeks ago while I was directing traffic on six-west at the terminal I noticed fine filaments floating through the air. There were thousands of them, and some were thirty to forty feet long. They were floating down at ground level and perhaps a thousand or more feet up in the air. They were so fine that they could only be seen if the sunlight caught them just so. These filaments floated past for over an hour. I've never seen anything like it. Some of the filaments caught on light poles and other structures. At one point I reached out as one went by and caught some of it on my arm and clothing. It seems to me that spiders wouldn't be flying around out on the Colorado prairie with winter setting in.

COBWEBS IN COBDEN

Living on Bell Hill directly across from Bald Knob, the tallest hill in Illinois, J reports that spray planes have been flying daily since Dec. 21, 2002 - with only a few days off. It looks to him that the pilots are using Bald Knob as a reference while working a line from the Mississippi River to the Ohio River.

J is seeing as many as a dozen spray aircraft during a single session. - mostly "stretch Lear jets" or similar executive-type bizjets - with an occasional tanker-size plane working back and forth, west to east, east to west and occasionally north-south over the ridgeline.

Collecting fibers dangling from tree limbs, J. recalls how Project SUCCESS sought to use updrafts along ridgelines to waft fibers spread by aircraft into the upper atmosphere, forming clouds.

Under computer-enhanced electron microscope magnification at 3200 power, he and a friend were able to clearly discern three fluorescing colors – red, green and blue – in the airdropped fibers covering his yard and farm machinery.

While any link to possible pathogens is strictly speculative without actual lab testing, J judges that the National Textile Center provides a clue when it discusses growing bacterium inside polymer strands using fluorescing colors to denote the level of biological activity. Green, for example, can denote E-coli. According to a DNA researcher, blue biomarkers indicates an RNA virus, red denotes sera blood product protein, green shows a DNA of bacteria.

J. and his astonished colleague watched through the microscope as the fibers broke into five parts, forming a ball "like a closed fist" before returning to a single strand containing chain-like or bead-like balls. Under high power, the balls showed a faint black line down the center with the knob and one end.

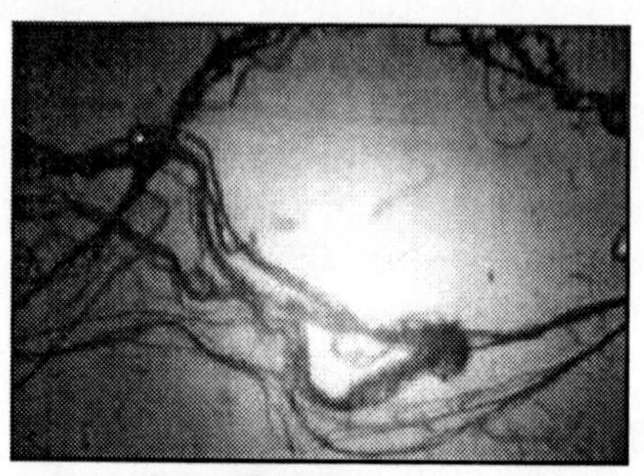

What Jay saw

> *"I noticed fine filaments floating through the air. There were thousands of them, and some were thirty to forty feet long."*

A doctor who provided special instruments for collecting cultures was very interested in J's investigation. Like many other residence in the surrounding area, the MD was suffering from a lingering upper respiratory illness that soon segued into body temperatures one or two degrees below normal - indicating the presence of a fungal infection.

But when J asked the MD for assistance in having the samples lab tested, the doctor demurred, fearing for his reputation and his medical practice if a lab flagged suspicious samples and notified the CDC or the FBI.

J also contacted an environmental organization, which had alerted Illinois residence that high chlorine levels in their drinking water, may be responsible for birth defects and congenital illness. When J suggested that a heavy loading of air-dropped bacteria could be worse than chlorine in the water, the group was very interested in his fibers. But after examining some of the material, J says they called and told him "Do not get it lab tested, do *not* get it lab tested." Instead, the environmental group suggested he draft a petition and "organize a protest". Whatever you do, they reiterated, "Do not have this material lab tested."

So J had had a professional lab "unofficially" look at his fiber samples. But on Dec. 14, 2002 he told this reporter, "Every time I talked to them it was something different. First they said it was a polymer. Then they said an acetate – then definitely *not* acetate. Most curious was the inability of the lab to match the airborne fibers with any of the many fibers in its extensive database."

Since then, J reports that the white sky "looks kind of plastic, the weather's been really screwy, and the leaves have fallen off the trees."

And everyone's coughing. Year round.

ANGEL HAIR IN KELOWNA

Half a continent away, in Kelowna, BC, David continues to monitor, photograph and log spraying events since 1998. While living in Pritchard between Kamloops and Chase on the Trans-Canada Highway, he witnessed six different occasions on which heavy spraying dropped 20 to 25-foot lengths of "spider web-like" material "everywhere".

His apple tree streamed with this strange "angel-hair". So did his fence and vegetable garden. Within weeks of the initial shower of "angel-hair", black mold appeared on their crops. David says that chemtrails are being laid "almost daily up here in the Okanagan," especially over Kelowna. Others in the area agree. "The evidence is everywhere," he insists. "But no one is telling us anything!"

Peering through high-power binoculars, David is seeing spray coming not from the engines of the aircraft. Instead, he says, "It most often is seen coming from the tail end of the fuselage."

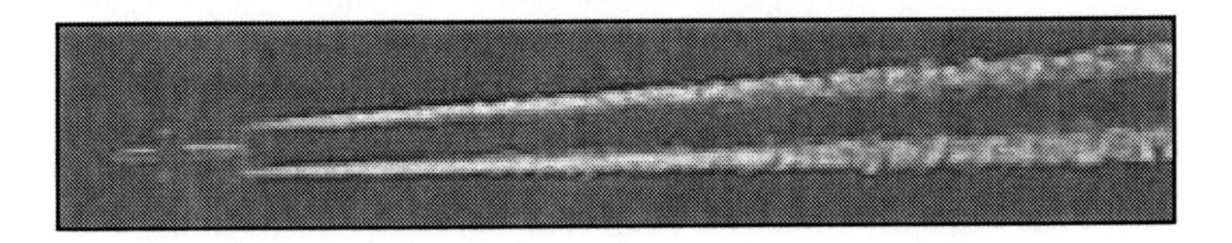

WORRIED ABOUT WEBS

Robert wrote from north central Texas to describe small planes over the Edgecliff area just south of Fort Worth "spreading some type of chemical." Half an hour later, he received a phone call reporting small planes sighted near Rio Vista also spraying something into the atmosphere "that appeared like spider webs."

His family watched two small jets race from west to east. This was odd because the normal flight pattern out of DFW and Love Field usually pass flying from north to south. "Soon after the two jet planes had passed," Robert recounts, "there were a lot of what appeared to be spider webs falling to the ground all around us."

Ushering his family inside, Robert called the local sheriff's office. He was told his call was among many inquiries about what the police were calling, spider webs. When Robert tried to get samples, "the webs turned to dust almost every time I attempted to pick one up and put in a Ziploc bag."

He did shoot some VHS video of thicker webs hanging from a relay tower almost in their front yard. When he took off his protective rubber glove, an "orangish-yellow area" on the palm prompted him to seal the glove in a separate bag.

"Something I also found strange is that these webs fell unto existing spider webs, but those spiders are not on their webs now," he explained. "Spider webs *do not* just turn into powder around here. This was over 25 of them that did this." Robert "never heard another word" about the small spray planes. "Why isn't this on the news?"

THOSE CRAZY CHEMTRAILS

Converted skeptics become the most ardent chemtrail claimants:

> The first time I heard about this on Art Bell, I thought it was "crazy". This is the reason it nags at me: Around 10 years or less, ago, I walked out a back door into a *huge* cob-web, I had to laugh at myself after I got over the shock of it, for no spider could be that big to weave it. It was at least 6 ft. tall and spanned across several feet also.
>
> It was springtime and I had on a jacket, for it was in the middle of the night. I started brushing this off me. It was sticky, but all of a sudden it started dissipating and disappearing.
>
> It was so unusual that I have often thought of it. It was on that night or around that time frame that it also rained in one spot only in the middle of this property. I walked back and forth through it in amusement. Maybe a 10'x10' area, or a little bigger?

> So both events stayed with me, and I never forgot them. I also remember sitting on my porch and telling my husband that the trails from jets were different now days, they stayed longer in the sky and looked different, he laughed at me. The web and rain was in the middle of the night, the jet trails I refer to I noticed during the day hours.
>
> But here is the bottom line: after the two first events I was diagnosed with Fibromyalgia and later with CFIDS. I am from NW Ohio. I have developed allergies and all kind of problems.

U-TURNS

Until April 2001, Lawrence was not having much luck getting people to look up:

> I'm a bicoastal person so I've been watching chemtrail activity for years across the skies over the Straits of Juan de Fuca, and also over the skies of New York City. The residents of Washington State seem to regard the crisscross and sometimes more bizarre patterns (loops, squiggles, circles) as natural phenomenon. And New Yorkers seldom look up. I was on the rooftop of a building in midtown Manhattan one bright blue day last fall. The sky was full of tracks, horizon to horizon.
>
> I've been trying to convince my dad for years that something very unnatural is going on in our skies. He finally started to come around when I pointed out a jet making a very tight U turn at about 20,000 feet, and then immediately making *another*

U-turn! While this was happening, another jet was crossing the wacky zigzag in the sky with more lines. Typically, the sky mural lasted all day, drifting and settling into that familiar greasy haze. I've recently been noticing the lines taking on a darker appearance at the edges, and shadows on them when they crisscross.

Another "cobweb" correspondent had his find lab-tested:

While driving back to Alaska on Nov. 11, 1999 traveling up I-5 approximately 30 miles north of Sacramento and continuing to Red Bluff, I saw a strange substance falling from or floating in the sky. I noticed strings of fiber-like material of varying lengths, a few inches to many feet long (up to 50), floating at various elevations above the highway. After maybe 10-15 miles of seeing this and noticing some along the shoulders and on the roadway I stopped at a rest area and saw many strings of this attached to trees, signs, and on the lawn. I used a straw and twirled strings of it into a ball about the size of a golf ball and put in a drink cup with lid and put in a zip lock bag.

That sample today is about half the original size. These ranged from clusters half the size of my hand, to rope-like diameters ballpoint pen-size, down to spider web size. As I collected the sample some of the thinner strings attacked to my arm and seemed to have a sticky, almost suction type attachment. A burning sensation followed for about 10 minutes after pulling off of arm, even after washing at rest area restroom. No apparent skin irritation appeared.

One rope-like strand, about 12-15 feet long was horizontal across the road at about 3 feet and stuck to my vehicle from the far left bumper, up across the headlights and grille and continued up across the hood to the bottom edge of the windshield.

> This is still visible today, although shrunk to a thin thread, however, it survived approximately 1,000 miles of rain and 1,600 miles of snow on the balance of the trip to Anchorage.
>
> I took the sample to a lab here in Anchorage and the CEO was amazed at it but said no lab here was capable of analyzing it and referred me to a lab in Colorado. He asked for my name and number (I thought that was strange since he couldn't help me), and the next morning he called me to say that I should be very careful with this material.
>
> He had done some research since I left his lab the day before and said *similar substances had been collected in 22 states over the past year and he believed it could have some harmful bacteria associated with it.*

These filaments finally came into the hands of computer consultant Clifford Carnicom, who examined them under a high-power electronic microscope. Photographs of enlarged fiber sections showing what *appear to be blood cells* are available on Carnicom's website [*www.carnicom.com*]. Carnicom describes the artificial fibers as sticky and unusually resilient – unlike any natural fibers.

But health researchers disputed this description. During three years working with human red blood cells in the Surgical Pathology department of a large teaching hospital in Michigan, Erminia Cassani is very familiar with their appearance under an electron microscope.

"I had seen human red blood cells, fixed on slides many times and was familiar with their distinctive appearance," she writes. "However, when I looked at the photos that Mr. Carnicom posted on his site of what he believed to be red blood cells, I immediately questioned that these were blood cells at all, and if they were, they were not likely human blood cells unless they had been very poorly prepared for the slide and their most distinctive tell-tale features had been lost. Human red blood cells typically present differently than what is seen in these photos." [*www.moonbowmedia.com*]

"MYSTERIOUS WEBS DROP FROM THE SKIES"

On Dec. 22, 2000 Oregon's *Wallowa Chieftain* reported sightings of "web-like material…falling from the sky." Some locals thought the filaments were falling "from three military jets that had been flying back and forth in an east-west flight pattern at high altitude."

Two years later, on Dec. 4, 2002, "Moonflowers" from Santa Monica, California (where else?) "found one of those white fibers floating thru the air that start to disintegrate upon touch. It was three-foot long when it floated by my office window, and about two-inches by the time I got it and brought it inside."

The previous Oct. 8, the Associated Press had reported, "long, floating spider webs bobbing through the skies of Santa Cruz, California."

A University of Wyoming microbiology professor quoted in an AP wire story attributed the Santa Cruz conundrum to a seasonal migration of hatchling spiders leaving their nests. The professor, who did not return messages left by a local resident at his home and office, told the wire service it was not uncommon to see "dozens" of webs floating across the plains of Wyoming. "But observers here were not reporting dozens of webs," the resident responded, "but hundreds of thousands.

A few weeks later, on December 21, the Galveston *Daily News* looked like a bad acid trip under a Stephen Kingish headline: "Mysterious Webs Drop From The Skies". The story by Michael A. Smith described skies over Galveston County on Friday "literally filled with floating, shimmering strands and fuzzy, luminescent wads that looked a lot like spider webs."

It was around noon when Lorenzo DeLacerta spotted the weird webs while delivering building material to a site a mile east of the San

Louis Pass Bridge. "It blew my mind," DeLacerta said. "I have never seen anything like it before."

Back at *The Daily News,* a half-dozen skeptical news minds were also being expanded as "people were forced to admit that there was, indeed, under way a slow, steady parade of slender web-like strands, some near the ground, some way up where the airliners ply."

The wacky webs remained visible in the air "for five hours, and poles were left wrapped with the sticky strands and fuzzy wads. So what were they? Official sky-web sources seem scarce. A spokesman at the National Weather Service Office in League City said the service had received no reports of flying webs, and that flying webs weren't really their thing."

A few weeks later, on Dec. 22, 2002 Oklahoma's *Duncan Banner* asked, "Just What Was That White Stuff?" Toni Hopper hopped on the story, asking, "What was that powdery substance covering vehicles throughout Stephens County on Wednesday? Was there a volcano eruption somewhere in the world, dropping ash on Duncan? Maybe it was some unknown chemical sprayed from an airplane as it flew over southern Oklahoma during the early morning hours. Was it acid rain? A terrorist attack? Fairy dust?"

Fairy dust seemed the most plausible answer as two library employees asked Hopper to follow them out o the parking lot. "I was astonished to see their cars covered in the powdery substance," Hopper hyperventilated. "I recalled seeing similar white spots on my vehicle earlier in the day. At the time, I hadn't given them a second thought. What was that stuff?"

At a nearby Wal-Mart, people shopping between 11 p.m. and midnight reported their cars were clean when they entered the store. But when they came out, they found their vehicles covered with white powdery. "Cokie Kifer felt sprinkles on her head when she was walking into Wal-Mart around 11:30 p.m. Tuesday. She assumed it was rain."

A local resident named Danny wrote his own "rain" report the next day:

> My car, all of my family member's cars, including a cousin in southeast Oklahoma whose car was covered as well. I don't know what it was, but I do know it was everywhere. The best way to describe it is kind of like rain, mixed with a little bit of

> snow, mixed with a little mud. It wasn't just simple water or dirty rain that ran off of things. It had substance and its appearance and the way it stuck to things just seemed unnatural.

That was weird enough. But Danny found the lack of "news" coverage even more boggling: "It's amazing that this stuff covered literally thousands and thousands of cars, and obviously many miles, but nothing has been said about it here in Oklahoma in the media."

SACRAMENTO TV

Aerial fallout over the Sacramento region has been heavy enough to finally break through into mainstream news coverage. One resident and her husband: were watching the 11:00 pm news on Friday, January 4, 2002, "here in Sacramento and we saw the first (to our knowledge) televised chemtrail report."

The segment was so short they did not have time to tape it…

> People were up in arms over a mysterious white powder falling from the sky. It covered a neighborhood around here with a thin layer of white powder. The news camera showed a HAZ-MAT (Hazardous Materials) team collecting samples, and then it cut to a sheriff's spokesman who said, "Our analysis shows this to be consistent with cement." And then he mentioned that the sheriff's office have only been getting these reports about once a week.

INCIDENT AT OAKVILLE

Human blood cells were found by a hospital lab technician in samples of gel-like material dropped over the tiny town of Oakville, Washington.

The mysterious sky gel first attained media attention in the summer of 1994, when this sky-goop splattered the startled populace of Oakville, Washington (pop. 665), covering a 20 square-mile area three times within a six-week period.

Local resident Maurice Gobeil told the TV host of *Unexplained Mysteries*: "I got sick, my wife got sick, my daughter got sick and everybody that lived here got sick."

Beverly Roberts remembers: "Everybody in the whole town came down with something like the flu, only it was a really hard flu that lasted from seven weeks to two or three months."

Officer David Lacey was on patrol with a civilian friend at 3 am when the sticky downpour began. "We turned our windshield wipers on, and it just started smearing to the point where we could almost not see," Lacy said. "We both looked at each other and we said, 'Gee this isn't right. We're out in the middle of nowhere, basically, and where did this come from?'"

Pulling into a gas station, officer Lacey pulled on a pair of latex gloves to clean his windshield. Lacey: "The substance was very mushy, almost like if you had Jell-O in your hand." Within hours, Lacey was in hospital unable to breathe.

The gel also fell on Dotty Hearn's porch. She started feeling dizzy. Everything started moving around and she started throwing up. An hour later her daughter and son came home and found Dotty sprawled on the bathroom floor. After a three-day stint in hospital, she was diagnosed with a severe inner ear infection.

Michael McDowell, a Registered Microbiologist for the Washington State Department of Public Health, reported "The substance covered a 20 square mile area on at least three occasions within a six-week period."

Cautioning that the Pseudomonas Fluorescens and Enterobacter Cloacae he found in gel samples could have come from the dirt on Dotti's porch, the RM remarked that the Jell-O-like substance resembled the matrix used to grow cell cultures in a Petri dish.

"We both looked at each other and we said,
'Gee this isn't right'".

PSEUDO BUGS

Another goo sample taken in Fairfield, California on Thanksgiving of that year was found to contain Pseudomonas Aeruginosa. An opportunistic pathogen that can infect the respiratory tract, resulting in a thick mucous, this particular pseudomonas is associated with pneumonia, Staph and bronchitis.

Primarily infecting the lungs. PA can also lead to ear infections, muscle and joint pain, upper respiratory problems, gastrointestinal symptoms, eye infections and meningitis –the exact symptoms being reported by eyewitnesses to the spraying.

Supposedly banned as a biowarfare simulant after being sprayed over San Francisco by the U.S. Navy in 1950 (resulting in at least one immediate fatality and many injuries) – Serratia marscesens was found in a sample of sky-gel that fell in Idaho in March, 19991.

JUST A DAB WILL DO YA

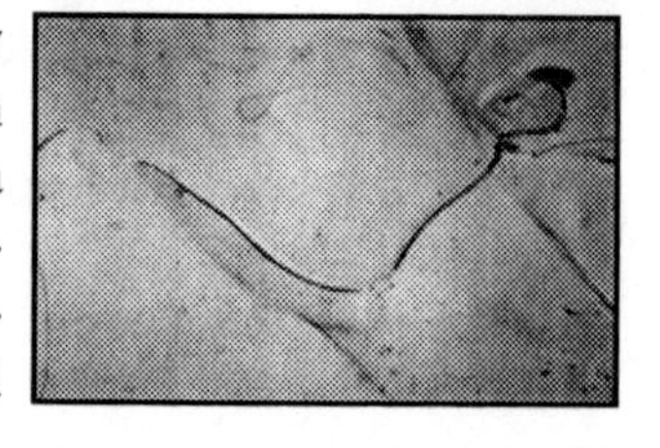

Gel drops by low-flying aircraft may be a separate experiment from the high altitude chemtrail spraying. An Arizona resident reports receiving "a really 'woo-woo' feeling" after finding "clear, gelatinous globs" all over a pickup truck parked in the mountains.

"This stuff did not melt, wouldn't disappear completely when rubbed between the fingers, only broke up into smaller globs."

From Hot Springs, Arkansas in early 1999:

> Most of the time when I watch the planes they are going from east to west. They leave the trails as they are going to the west; they come back with no trails, then go to the west leaving trails again in a parallel design. But I have seen other days that two or three planes will do a criss-cross design. I have only seen the brownish jelly-like goo. I usually saw it on the ground or on pieces of wood from trees.

In what may be descriptive of a separate experiment, reports of "goo" stick to low-level airdrops, not high-altitude chemtrails. In Aptos, California on January 25, 1995

> I was outside doing some gardening at about noon when I heard a very loud and low-flying helicopter. I couldn't see

> which it was as it was slightly foggy. I was in the military. I knew it was flying far below where a normal helicopter would fly. I found the noise deafening, and covered my ears. About a minute or so later, I had to reposition myself to poke another plant into the soil. I noticed that where there had just been nothing but damp asphalt, there was now a small lump of a clear gelatinous like substance. This goo was clear, not green.

A Seattle resident remembers how in 1998, "The gel stuff appeared in a parking lot. Sanitation workers scraped it up into garbage bags and disposed of it. I believe that was on local TV and I have an acquaintance whose children watched some of the clean-up."

The brown gel is especially nasty:

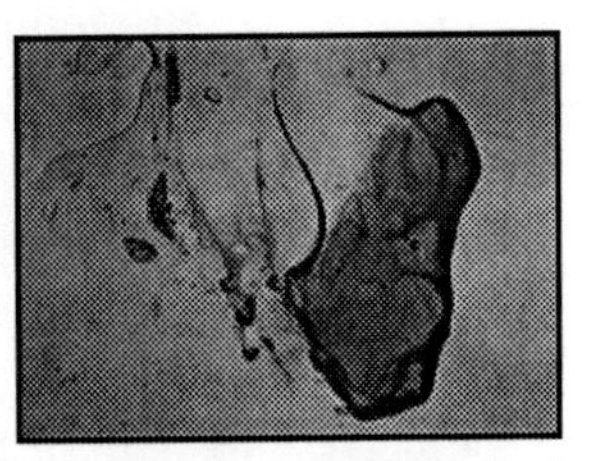

> I have only seen the brownish jelly-like goo. Last fall I had been out in my yard all day, and that night I awoke to go to the bathroom and when I stood up I fell back down into my bed so dizzy it was like I was on a merry go round. The next day I was dizzy with vertigo and throwing up constantly. I was sent to the hospital for a week but they could not help me. I was sent to an ear specialist but he could not find anything wrong. I watch my guinea chicks while they are getting drinks at a nearby spring, and lately I notice a blotch of oily substance at times landing on the water. It appears suddenly, as if from the sky.

"We see these all the time now," reported a Seattle resident early in 2002.

> A glob fell on my face and I got an inner ear infection (as far as the doctor could tell) and I was sent to ER...Another older lady in ER had the same thing I had and I heard her talk about it was the second time recently she got it. I had vertigo so bad I couldn't get out of bed for three days. It was later, when I saw and took pictures of the chemtrails, that I put two and two together since that is one of the symptoms.

In April 2003 there were a lot of chemtrails from Spokane to Ellensburg and while In Seattle, I came down with a bad case of bronchitis (another symptom of this crap in the air). If you have noticed, more and more people are getting allergies and flu-like symptoms and respiratory problems. A lot of people you tell this to, think you are crazy and that it's just contrails. Well, if you study them any at all you can see the difference. Besides commercial planes don't go up in the sky and play tic-tack-toe.

SPLATTERED IN IDAHO

In what appears to be a repeat of the Oakville incident, on Friday evening, Sept. 29, 2000, low-level "gel" expert Erminia Cassani was alerted by her Webmaster, Kathy Gillogly to yet another goo drop – this time over the town of Middleton, Idaho.

An ABC affiliate in Nampa, Idaho ran the story. Video footage of houses splattered with the red-brown spots in a north-south pattern accompanied interviews with local residents – including the almost obligatory media debunking of an "Idaho UFO organization".

Reporting on Cassani's "Moonbow Media" website, Gillogly related how she and a colleague took photos and collected samples from the home of a couple who were "extremely frustrated and angry about the difficulty of getting anyone to take the situation seriously."

It turned out that for the past four months or so, residents of a subdivision in this rural Idaho community had their homes and cars splattered almost daily with smelly, sticky goo. "When you get it wet to try to clean it up, it smells like poop," said one resident Gillogly interviewed. But just as in the Michigan goo drops, the FAA stated that the strange substance could not be from airliner toilets since it did not contain the characteristic blue coloring used in all airplane sanitation systems.

"We find new batches of it daily," said another Middleton resident. "It's nearly impossible to get off of the car and the travel trailer and we've given up on trying to remove it from the siding and the driveway. Just regular washing isn't enough and if you do manage to clean it up, the next day we get it again."

Though many planes fly over Middleton, she continued, no one has ever seen them spraying or dropping anything. "But my daughter was outside one evening and felt a wet, sticky mist hit her just after a plane had flown over. She immediately came in and took a shower and threw her clothes in the washer."

Said another man, "It sure can't be dismissed as an isolated, accidental drop from one plane. It happens every day." Pointing to a nearby school, he added, "We put a piece of white paper down on the strip of vacant property between the subdivision and the elementary school over there. Within a few hours, it was covered with the stuff."

Chemtrail fallout – Saskatchewan

LET LOOSE

Now there is weaponized fungus among us. A woman leaving a restaurant in Perrine, Florida was relived to see clear blue skies. Then she spotted "a fat, long contrail to the east, going from north to south."

> *Oh noooo.* Soon as I got home, got my camera and took three pictures. I called my daughter Lorrie right away. She wasn't home, but her son Sean went outside, saw it, and took pictures. I came back out to check.
>
> *Omigod.* The contrail had come right over my house, grown very wide, and now was *crossed* over with another huge, fat, long contrail. I took a good video shot of it, speaking the date,

> March 6 ['99]. Lorrie called. She had seen the same X while filling her car with gas. Contrails continued to be made – till there were six or seven of them, another "X" and a "3".
>
> I went for a live cell blood analysis and have *mycoplasma* in my blood. Throat burning. Typical red crescents on throat. Have been sneezing blood, weak, dizzy. Many, many people are sick here, with headaches, respiratory ailments, eye problems, sinus problems, "walking pneumonia". Friends who work in the hospital tell me that they can't keep up with the medical records.

MEET MR. MIKE

Mention of mycoplasma is especially worrying, as it is another indication that this once rare infective germ and pet pathogen of bioweaponeers is spreading among civilian populations. A primary agent of transmissible Gulf War Illness currently afflicting more than 200,000 Desert Storm veterans, spouses and children, merely mentioning mycoplasma raises many bright red flares.

Professor Colman Salloway teaches Epidemiology at the University of New Hampshire. During last winter's "flu" epidemic, Salloway was surprised to learn that the university had been treating the problems symptomatically. No cultures had been taken to test for the Type A Sydney influenza said to be afflicting students.

Salloway saw that the on-campus illnesses – referred to by students nationwide as "the plague", were more likely mycoplasma. "The symptoms of the mycoplasma are similar to that of the Type A Sydney; they both cause upper respiratory infection and fever. The difference between them is that the mycoplasma leaves a cough that can last up to four weeks. The influenza is a five to seven day disease."

Lacking identifiable cell walls, the tiny mycoplasma responsible for transmissible Gulf War Illness, autoimmune dysfunction and sudden severe pneumonia requires specialized detection equipment. Few laboratories are equipped to test for a bacteria-like pathogen one-tenth the size of normal bacteria - especially after this ultimate stealth weapon was modified and patented for the U.S. military by Dr. Shyh-Ching Lo of the Armed Forces Institute of Pathology *for use in vaccines*.

Awarded on Sept. 7, 1993, the patent for the invention of "pathogenic mycoplasma" linked Mycoplasma Fermentans with pneumonia, chronic fatigue, respiratory distress and lupus.

As Harvard-trained Dr. Len Horowitz observes:

> It's only been recently that the mainstream media has acknowledged that hospital emergency rooms are filled with patients with this bizarre upper respiratory infection that doesn't quite seem to be a virus – a flu that the flu vaccines were ineffective against. People have been hacking and coughing with this bizarre illness that does not seem to follow any logical viral or bacterial onset and transition period. It was something that did not cause a high fever. It was something that lasted weeks, if not months...and that's exactly what has been developed and patented by the Armed Forces Research Institute of Pathology. A 'pathogenic mycoplasma.'

Extensively tested since the mid-1970s by American and other bioweaponeers, live mycoplasmas were accidentally delivered in supposedly "attenuated" anthrax shots given to Desert Storm soldiers. As my Gulf War book documents, nearly a quarter million soldiers and their families have since become gravely ill with debilitating Gulf War Illness. [*Bringing The War Home*]

> *"There's no question chemtrails are real.*
> *There's no doubt about that."*
>
> – Len Horowitz

The first hard evidence of mycoplasma infection following heavy chemtrail spraying came in March 1999 when a woman wrote:

> Do you recall that I quickly got a very bad Mycoplasma infection after spending 25 minutes outdoors videoing and photographing chemtrails in March 1999? A live blood microscopy test showed them in my blood, and I had the red crescents in my throat. Boy, was I sick. The worst sore throat I ever had in

> my life, even strep wasn't as bad. 'Flu-like' symptoms. Also, swollen glands, leg and joint aches and just could barely drag around for a long time.

Another chemtrail correspondent sent a similar report:

> My family in Virginia has also been ill. My mother has developed an asthma condition over the last year that she never had before in her life. She also had mycoplasma pneumonia a couple of times last year, which she had never even heard of till she got it. She lives in the Norfolk, Virginia area. I have seen spraying there each time I've visited over the last year.

Chapter 4

LOW FLIERS

C-130 demonstrating low-level spraying capability

In November 1998, veteran health researcher Erminia Cassani heard of a strange incident involving air-dropped waste on a suburban Michigan home. Proceeding immediately to the site, Cassani took one look at ominous splatters of what looked like dried blood and knew that this was not toilet waste from an airliner. It did not have the characteristic blue preservative agent that is poured into airline waste holding tanks – which in any case, cannot be jettisoned in flight.

Cassani videotaped the reddish-brown gel across the entire garage, driveway, and parts of the back of the house. The splatter pattern on the garage, she saw, "could only have been caused by a higher velocity spray."

After collecting samples with saline-soaked Q-tips and placing them in plastic Ziploc bags, Cassani called Dr. Peter Maier, a marine biologist at the University of Michigan. When Dr. Maier turned up the magnification on his microscope, both bio-sleuths were startled to see minute protozoan life forms "swimming on the slide quite vigorously." This was strange because the samples had been outside in cold weather for a while.

"They should not have been alive and yet were," Cassani later explained. When Dr. Maier attempted to grow the algae-like material in Petri dishes, and several colors blossomed on the cultures – indicating that several different organisms were present in the sample.

Erminia Cassani next hired a commercial lab to identify her samples. Normally taking three or four days to grow in a Petri dish, Cassani's bacteria-laden sample "flowered" floridly over the weekend. Surprised by how quickly the samples grew "all over the plate," the head of the lab told Cassani she had never seen anything grow so quickly. "Where did you get this bio-hazard material?" she asked Cassani.

Surprised to learn of its origins, the lab tech guessed that it must be some type of biohazard materials that accidentally fell out of a plane descending to a nearby airport, "as the combination of organisms indicated more a clinical setting rather than a natural, environmental setting."

But Cassani pointed out that there were "no containers, no broken glass, no boxes, nothing to suggest a biohazard accident."

The lab found:

Pseudomonas fluorescens – a bacterium that glows like a fluorescent light. Cassani also knew that PF "is commonly found in soil and water and is also associated with food spoilage of protein." Used to eat oil spills, Pseudomonas fluorescens thrives on fuel. It is also an opportunistic pathogen, causing urinary and blood infections in susceptible humans that can lead to fatal shock.

Bacillus amyloliquefaciens – also common to soil. But what was this restriction enzyme doing splattered on aluminum-sided buildings? Employed in biolabs as a natural genetic "scissor" to restrict or cut DNA, this bacillus is used to transfer genetic traits between separate organisms.

Vibrio splendidus 2 – found in coral reefs. Used as a bacterial "marker" in medical and food research, its "day-glow" luminescence can signal the presence of pathogens without putting samples through elaborate tests. "Theoretically," Cassani explains, "if someone were later wanting to test for the presence of 'their' organisms, which they dropped into the environment for whatever reason, the inclusion of Vibrio splendidus would allow them to pick out their organisms from naturally occurring background organisms."

Staphylococcus – a predominant organism in the Michigan samples. This fairly common bacterium is responsible for many infections of the skin and the blood.

Aureobasidium pullans – causes an opportunistic infection in humans that can lead to a severe fungal form of pneumonia.

Streptomyces – another fungus-like bacteria. While more than half of all antibiotics are derived from Streptomyces organisms, the "raw" form found by the lab in Cassani's samples is parasitic to plants and people.

Nigrospora – commonly referred to as a black mold, these illness-causing spores are easily taken into the lungs.

Still skeptical of the link between this chemtrail fallout and widely reported illnesses, Cassani herself fell victim in May 1999. Within 24 hours of finding herself under a "huge, vertical river" of chemtrail chemistry that left a "hairspray-like" material in her hair, the health investigator was stricken with extreme vertigo, a serious upper respiratory infection, swollen lymph glands, sore throat, and general "flu-like" symptoms.

By then, Cassani had taken a second "gel" sample to the same lab for analysis. Sent from Pennsylvania in January 1999, neither Cassani nor I thought it would reveal much since the original incident had occurred the previous January.

This earlier airdrop had been seen by a neighbor who described the plane as "huge, dull gunmetal gray, unmarked" – flying so low, this witness was sure the plane was going to hit his barn. Windows shook as the plane – possibly a C-130 Hercules – swooped overhead to spray several sides of his neighbor's three-story farmhouse.

The homeowners videotaped the damage, and sent a copy of the tape – as well as samples of the reddish-brown material – to Cassani after she made contact a year later. The same Michigan lab tech was as shocked as she was to find the powder-dry material flowering rapidly in the culture dishes.

Their findings included:

Bacillus amyloliquefaciens – also present in the Michigan sample, this airdropped organism from Pennsylvania "was present in an overpowering amount."

Turicella otitidis - the second organism identified can cause nasty middle-ear infections.

Streptomyces – also found in the Michigan samples.

Rhizomucor – a mold that grows on corn plants or bread. It is used to create penicillin.

JUST TESTING

There is plenty of pattern and precedent for unannounced biowarfare experiments on the American public. Two congressional investigations in 1977 and 1994, as well as recently declassified British defense documents, detail five decades of "open air" testing that spread biological warfare simulants from spray-equipped ships and aircraft to hundreds of cities and millions of unsuspecting taxpayers across the U.S., Canada and the U.K.

Even as aerial atomic detonations were being conducted upwind of U.S. cities to test the effects of fallout on unsuspecting residents, airborne biowarfare tests began in earnest in 1957 and 1958 when a cargo plane criss-crossed the country, spraying highly toxic zinc cadmium sulfide chemicals.

A U.S. Army report states, "Virtually, the whole country of the United States was covered with this material."

Prof. Leonard Cole testified at the first congressional investigation into large area biowarfare experiments. The author of *Clouds of Secrecy* described how:

> The plane would take off from the Canadian border, and fly slowly down to the Gulf of Mexico. These materials would be spread, and were found to be landing as far away as New York State. So you know that, as the air would push the zinc cadmium particles around, most of the people who were residents of the United States during that time were inhaling at least some of the zinc cadmium sulfide. And the cadmium in that compound was clearly known then to be toxic, even in small amounts.

Five decades of "open air" testing cynically and clandestinely used millions of people living in the U.S., Canada and Britain as guinea pigs.

Congress also learned that in 1953 the U.S. Army sprayed fluorescent particles containing carcinogenic cadmium sulfide over 25-square-block areas of downtown St. Louis, including what the army called a "slum area". The U.S. Public Health Service's toxic chemical registry warns that cadmium sulfide can lead to lung cancer, high blood pressure and damage to the kidneys, lung, liver – as well damaging the nervous, reproductive and immune systems.

In 1956, U.S. military personnel released mosquitoes infected with Yellow Fever over Savannah, Georgia and Avon Park, Florida. Hog cholera was also released over Eglin AFB in Florida. Following each test, Army agents posing as public health officials tested victims for the effective spread of this disease.

The Army noted that small particles were chosen because they are "considered most effective in penetrating into the lungs."

Also that year, as Prof. Jones of the California Polytechnic Institute points out in his "Short History Of US Bioweapons Testing On Innocent Civilians", Serratia marcescens was sprayed over San Francisco from a U.S. Navy warship steaming just offshore.

Jones notes:

> This organism is especially nice because it produces a red/pink pigment when grown on certain media, which makes identification very easy. At one point, 5000 particles/minute were sprayed from the coastal areas inward. During this time, one man died (in the hospital) and 10 others became infected in what was described as "a mystery to doctors."

"Where did you get this bio-hazard material?"

In 1977, Senate hearings found that 239 U.S. populated areas had been contaminated with biological agents between 1949 and 1969. Some cities included San Francisco, Key West, Washington, D.C., Panama City, Minneapolis, and St. Louis. As recently as 1997, 61 secret tests sprayed Minneapolis residents with germ warfare simulants over a period of several months. Respiratory illness increased sharply in the sprayed areas.

In 1966, more than a million New Yorkers were exposed to biological attack, not from the Soviet Union, but by U.S. Army bioweaponeers who diabolically dropped light bulbs filled with Bacillus subtilis variant Niger through that city's subway ventilation grates.

Similar biowarfare canisters were released in London subways. In the 'Sixties and 'Seventies, British germ-warfare trials also spread Bacillus globigii and E. coli from a ship and a Canberra bomber converted with stainless steel tanks and sprayers. For people with breathing problems or poor immune systems, these bacteria can cause septicemia, fever, pneumonia and chest infections. [*Dorset County Council News* April 16/98]

TITLE 50, SECTION 1520

In the United States, at least, experimenting on the public is legal. Recently revised after decades of silent sanctions, U.S. Code Title 50, Section 1520 still states that the Secretary of Defense may conduct tests or experiments "involving the use of a chemical agent or biological agent on a civilian population" – if they are related to research activity.

Amended in 1997, the law now stipulates that biowarfare tests can be carried out on Americans only if Congress is notified 30 days in advance – and "only if informed consent to the testing was obtained from each human subject in advance of the testing on that subject."

Adhering to Title 50, in June 1999 the Los Alamos National Laboratory announced that it would soon be commencing "open air" tests of biological warfare detectors using the same "harmless" globigii bacillus used in biowarfare simulations on one million Britishers.

The resulting public outcry across the American Southwest caused these tests to be canceled.

1-800-I-GOT-FLU

Perhaps not coincidentally, pervasive radio and TV ads during ongoing epidemics over the past two years have urged Americans to phone special "1-800-I-GOT-FLU" tracking numbers. Startled callers learned that they must qualify for the study by contracting specific symptoms within a limited radius of exposure within a certain time frame.

Similar ad campaigns continue to provide 1-800 meningitis and migraine numbers. Are these ways of tracking nationwide reports of accidental or deliberately induced illness?

ESPANOLA'S EXPERIENCE

What residents described as "frequent spraying" over Espanola began in March 1999. By July, mounting public pressure compelled the provincial Ministry of Environment to dispatch an air monitoring van. At the raucous August 10 town meeting, environment officials pronounced the air "safe" – but reportedly refused to make public the actual air sampling analysis.

On Aug 29, 1999, CBC Newsworld reported from Espanola, Ontario: "Residents of a small town west of Sudbury, Ontario are anxious. They think they're getting sick, and they think they know why. It involves the U.S. military, the government and strange planes overhead."

Canada's national news network noted, "Tempers at the Espanola town council run high. Residents want to know what's flying over their community. Shelly Jordan thinks strange planes might be making her kids sick...In fact, many in the community have reported respiratory problems and strange aches and pains. Town council heard that some believe military jets are dropping material over the town as part of a weather experiment."

The MOE also tested particulate samples collected in by a resident in March 1999. The provincial lab analysis found traces of mica and large quantities of highly reflective quartz grains. Following a fresh snowfall, this reluctant activist discovered "a four-block area covered in carbon. Environmental officials swear it's not from Sudbury, or the town's paper mill." While admitting the use of carbon in weather modification activities, the U.S. Air Force denied flying its planes over Espanola.

Residents countered with eyewitness reports and photos of USAF tankers spreading broad white plumes over the region.

An independent Ontario lab also analyzed McNenly's samples of rainwater collected after falling through thick chemtrail plumes. The lab looked for EDB (a carcinogenic jet fuel additive) – and did not find any in measurable quantities.

Fresh rainwater sampled on May 31, June 4 and June 7 in Espanola did find an overgrowth of bacteria and a high count of 80 Coliform per 100ml. (Samples were collected in stainless steel pots sterilized with 3% peroxide and placed on an outdoor table four feet off the ground.)

More than 550 residents of this small Ontario community petitioned to parliament to "ban all cloud-seeding activity by civil or military aircraft, foreign or domestic."

"Quartz is probably the biggest part of this," a HAM radio operator told this reporter. "A really big deal."

Noting powerful electronic interference audible across shortwave bands when the Prime Minister's campaign plane made a forced landing in the area because of "electrical problems", this source explained that electromagnetically conductive quartz is a "very unusual technology" used in many of Tesla's experiments.

The CDC calls talcum-fine quartz a hazardous substance: inhaling it can cause silicosis. Despite it's known health risks, quartz "fine as flour" began sifting down over Espanola in March 1999. Around midnight one resident went outside. "I could see it coming down – totally bizarre. It was wintertime and it was sparkling. And it wasn't snow."

A sample "gingerly" scraped off a car was subsequently lab-tested at 80% quartz grains. The remaining wood fiber concentration probably came from a woodchip pile two blocks away.

The lab did not classify any of the 1600 molds/fungi found in the rainwater, reporting only that "no one species was dominant."

But the level of aluminum in the chemtrail-contaminated sample was .53 (ppm): 7-times over the previous "safe" threshold set by the Ontario government for drinking water.

Describing the mysterious malaise that began in the wake of the tanker overflights as "free-floating, abstract, can't really put your finger on anything," one resident noticed "a lot of depressed people in Espanola." In addition, "A lot of people here in town are complaining of short term memory loss." People can't remember simple errands, or where they parked their cars. It's become, he added without humor, "a running joke."

Blaming the chemtrail spraying for widespread respiratory problems and strange aches and pains that were suddenly endemic over a 50 mile area, more than 550 residents of this small Ontario community petitioned to parliament to "ban all cloud-seeding activity by civil or military aircraft, foreign or domestic."

COMMITTEES OF THE HOUSE PROCEDURE AND HOUSE AFFAIRS PETITIONS: AIRCRAFT EMISSIONS (Nov. 18, 1999)

Member of Parliament Mr. Gordon Earle:

Mr. Speaker, over 500 residents of the Espanola area have signed a petition raising concern over possible government involvement in what appears to be aircraft emitting visible aerosols. They have found high traces of aluminum and quartz in particulate and rainwater samples. These concerns combined with associated respiratory ailments have led these Canadians to take action and seek clear answers from this government. The petitioners call upon parliament to repeal any law that would permit the dispersal of military chaff or of any cloud-seeding substance whatsoever by domestic or foreign military aircraft without the informed consent of the citizens of Canada thus affected.

The Department of National Defense eventually replied: "It's not us."

But more lowdown aerial spraying was also taking place at treetop level over Espanola that had nothing to do with weather modification.

Retirees "Bob" and "Jean" (not their real names) spend several months every year on Birch Island near Espanola. After nearby residents reported air force C-130 transports dropping a red powder that appeared to be making children sick, health investigator Erminia Cassani found the retired couple in their beautiful home overlooking McGregor Bay:

> On July 18th, 1999, as they were sitting out on their patio that overlooks the Bay, Jean suddenly caught sight of a nearly silent, extremely low-flying, very large, gray plane literally gliding over the roof of their home, skimming the treetops of their property. It was that low, no more than 50 to 100' off the ground! Seeing her surprise, Bob jumped up to see this huge, completely unmarked plane gliding right over them and their patio. Stunned, and too afraid to move, they stood watching the plane glide silently out towards the water, trailing a reddish-brown powdery trail, which covered their patio, their dock, and their neighbors dock. They ran to the water's edge and watched the plane glide silently down the bay until it was out of sight, all the while dropping the reddish powder that fell quietly and disappeared into the waters of McGregor Bay.

Cassani and another chemtrails investigator from Espanola collected samples, as well as interviews. It was spooky, Cassani recounts. "The powder must have reconstituted somewhat from water in the bottom of their neighbor's boat as the entire bottom of the boat was covered with a very red sticky film, almost as if blood had been wiped from the bottom and sides of the boat."

After videotaping the scene, Cassani covered her hands with surgical gloves before scraping a big Q-tip along the bottom of the pail. "What came up on the Q-tip was incredible, a blood-red substance that adhered to the Q-tip like a gelatinous gob."

Without prompting, Bob identified the spray plane as a C-130 Hercules transport plane. He and Jean told Cassani and her companion that they and their neighbors – even the neighbors' dog – became ill with fever, chills, a "flu-like" malaise soon after the red powder was dropped over their property. The neighbors' boy swam in McGregor Bay. He came down with pneumonia after returning home to Toronto that weekend.

A concerned Cassani took the Birch Island samples to the same lab that had analyzed the previous two samples.

The new samples turned out to be very similar to the Michigan and Pennsylvania samples. The bacteria found in the low-level Birch Island drop included: Pseudomonas, Staphylococcus and Bacillus. The fungi found included a primitive mold, Penicillium, and Acremonium – "a rather nasty organism," Cassani comments, "found in patients who are immunocompromised, most frequently AIDS patients."

By then, Erminia Cassani had spent more than a year investigating low-level drops of pathogens across the U.S. A total of 29 fly-overs dropped "goo" in the state of Utah alone, where Cassani interviewed eyewitnesses and officials:

> What's so special about Utah that they might have such occurrences? The fact that Dugway Proving Ground is only minutes away from where all these drops occurred might shed some light on the phenomenon. If anyone there were talking, that is. Dugway, in Provo, is one of the country's centers for biological open-air testing and development.
>
> Could these fly-over goo drops in Utah have been part of either open-air biological testing or accidents of transport of some biological materials? Maybe.
>
> When talking to a few of the "victims" of these fly-over goo drops, it was learned that all of these occurrences happened at night, with the homeowners waking up and finding their houses splattered with this brownish goo.
>
> A young man whom I interviewed told me how he and his family were housesitting their parents home while they were away on a religious mission in another country. They woke up to go to work in the morning at 7 a.m. and found the garage, driveway and part of the house splattered with this material. Bryan also told me that the local HAZMAT team, complete in head-to-toe biochemical hazard gear, was quickly dispatched from the Fire Department. They didn't take samples. They just quickly sprayed the entire area down with bleach after taking photos.

Bob jumped up to see this huge, unmarked plane gliding right over their patio.

Another Utah home was hit on April 10th, 1999. On discovering the "goo", this family immediately contacted the Salt Lake County Fire Department. At first reluctant to wash away the material, fearing it could contaminate storm-water systems, the fire department told the homeowners to contact a private biohazard-cleanup company, who also balked at cleaning up the mystery material.

A day later, the Fire Department relented and eventually cleaned off the goo, employing a bleach concoction, which is used in laboratories to kill bacterial and viral contaminants. The family was told to keep themselves and their pets out of the yard. But officials declined further explanation for these drastic restrictions. Cassani's questions to the Director of Public Health were left unanswered. A secretary referred the health investigator to a lab testing a few samples of the residue.

But numerous calls by Cassani were never returned as the public health director issued a public statement stating that the material contained was "sewage" dropped by a pilot "prankster" over the city.

Twenty-nine times.

From late 1998 through June, 1999 Erminia Cassani has documented 33 low-level drops – many taking place in the same areas. She wonders if similar treetop-level drops at opposite end of the country are meant to combat some sort of mutant fungi spawned by global warming, or leaky biowarfare labs in Ontario and other locales.

The HAZMAT team didn't take samples before spraying the area with bleach.

In October 2000 a school bus driver from Orcas Island commented on the gel's strange consistency:

> I just want to let you know that, about two years ago, I and two or three students saw two to three apple/orange-sized hunks of a gelatinous substance on the ground and sidewalk outside the

> school bus-barn located at the Doe Bay Fire-house, on Orcas Island, Washington. I was curious, suspicious, and cautious. I found a small twig and used it to "feel" the material. It felt quite firm, dense, solid; its appearance reminded me of a jelly-fish; the substance laid as though it had been "knocked-out" of a small Jell-O cup-mold dish; sort of flat on the side of the material in contact with the sidewalk. It stayed in place for a good many days.

There is no indication that the fungi found in lab tests of samples taken from low-level air drops can be used to interdict invading weeds or fungi. But some fungus is an effective killer of other plants. A 1977 Army report to Congress on a secret program that doused wheat fields in North Dakota with a fungus to test ways of killing livestock and crops to starve families in commie countries.

KILLER FUNGUS

Writing in May 2000 for the *Third World Network*, Chakravarthi Raghavan reported from Geneva that the "Sunshine" organization from Seattle and Hamburg was hoping to halt U.S. government experiments using "agent Green" fungi to kill narco-crops. These microbial pathogens pose risks to human health and all life whose web sustains us all. Prohibiting the use of microbial fungi in the United States has not stopped Congress from approving $23 million for the testing and development of Pleospora and other fungi aimed at killing opium poppies and marijuana in other countries.

While it is clear that low-level drops of fungi and molds in mainstream American suburbs have not been pot shots fired at pot growers, experimental and naturally toxic fungi are proliferating. According to the air force, specifically modified aircraft are used by the 757th wing based at Youngstown, Ohio, for aerial spraying. A magazine published by the Reserve Officers Association of the United States describes 910th airing training in May 2000 to deploy pesticides from their C-130s.

According to Ohio chemtrails activist Kim Weber, "The training included working with weather personnel and using maps to coordinate and calculate the amount of pesticides needed." [*The Officer* July 2000]

The 757th has six Modular Aerial Spray Systems and four MASS-modified C-130s. Each MASS has a 2,000-gallon capacity and flow rate of 232 gallons per minute.

The aircraft makes its spray runs at 200 Knots at just 100 feet, laying a 100 foot-wide swath of the herbicide glyphosate over targets including illicit Colombian coca plants.

Pesticide spray tanks being loaded aboard C-130s

Colombian farmers hit by this new "Agent Orange" complain that wind-drifted fungi banned by the UN are hitting adjacent agricultural fields.

"The fumigation has caused damage to our yucca and sugarcane crops and has caused sickness in our children," said Francisco Tenorio, president of the Regional Indigenous Organization. Across Columbia, communities report that indiscriminate fumigation is causing illnesses, destroying pastures and food crops, poisoning livestock and contaminating water supplies. Photos displayed at a press conference showed food crops destroyed by fumigation alongside thriving coca plants that somehow escaped the herbicide.

About 500 bird species also inhabit the region targeted by USAF C-130 spray planes. The Environmental Protection Agency's own study on the herbicide published in 1993 noted that in California, a state that is required to report pesticide poisonings, glyphosate was ranked third out of the 25 leading causes of illness or injury due to pesticides. [*Inter-Press Service* Nov. 22/00]

"From a global bio-diversity perspective, defoliating and poisoning vast areas of Colombian forests is like dynamiting the Taj Mahal, a global jewel of humanity's cultural heritage," said David Olson, director of the conservation science program at the World Wildlife Fund. Olson said large areas of forest are being contaminated and stripped of their leaves, causing a loss of habitat for species and increased fragmentation of intact forests.

Just like the USAF defoliation operations that devastated Vietnam.

Mike Castle, the Ohio-based environmental consultant and self-described "polymer chemist" who discovered the 1994 Hughes Aerospace chemtrails patent for "Reduction Of Global Warming", now says he has identified genetically-modified fungal "bio-control agents" in air-dropped polymer strands.

Castle says the "Fusarium" he found in a Seattle sample is aimed at killing any plants containing THC - the active ingredient in marijuana responsible for reducing anyone exposed to official "spin" to helpless laughter.

POUNDED IN PARHUMP AND PEGOSA

North Americans are also being hit. In May 2000, a former pilot/mechanic wrote from Pahrump where he and his wife have been living for six-and-a-half years.

"My wife came down with kidney cancer in Dec 97 and I caught viral meningitis in Dec. '99," Jim wrote. "We are both in our mid- thirties. Her doctor was absolutely surprised to see someone her age with her form of cancer. I hate to open up an additional can of worms, but my infection came down 48hrs after an extremely low pass at 160 and Basin by a C-130 that was leaving a black trail. One trail from a four-engine airplane. It smelled strongly of jet fuel.

Crossing the street in Pegosa Springs, Colorado in the summer of 2000, I stood stunned as a throttled-back, camouflaged-colored C-130 Hercules swooped silently over this remote resort town. Pulling out at 500 feet, well below the 1,000-foot separation from structures mandated by federal regulations, I watched two spray trails spurt from the wings outboard of the engines. Continuing into town, I was not surprised to find many store employees coughing and sneezing.

WHO IS BEHIND THE LOW-LEVEL SPRAYING?

Investigative reporter John Titus presented a possible clue to this key question. In his updated story, "Who's Who in the C-130 Scandal," published in the March/April 1997 edition of the *Portland Free Press*, Titus documents the diversion of an estimated 42 former Navy P-3 Orions and spray-equipped Air Force C-130's from firefighting duties with the U.S. Forest Service to the CIA.

It is well documented how C-130s have been used by the CIA for drug smuggling to procure arms for the Contra terrorists and other covert operators. As Titus reveals, "Tail number N69-P operated on contract for the U.S. military's Nuclear Defense Agency and was later busted by the DEA in Miami, Florida, on a cocaine smuggling mission."

But the ubiquitous Hercules can be leased or purchased without range-reducing spray gear. Why does the CIA need spray-equipped C-130s? Is there any tie-in with the many reports of low-flying C-130s spraying communities across the U.S. as well as Canada?

FUNDING THE SPRAY PLANES

An investigation by *Mother Jones* magazine has documented how $100 million-a-day "back door" transfers of tax dollars are used to fund the Pentagon's black operations. None of this money – or the projects it funds – is accountable to Congress or the American people.

SPRAY PLANE BASES

Outside Dobbins Air Base in Marietta, Georgia, one observer writes: "We drove up to a light and saw the runway, and saw a large, white plane, with a blue stripe, no markings at all, taxiing to take off."

Alleged spray jets - Oregon 2003

A delivery person at Tinker AFB states "I have seen more than 30 of these white, KC-135s parked on the tarmac. I have seen six to 10 take off, one after another. They are, indeed, white with no markings."

The white planes have also been spotted at a former AFB near Phoenix, and at the previously closed George AFB in the Mojave Desert. Unfortunately, few people travel with telephoto cameras. No close-up photographs have been obtained to corroborate these ground sightings.

But at least one correspondent claims to have personally seen the spray planes taking off from and landing at McGuire AFB in New Jersey. Active in the Canadian military "since my birth," Bryan says, "What I have noticed is that unusual trails have been coming from white USAF KC-135s heading to Shilo, Alaska."

A front-page article published in the *Journal* identified an obscure program at Kirtland AFB called "Agent Conceal Weapon." The logo showed clouds with big blue drops coming out of them, and a beaker of bubbling chemicals, divided by a bolt of lightning.

GUESS WHO'S FLYING THE JETS?

The tip-off to the tankers came on March 2, 2000 when the Associated Press reported that hundreds of KC-135s had been grounded to fix problems in their tail feathers. The next day, the chemtrail tracking center in Houston reported that daily spraying over the U.S. had suddenly dropped from 24 to just two locations. As the big jets were returned to service the following week, Chemtrail sightings climbed right back to previous levels.

Phoenix Feb. 15/00

PHOENIX RISING

Sid has been investigating chemtrail activity for more than four year. It's hard to avoid, living in Phoenix. "As you are probably aware, we have missed our monsoon season for the last three years," he writes.

"No accident! I've watched the Citation and Lear type jets destroy the oncoming storms for the last three years. KCs also!"

On Oct 6, 2002, while visiting Deer Park airport outside of Phoenix, Sid "got lucky, and got up close and personal photos from a few feet away of the adaptations made to the engines of a Citation Bravo aircraft."

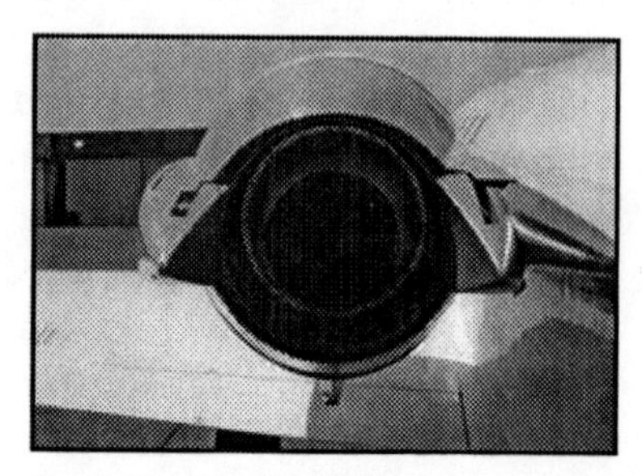

(Note the big vent in the fuselage and small nozzle under the engine on the right.)

Sid sent copies of his photos to Cessna and Pratt & Whitney's corporate headquarters.

"P&W responded with a phone call and subsequent emails," Sid relates. "What I can tell you now is that the engineers had no idea what the modifications were for. I think they do now! As far as I'm aware, it's the only photographic proof of the engine modifications used to spray DynOMat or whatever to suppress rain clouds."

A check of the aircraft tail number by this reporter found a Hughes helicopter listed by that N number.

Chapter 5

FUNGUS AMONG US

Brampton, Ontario July 17. 2002

Warmer wetter weather worldwide has resulted in an explosion of *Stachybotrys* (Stack-ee-bot-ris) – an especially lethal black mold – growing in wet wood and paper products in damp homes and office buildings.

Stachybotrys is no joke. Loaded as an air-dried powder into SCUD missiles fired by the Iraqi Chemical Corps against coalition troops during the Gulf War, this household mold is responsible for lost memory, lost jobs, serious breathing difficulties, memory and hearing loss, severe dizziness and flu-like symptoms, even fatal bleeding in the lungs. At least one Texas dream home has been quarantined behind stern signs warning:

"DO NOT ENTER – BIOHAZARD"

Time correspondent Arnold Mann cites 1996 and 1999 studies at the Eastern New York Occupational and Environmental Health Center, which found that people with long exposure to Stachybotrys and other fungi experience chronic fatigue, loss of balance, irritability, memory loss and difficulty speaking. College graduates used to functioning at a high level are reduced to a haphazard, stumbling existence.

Mann mentioned a 1999 Mayo Clinic study that pegged nearly all the chronic sinus infections afflicting 37 million Americans to molds.

Other recent studies have linked molds to the tripling of the asthma rate over the past 20 years. Modern airtight homes, with air-conditioning and heating systems recirculating contaminated air, are more prone to moldy malaise than older houses.

Colonies of microscopic mycotoxins can haunt new buildings, whose inhabitants puzzle over headaches, dizziness and fatigue, followed by respiratory and sinus problems. Some victims cough up blood, suffer profusely bloody noses – and test negative for allergies. Reporter Jacqueline Marino describes the grief of Merunas Dautartas after her daughter Katelynn died from bleeding lungs caused by black mold growing in a flood-damaged home. "Every person I meet, I say, 'Have you heard about [black mold]?' You go out on the street, and everyone knows about AIDS. Everyone should know about this, too."

A survey of chemtrail-stricken patients found 99% with fungus in their blood.

Bu global warming alone cannot account for a new black plague of extremely toxic mold spreading through basements and bedrooms across North America. A specialist who conducts environmental sampling of indoor environments later confided that the contamination he is seeing is so extensive it's making all of his team's hard work remediating infested homes a total waste of time. He wonders if the mystery mold is "dropping our of the sky."

Puleo and Horowitz note how dormant fungus can be "raised from the dead" by exposing it to ultraviolet light. Could fungal spores colonizing the fuel tanks in jet tankers be inadvertently sprayed and activated by high levels of high altitude UV, mutating them into mycotoxins?

WHAT HAS CHANGED IN YOUR PERSONAL ENVIRONMENT?

Whatever their origins, there is increasing fungus among us. Some, like the recent Pfeisteria hysteria, have escaped from long dormancy, emerging suddenly in populations and bloodstreams like creatures from the Black Lagoon. Others, like mycoplasma fermentans, have been genetically modified to inoculate and infect soldiers.

Chemist and botanist Bruce Tanio's list of symptoms is familiar to many people exposed to chemtrails:

- Abdominal pain, gas and bloating, indigestion, heartburn, constipation, diarrhea, gastritis.
- Poor memory, headaches, and light-headedness.

Tanio is describing what happens when microscopic fungi invade the body. But despite the upsurge of damp-loving fungus in North American homes and offices, it is inconceivable that millions of people would be simultaneously stricken on the same weekend, jamming hospital emergency rooms with acute allergies to long-accruing natural molds.

A good doctor asks: "What has changed in your environment that could be making you ill?" In almost every case among the more observant, the answer must be: "Chemtrails!"

In late 1999 the *Idaho Observer* observed "Last year, north Idaho naturopaths determined that the upper respiratory infections that would drag on for months were not viral or bacterial but were fungal."

In a recent survey among 179 patients reportedly suffering from CRI:

- 22% had been to a hospital Emergency Room.
- 34% exhibited rashes and sores.
- half or more had experienced disorientation and suffered from stiff neck and gastro-intestinal problems.
- 72% had a sore throat.
- 78% reported severe headaches.
- 81% complained of congestion.
- Almost everyone surveyed experienced short-term memory loss and difficulty in concentrating.
- Fully 99% were found to have fungus in their blood

"Weaponized" fungi remain prime suspects in outbreaks of inexplicable illness across the United States, Canada and other allied nations.

Because they are non-inflammatory, bio-engineered stealth viruses also stay hidden, while infecting the brain and nervous system. The long incubation period of these "slow viruses" result in prolonged degenerative disorders that feed on a nasty fungal feedback loop.

In *Healing Codes For A Biological Apocalypse*, Horowitz and Puleo point out: "As fungi grow in the body, their fermentation products further acidify blood and tissues, further taxing the immune system and leaving people more susceptible to opportunistic infections and even certain cancers."

Fungus can also "morph" into bacterial infections. Puleo has found that low fluctuating body temperatures among "those with the first horrible cough: 95.6, 96.8, 97.4, 97.6 – encourages the formation of bacterial crystal chains as fungal infections flip to bacterial states."

ANOTHER CHEMTRAIL CONVERT

As blatant chemtrail spraying, and inexplicable illness on the ground, continued in tandem across the USA, Canada and a dozen other allied nations. Trent told me,

> I thought you were "all wet" on this subject of "Chemtrails" but I have to say I have observed one somewhat strange "contrail" on Mach 15, 2001 at 6:30 pm. What I saw was two large jets flying in close formation at a high altitude. This formation of jets was flying from north to south over Melbourne Florida. Both jets were emitting large sustained and spreading white "contrails".
>
> I thought it looked a little strange in and of itself but the thing that really got my attention was that all of a sudden one jet still in close formation with the other stopped emitting the "contrail" while the other one continued! This made it clear to me that this "contrail" was indeed some sort of "spray" based on the way it could be suddenly turned on and off next to another jet which continued to emit the "contrail"!

CHEMTRAILS STREET THEATER

Lawrence described a solo street performance in Toronto:

> On Sunday April 15 at 4.30 p.m., a lady about 25-30 years old

approached my wife's friend Marie in downtown Toronto. Marie said that the woman had a book, a petition to be signed and a sign or placard about chemtrails. Marie was on her way to church and told the woman that she was in a hurry and didn't have time to sign a petition.

My wife and I heard this from Marie today, April 22, 2001. When we were getting into my car, intending to leave the corner of Dufferin Street and Lawrence Avenue West, I happened to look up and saw eight chemtrails crisscrossing the sky. Then I mentioned the word chemtrails to Marie and she told us what had happened on the 15th. It was 3 p.m. today when we saw the trails. I looked and saw that one aircraft looked large and silvery.

When I phoned my friend Harry tonight to tell him about the incident, he said that he was bicycling at 4.30 p.m. his eyes started to water, he looked up and saw chemtrails spreading across the sky and blotting out the sun. We have to keep on the trail of the trails. My wife went to bed an hour ago, complaining of a slight headache and some nausea.

As chemtrails continue to contaminate the new millennium, George wrote from Phoenix on Jan, 8, 2002:

This morning at approximately 8:20 am, southeast Phoenix, had a blitz of contrails finishing around 12 noon. I stopped by an environmental emissions site and asked the supervisor to come out and look up. The sky was littered with the trails of planes as they turned and crisscrossed past South Mountain, returning over Scottsdale. The wind was lightly blowing northeast.

The state employee said he'd contact someone higher just to make sure the airport knew. I pointed out to him to look at the one directly overhead; it was dissipating horizontally widening to over 300 ft across.

On a clear day with a lovely blue sky these aircraft cross-hatched the sky to such an extent that they appeared to be ribbons of white and blue. The contrail planes were at altitude too, as the airport was having its own passenger plane business. Later it was great to see the feathery cirrus clouds that came from the west, just to reaffirm nature. I'm concerned for the safety and well-being of the people who are working in Light and Love in this region.

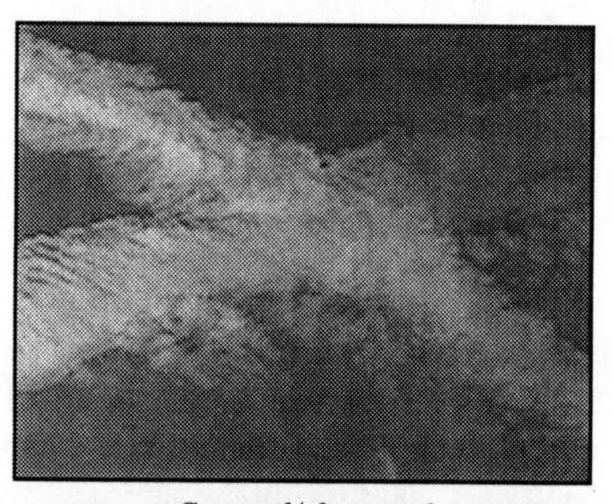

Contrail/chemtrail

ENMOD

Concerned over the 1967-1971 Operation Popeye weather modification program over Vietnam and Laos, Senator Claiborne Pell - chairman of the Senate Subcommittee on Oceans and International Environment and later chairman of the Foreign Relations Committee – led a Congressional revolt of "doves".

"Rainmaking as a weapon of war can only lead to the development of vastly more dangerous environmental techniques whose consequences may be unknown and may cause irreparable damage to our global environment," Senator Pell pleaded. "This is why the United States must move quickly to ban all environmental or geophysical modification techniques from the arsenals of war."

The 1977 "Convention on the Prohibition of Military or Any Other Hostile Use of the Environmental Modification Techniques" specifically prohibits "the use of techniques that would have widespread, long-lasting or severe effects through deliberate manipulation of natural processes and cause such phenomena as earthquakes, tidal waves and changes in climate and weather patterns."

ENMOD was signed by Washington and Moscow.

Chapter 6

SEE NO EVIL

Chemjet

In September 1999, John Volkerdin of the New Mexico Environmental Protection Division responded to a letter from Alan Hutner of the Santa Fe-based Skywatchers organization. The environmental enforcement specialist stated that after contacting the National Guard, U.S. Army, New Mexico Agricultural Department, New Mexico Department of Military Affairs, and the Federal Aviation Administration – "the data does not suggest that any illegal or clandestine activity is occurring."

Another Santa Fe resident was contacted after complaining about the chemtrails: "I have finally received responses from the Health Dept. and Attorney General here. Same o' same o'. Just normal contrail activity. Meanwhile, I just had some clients cancel their appointments because the whole family of six were down with pneumonia."

A July 29, 1999 Skywatchers' letter to the office of the Attorney General of New Mexico received a November 30 response from Assistant Attorney General Donald Trigg and researcher, M. Kimber Johnson. As Trigg told it: "Based on the information I reviewed, there is substantial evidence that the activity and contrails you observed are well within the range of normal aerial and contrail activity."

NOAA RESPONDS

All chemtrail questions to the National Oceanic and Atmospheric Administration are directed to Jana Goldman who told reporters that she "can't comment" on chemtrails.

THE EPA RESPONDS

November 30, 1999
Subject: Complaint regarding Contrail/Chemtrails

Thank you for contacting Ohio EPA...Our authority is over those facilities and companies in Ohio that generate waste materials, emit pollutants or discharge wastewater into waters of the state.

Ohio EPA does not have regulatory authority over aircraft, aircraft emissions or the situations you describe...At this time, Ohio EPA does not have the legal authority, resources or documentation to investigate this matter. While we are unable to complete an investigation into all the claims expressed in your original Email, we do appreciate your concern over the environment.

Sincerely,
Tracy Freeman
Public Information Coordinator
Ohio EPA

DEPARTMENT OF HEALTH AND ENVIRONMENTAL CONTROL REPLIES:

Like so many states, South Carolina's DHEC notes that there are "no [state] regulations on emissions from mobile sources."

A VICE-PRESIDENTIAL CANDIDATE QUESTIONS CONTRAILS

On March 5, 1999, Senator Joseph Lieberman wrote to EPA head

Carol Browner regarding constituent concerns "about the possible release of toxic chemical substances from jet contrails" and "reports of toxic spraying over populated areas in 41 states." In calling for a response from the EPA, Senator Lieberman noted that "My constituents further point out recent outbreaks of flu-like symptoms and other sicknesses in Connecticut and other states that may possibly be linked to jet fuel exhaust fumes."

No reply from the EPA was ever forwarded.

Sky watchers are still awaiting the outcome of New Mexico Representative Tom Udall's March 13, 2000 request to the House Transportation and Infrastructure Committee to hold oversight hearings on the "chemtrails" issue.

> *"One jet still in close formation with the other stopped emitting the 'contrail' while the other one continued!"*

A METEOROLOGIST RESPONDS

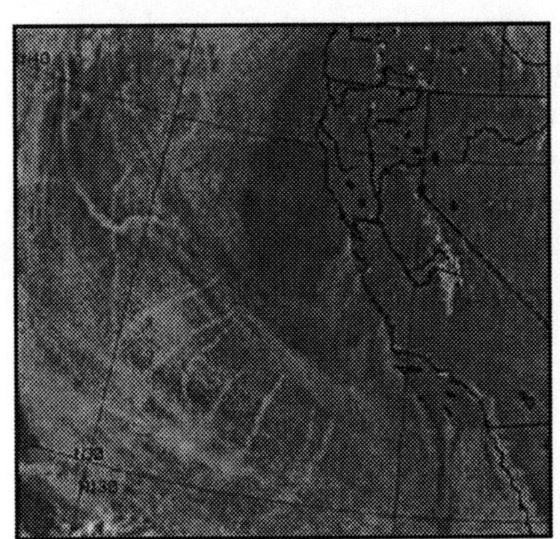

"Do you know what a shiptrail is?" asks David Jones. "Do you realize that one of the websites you referenced regarding these spooky cloud formations has a front page with an image of a shiptrail on it?"

Shallow stratus clouds sometimes trail the tracks of large ships. Called "ship tracks", they are sometimes mistaken for contrails or chemtrails in satellite photographs. Caused by condensation around particles wafting skyward from the ships' funnels, these linear clouds form above the wakes from ships. A field study called MAST (Monterey Area ShipTrack) conducted during June 1994 off the central California coast found them to be up to 5 km wide and "remarkably long-lived".

[*Geophysical. Research*]

CONGRESS RESPONDS

Concerned citizens have asked many mayors and congressional representatives to intercede. Among those contacted in writing are senators Ben Nighthorse Campbell, Wayne Allard, Jesse Helms, Edwards, McCain, Murray and Bingaman. In the House of Representatives Jon Kyl, Charles Taylor, Tom Allen, Bob Stump and Wayne Allard have also been contacted.

Senator John McCain contacted the U.S. Air Force. On August 3, 1999 Col. Michael Anderson of the USAF Legislative Liaison must have forgotten megatons of Agent Orange and more than one million deformed children of Vietnam when he replied: "The U.S. Air Force does not conduct spraying operations over populated areas."

Commenting that McCain's complaining constituent may have been looking at normal contrails, the colonel continued: "The Contrails are safe, contrary to misinformation on the Internet and other sources. Emissions from jet engines are basically the same as from car or diesel engines."

Contrails composed of water vapor *are* safe – at least for people. But as another constituent comments:

> I recently wrote to my representatives from Maine. I received a call from Rep. Tom Allen's' office telling me that they had assigned my complaint to the student intern in the office. They made a request for info to the FAA and the EPA, both of whom wrote back saying that the Chemtrails were just normal jet contrails and that the stupid public was simply being misled by erroneous reports on the Internet. Clearly, they are in deep deep denial and are treating the public with total contempt.

THE FAA RESPONDS

Speaking from his Los Angeles office, head of the FAA's Western region, Charles Lieber, told this investigator "There are no unidentified aircraft flying over the USA. There's different people looking at different types of aircraft flying back and forth across the country."

Three regional FAA Centers in the East, Central and West United States track all transiting aircraft flying at or above 18,000 feet. Each must file a flight plan identified by a flight number. "We know where they are all the time," Lieber affirmed. Not quite. Airspace may be cleared for aircraft on military or covert missions that are not required to "squawk" identifying civilian transponder codes. Or file a civilian flight plan.

After I relayed our conversation to the person who set up the interview, my intermediary informed me: "I just called and talked with Charles Lieber in the LA Regional office of FAA. He said he hadn't talked with you. I quoted what you said you were told by the FAA person, and he said he hadn't made those comments."

Though no noise complaints have ever been received in connection with whisper-quiet chemtrails, Lieber recommended that reports concerning unusual airplane activity be sent in writing to the Noise Ombudsman in Washington, DC.

Is this "file-a-noise-complaint" response a cover-up for clandestine flights in which airspace is specially cleared by the FAA and therefore requires no flight plans to be filed?

When a Toronto chemtrail observer called the Pearson International Airport authority in the spring of '99, he was startled to hear "an obvious military voice" on the phone. Pretending to be an airplane buff, the caller excitedly asked where the air show was.

The airport authority was taken off guard. "There's no air show today," he stammered.

"Well," the caller responded, "I'm watching KC-10's and KC-135s painting low contrails over the West end of Toronto. I'm looking at them right now."

"Contrails!" The official was clearly taken aback, almost shouting the word "I have no information on that!" To the caller he actually sounded scared...before giving out the FAA number for noise control.

The U.S. Air Force does not conduct spraying operations over populated areas.

Perhaps the most ludicrous official response came in March 1999 when a Michigan caller complained of three bouts of illness suffered by him and his girlfriend after heavy chemtrail activity. An FAA representative calmly explained the unusual aerial activity as "delayed Christmas traffic."

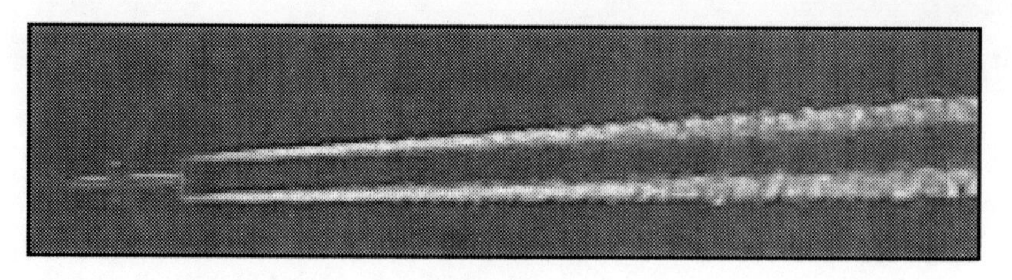

MORE NOISE FROM THE FAA

Another correspondent has been trying to report what's going on in the skies above the SF Bay Area. But as of March 28, 2003 he was still having difficulty finding anyone to talk to at the Oakland International Airport: "The operator will not give me a number for Air Traffic Control, saying it's against the law to give it out. They say they cannot connect me to any live person, telling me they will connect me to the voice message service for noise complaints."

Sydney also "tried the FAA, EPA, Calif Highway Patrol, Berkeley City Police Department and many more. I was able to get through to the aides for Congresspersons Dennis Kucinich and Barbara Lee, but I did not feel heard. The heaviest spraying I've seen in the last one and a half weeks of bombardment, was on International Women's Day, March 8th, a day on which there were many, many peace marches and rallies."

The man Sydney finally reached at the office of Bay Area Air Quality Management "said hello with a cheery voice which shifted to slight ridicule when I mentioned chemtrails." His office "did not take reports" of chemtrails, which the official said had had looked into and "determined to be bogus."

Sydney said that since Rep. Dennis Kucinich had included a ban on chemtrails in the appendix his October 2001 peace-in-space bill to Congress, they could hardly be bogus. Other staffers reached at the EPA in San Francisco "seemed friendly and helpful, but had never heard of them and didn't know where to tell me to go," Sydney said.

"The data does not suggest that any illegal or clandestine activity is occurring."

CHEMTRAILS CALLING

Another concerned citizen made a series of phone calls to the FAA, the Miami International Airport control tower and nearby Homestead Air Force Base during heavy Chemtrail spraying here in the Miami area. Amazingly, his phone call *to each location* "were transferred to a man who sounded just like Jethro from the Beverly Hillbillies and also sounded drunk!"

"This is apparently how they handle inquiries about Chemtrails," he later wrote, "by having you talk to a CIA/FBI/NSA/NRO/DIA etc operative who sounds completely incompetent."

Other chemtrail callers in the Bay Area report being instantly transferred to a gruff, military-sounding voice demanding personal identification. The intimidation usually works.

> *"Our KC-135 jet aircraft operate at altitude below 33,000 feet which is typically the altitude where jet contrails form."*

THE AIR FORCE RESPONDS

Initially responding to complaints by citizens suffering adverse chemical reactions under high-flying aircraft, U.S. Air Force representatives pointed to "routine fuel dumping" over Las Vegas and other populated areas by fleets of multi-engine jet aircraft criss-crossing those skies for hours.

The air force has since repeatedly declared, "Those are not our planes."

The official word is that those definitely are *not* contrails coming from KC-135s. According to Major General Gregory P. Barlow at the Office the Adjutant General, Camp Murray, Washington: "Our KC-135 jet aircraft operate at altitudes below 33,000 feet which is typically the altitude where jet contrails form."

So what are the KC-135s emitting?

U.S. Air Force spokeswoman Margaret Gidding informed *The Spokesman-Review* of Spokane in November, 1999: "The Air Force doesn't do anything that emits anything other than a normal contrail, which is vapor."

So is Gidding's response. In fact, Air Force pilots say they routinely jettison raw JP-8 fuel to lower aircraft weight within specified limits for in-flight trim and safe landings.

This is not good news.

> *"'Spraying' from a tanker is not unheard of."*
> *–Lt. Col. Ardinger*

FORMER TANKER PILOT ADMITS "ROUTINE" FUEL DUMPING

Veteran USAF tanker pilot Lt Col Den Ardinger, (Ret) has flown enough tanker missions to know a chemtrail when he sees one…

> One of the things I want understood is that "spraying" from a tanker is not unheard of regardless of what anyone tells you. It's what is being sprayed that is the puzzle.
>
> I have a photograph here in my collection that I personally took in 1969 when flying in a KC-135A tanker on a trip from Seymour Johnson AFB, NC to Pease AFB, NH. After we took off and reached altitude, most likely over Virginia, we lowered the refueling boom in the bottom rear of the aircraft and 'dumped' 3,000 pounds of JP-4 fuel into the atmosphere just to trim out the aircraft and improve its weight and balance. Nothing was considered unusual with this procedure. The reason I bring it up is to show that there are reasons for a tanker to sometimes spray fuel into the atmosphere.
>
> What we are seeing today is not the occasional spraying I am talking about. When we dumped fuel we didn't fly in a grid pattern.

JET FUEL HAZARDS

Lab test MEL 97-1140 done in September 1997 on a sample of JP-8 jet fuel by Aqua Tech Environmental Labs in Ohio found 51 toxic substances, including trace amounts of ethylene dibromide (EDB). Banned in 1983 by the Environmental Protection Agency in a rare emergency order, EDB is a potent pesticide and chemical irritant. EDB

attacks the liver, lungs and skin. Exposure effects are cumulative.

The *Hazardous Chemicals Desk Reference* and EPA's seven-page "hazard summary" call EDB a "confirmed carcinogen."

The EPA's ethylene dibromide hazardous materials list is seven pages. Its "Hazard Summary says:

> Ethylene dibromide is a carcinogen and must be handled with extreme caution. It may damage the developing fetus, and the male and female reproductive system, and may lead to cancer, liver and kidney damage, pulmonary edema, damage to a developing fetus and reproductive organs of both men and women.

An Air Force-funded study conducted at the University of Arizona at Tucson in the late 1990's found that "exposure to only seven days of JP8 jet fuel for one hour/day at a concentration of 500 mg per cubic meter can produce lung injuries."

But "accidental use" of JP8 also resulted in: "general weakness, vomiting, diarrhea, chest pains, coughing, shortness of breath, cardiac insufficiency and uterine hemorrhaging." Following death, autopsies found: "upper respiratory tract irritation, swelling of the pulmonary lymph glands, advanced deterioration of the heart, liver and kidneys, and hemorrhages in the respiratory tract."

Mark Witten, a respiratory physiologist involved in the official US Air Force study on JP8, told *Scientist* magazine in March 1998 that crew chiefs "seem to have more colds, more bronchitis, more chronic coughs than the people not exposed to jet fuel."

So severe and sustained are the effects, Witten and his colleague David Harris also worry that repeated exposure could increase the risk of autoimmune diseases and cancer, especially in the presence of other risk factors such as pesticides. According to Witten, another leukemia and immune-deficiency disease cluster lies at the end of a San Diego runway used by Coast Guard and civilian jets. He adds that Italian troops who used JP- 8 in Bosnia are also reporting a cluster of leukemia cases. Many more cancer clusters await discovery around airports and air bases.

Hyperactivity, memory loss, vision impairment and a loss of the sense of one's bodily location are other symptoms of JP-8 poisoning.

Short-term exposure to the fuel also causes rashes, respiratory and skin problems. "I went up to a Montana Air Guard base in Great Falls and the workers and mechanics who had contact with the fuel had hands like crabs," Witten said.

David Leith, an environmental engineer at the University of North Carolina School of Public Health is measuring JP-8 aerosols released by jet aircraft. In a trial over Alaska, the microscopic plume of highly toxic JP-8 pegged the needle on his monitoring instrument.

The effects of exposure to aerosols and spills on children and pregnant women have yet to be studied. But when pregnant mice are exposed to jet fuel, up to 70% of offspring die and surviving pups have abnormal white blood cells. Hydrocarbons in JP-8 such as naphthalene and benzene are capable of causing the sorts of genetic damage seen in childhood leukemia.

TROUBLE WITH TANKERS

Growing health concerns, aging airplanes, a growing exodus of tanker crews, and additional refueling burdens brought on by 9.11 and a pretender president's declaration of "never-ending" war against 60 nations have pushed Congress into approving the costly lease of additional airliners for conversion to operational tanker status.

Back in July 1999, nearly 18 months after North American chemtrail operations kicked into high gear, the Air Force asked the Secretary of Defense for a "reprieve" in the number of missions they would have to fly "over the next six to eight months."

More than a decade earlier, during Desert Storm, KC-10 and the KC-135 tankers conducted some 51,700 mid-air refuelings. Ironically in this conflict over oil, hard-pressed tanker crews exceeded Saudi refining capacity while pumping 125 million gallons of fuel into tactical aircraft – and, through their engines, into the atmosphere.

Downsized 40% afterwards, the Air Force was next ordered to commit almost half of its remaining people and planes to bombing Kosovo. The 1999 annual *Readiness Review* prepared by the House Committee on

Armed Services found that the demands of refueling aircraft bombing Kosovo had once again taxed tanker squadrons to operational limits.

The congressional committee's "Strained to the Limit" report revealed that Operation Allied Force over Kosovo had "overextended" U.S. Air Force tanker wings, already tasked with enforcing No-Fly zones over Iraq and Bosnia. Such sustained refuelings, it read, "has taken its toll on personnel, equipment, and training."

The jets they refueled also took a toll on the people of Kosovo, killing more than one thousand civilians while leaving the Serb army and armor essentially intact. The resulting ecological disaster from wrecked factories and refineries combined with cancers triggered by radioactive Depleted Uranium munitions are also part of the tankers' legacy. [UN reports]

Back in the USA, the congressional review committee raised serious doubts about whether the Air Force has sufficient forces at proper readiness levels to execute the two major theater war requirement called for in the National Military Strategy."

The heavily-laden flying gas tanks are also alarmingly ancient. The first KC-135 Stratotanker took to the air in August 1956! A modified version of the first jetliner to see widespread commercial use at the dawn of the jet age, each $52 million reconfigured Boeing 707 carries 150,000 pounds of transferable fuel and costs $3,448/hour to operate.

The last KC-135 was delivered to the Air Force in 1965. Today, the Air Mobility Command operates more than 442 Stratotankers. The Air Force Reserve and Air National Guard fly just over half of these aircraft.

Almost 400 of these old warplanes have been retrofitted with new CFM engines. Born-again KC-135s can now carry 225,000 pounds of fuel. They're new "hush kit" engines are also nearly 100% quieter than the Boeing 707 - which is so loud, commercial 707s are now banned from taking off from US airports.

A modified Boeing DC-10 airliner, the KC-10 entered service in

1981. The three-engine KC-10 carries about 320,000 pounds of transferable liquids.

The 305th Air Mobility Wing at McGuire Air Force Base, N.J. and the 60th Air Mobility Wing, Travis AFB, Calif flies these newer tankers.

Then came Sept. 11. Two months after a handful of fanatics armed with Exacto knives defeated trillion-dollar North American defenses, *Aviation Week & Space Technology* reported refueling tankers were "stretched thin after three weeks of intense operations" protecting nuclear reactors and key US cities.

The December, 2002 Defense Appropriations bill required the tanker-challenged Air Force to lease and convert 100 Boeing 767 airliners for aerial refueling duties over a 10-year period. These are planes even the Air Force doesn't want.

It would be cheaper to buy the planes outright. Instead, the Air Force was initially ordered to lease 100 planes at $20 million per plane *per year*. Converting each plane to carry jet fuel will add about $30 million per plane. Like any leased Lexus, the Pentagon must return the planes to Boeing in the configuration and condition in which they were purchased, at another $30 million or so per plane – another $3 billion.

Though federal laws prohibit lease arrangements that are more expensive than direct purchases, Congress was prepared to waive those rules in appropriating the money for Boeing, which lost out to Lockheed on the multi-billion dollar advanced fighter contract.

But now that deal was scuttled after Pentagon profiteer Richard Perle's failed to disclose his financial ties to Boeing - while championing its bid for a controversial $20 billion-plus defense contract. Perle had earlier been forced to resign as head of the Defense Policy Board, which promotes a perpetually profitable war agenda within the Bush administration.

Perle's tanker scam "stinks to high heaven," said Keith Ashdown of Taxpayers for Common Sense, a Washington-based federal budget watchdog group. The tanker deal has since been placed on hold pending an audit of suspected contracting improprieties that led to the resignation of Boeing's chief executive. In November, US lawmakers allowed the lease of no more than 20 tankers and the purchase of up to 80 - rather than accept Perle's $5 billion scam.

Boeing has since admitted in an internal e-mail that it "ghost-wrote" several influential Opinion pieces by prominent figures in favor of leasing tankers rather than buying them outright, as has been standard weapons-procurement policy. *[Reuters Dec7/03]*

A man named Edwin has two friends with tanker refueling experience in the U.S. Air Force. "They have commented that these planes *will not* be used for air-to-air jet refueling, they will not say what they are to be used for and often appear nervous when I discuss this subject in detail. This leaves only one other option."

This year, the active duty Air Force, Air National Guard and Air Force Reserve are projected to be short a total of 3,200 pilots.

TANKER CREWS BAILING OUT

But who will fly them? In the past five years, the percentage of Air Force pilots leaving the service is up *322%*. At least two pilots are quitting the Air Force *every day*. And they are not being replaced.

This year, the active duty Air Force, Air National Guard and Air Force Reserve are projected to be short a total of 3,200 pilots.

Many of tanker pilots are being joined in the exits by crewmembers and fuel handlers concerned over recent Air Force findings showing that constant exposure to jet fuel and fumes can cause serious health problems. And naturally-occurring fungal contamination of jet fuel may be an additional health hazard to anyone repeatedly exposed to jet traffic overhead.

TUNGSTEN IN YOUR TANK

Dee Lewis, a grassroots organizer of for the Citizens Response Initiative to climbing cancer incidents in and around her subdivision just north of Elk Grove, CA. Convinced that something is loose in the local environment, Lewis is looking at a small airport about three miles southwest of the Leukemia clusters in her own neighborhood.

Since 1999, a neighbor and member of the International Citizens Activist Network says he has "seen KC-135 and [KC-10] tanker planes" come out of the north to spray something that lingered in the sky for hours.

George suspects the tankers are dumping fuel while preparing to land. Though tungsten is reportedly missing from earlier tree ring samples, George says that tungsten has been found in tree samples near the leukemia clusters. "Tungsten is used to harden turbine blades in jet engines," he notes. Aluminum oxide used in chemtrails and fed through those engines "is an abrasive."

George points to a Feb. 2003 medical study linking high levels of tungsten to childhood leukemia clusters in Nevada, Arizona and California. Two clusters are close to military bases and pipelines carrying highly toxic jet fuel. Two years previously, in June 2001, a senator demanded that the U.S. Navy hand over documents concerning possible links between JP-8 and a cluster of 14 childhood leukemia cases near a Nevada naval airbase.

The low volatility of JP-8 means it lingers longer on skin and clothing, releasing fumes and passing directly through the skin into the body.

Ground crews complain of smelling and tasting JP-8 for many hours after exposure. Headaches, dizziness and light-headedness are common side effects, along with upper respiratory and skin irritations. And apparently, cancer.

According to George, "At least three laboratory studies have linked the fuel to DNA damage. Last year, Congress authorized $5 million for a study of the fuel at six Air Force bases and the Pentagon has even commissioned studies to determine whether JP-8 exposure contributed to Gulf War syndrome."

The Pentagon continues to view JP-8 as a "universal battlefield fuel" capable of powering trucks, tanks and even infantry stoves, as well as planes. It is also a universal immune system destroyer. Mark Witten is still freaked after seeing what JP-8 does to mice inhaling it. "It's just wrecking their immune systems," he says. "I've never seen a chemical that can so completely wipe out an animal's defenses."

FATHER KNOWS BEST

The commercial-grade jet fuel tested by Aqua Tech of Ohio came from an airport in Coarsegold, California where residents have been watching unusual trails in the sky. A story published by WorldNetDaily in 2001 – "Californians Concerned Over Chemtrails" - was one of the first to take eyewitnesses seriously.

Reporter Lance Lindsay interviewed David Oglesby. Just after sundown two months previously, the World War II veteran spotted nearly a dozen white trails, dissipating slowly over his home. "The trails formed a grid pattern," Oglesby told Lindsay. "Some stretched from horizon to horizon; some began abruptly and others ended abruptly. They hung in the air for an extended period of time and gradually widened into wispy clouds, resembling spider webs. I counted at least 11 different trails."

Lindsay also examined dozens of photos taken over 12-months by Paula Glick. Her father Gene Shimer served four years as a radar technician during the Korean War. The retired U.S. Air Force sergeant does not believe the patterns over his Coarsegold home are normal contrails.

"I was talking to my dad," Glick remembers, "and he said, 'They're gridding us up here'. I thought, 'Yeah, right dad. Sure they are.' I didn't believe him."

Four months after moving from Ventura to Coarsegold, Glick had to reassess her father's assessment. "I had to watch them do it," Glick told Lindsay. "And as I watched them everyday doing it, it became apparent that we were being sprayed. And so I had to believe. I saw what was normal and I saw what was abnormal."

Shimer contacted the Military Operation Control at Travis Air Force Base, which controls all military operations in Central California. Shimer asked the colonel to identify three planes flying over his home at that very moment. "What would you say if I said there are three aircraft up there right now?" Shimer asked. "Are they there?"

The colonel replied, "No. They are not there."

Navy operations told Shimer there were no operations at all. The flight-control office at Fresno Yosemite International Airport said no flight plans had been filed.

But Ira Plumber is a retired lieutenant colonel in the U.S. Air Force who regularly watches the sky over his Coarsegold home. Several times a week, he sees planes emitting significant sky trails that do not appear to be normal contrails, Plumber says.

As Lindsay chronicles:

> One morning, about two years ago, Shimer spotted a long, thin string resembling a spider web floating in the sky, he said. It was about 20 feet in length and could only be seen in the reflection of the sun. He looked up, saw trails, and then saw something that appeared to be a glob of foam falling from the sky. "It came floating down, free-floating," Shimer says. "I caught it with a spatula, scooped it off the ground, and I watched it as it shrank. It was about the size of my fist when it first started. It looked like a cross between soap bubbles and cotton candy."
>
> He placed the substance in a plastic bag and kept it. It is now about the size of his thumbnail, he says. It has hardened, now appearing to be made of plastic. He did not have it lab tested. He doesn't have enough faith in any lab to give them his only sample, he says. He believes it is probably polymer.

USAF CALLS CHEMTRAILS, A "HOAX"

A Nov. 2001 public information paper released by the USAF calls chemtrails a "hoax" perpetrated by people confused over contrails. "The 'Chemtrail' hoax has been investigated and refuted by many established and accredited universities, scientific organizations, and major media publications," the statement claims.

An even bigger whopper, considering the activation of weather-altering HAARP and other atmospheric experiments: "The Air Force is not conducting any weather modification experiments or programs and has no plans to do so in the future."

NO BOGIES

Why do some Air Traffic Controllers insist there is nothing on their scopes, while callers are watching sets of aircraft weaving chemtrails directly overhead? The answer lies in the mission and capabilities of air traffic radars today, and in military flight procedures. As Ron Garrett of the South Carolina Dept of Health and Environmental Control explains, Air National Guard and other military aircraft fly between 25,000 and 30,000 feet, while commercial aircraft fly at higher altitudes, between 35,000 and 40,000 feet. This separation allows military flights to operate independently of civilian air traffic control.

DISAPPEARING PLANES

Experimental "cloaking" techniques also render military jets invisible to ground observers. When it comes to rendering large airplanes invisible to radar and the human eye, U.S. military technologies, in the words of one air traffic controller, is "a little advanced."

Writing in June 2000, a concerned chemtrail observer complained, "On clear days my wife and I hear loud jets going right over our house, but we can't see the jets. First time I can't spot those death jets. The only explanation I have is that they are using the military's new cloaking device. But the cost of building them on to the jets entails mega bucks. And for what purpose since we can hear them anyways. Whole thing is crazy?"

Linda describes herself as "a system engineer in central New Jersey – a place where for two years you can witness daily spraying in tic-tac-toe formations in the sky." She wrote to John Quinn about "a peculiar phenomenon regarding the aircraft used for chemtrails which I have on occasion noted as well. At times the jets seem to just 'disappear.'"

> I have seen about four times now, these spraying planes virtually 'vanish' in thin air. The first time I saw it disappear I was driving to work. The plane was so high up in the sky, when I turned the corner and didn't see it spraying anymore. I assumed it went beyond the clouds.
>
> The next time (a month later) I was driving to work in the am and saw the high altitude plane. I was mad that I couldn't breathe that morning – tic-tac-toes and circles all over the sky.

> While at a stoplight I looked up and to my amazement I saw it literally vanish in thin air!
>
> The last time (two weeks ago) I saw a plane vanish, I took it quite seriously. I was not driving in a car but sitting in my back yard. I looked up – saw this high flying plane in our clear sky and thought to myself it will probably start to create that fake line cloud spreading out thing – but, to my amazement it flew low, very low, and just poof – vanished in thin air – no noise, no anything.
>
> I sat outside for a while waiting for it to reappear, but it did not. I didn't even tell my husband about any of these occurrences 'cause he would think I was nuts. But I know what I saw on all three occasions. I am a system engineer at a major telecom corp. I am starting to fear for my children's future.

The "News Hawk" editor responded:

> The aircraft may have been utilizing a technology more like camouflaging. The state-of-the-art in camo these days is pretty damn effective. Multiple miniature cameras on one side of an object or person transmit pictures of what *is* visible on that side to the opposite side of the object or person, where it's displayed on multiple small screens. Thus when an observer looks at one side of an object they can "see" what's on the other side of it – as if looking through the object or as if it wasn't there.

"Poof – the plane vanished in thin air."

A former US military technician confirms Quinn's description of "Active Camouflage". Describing patents held by Hughes Aircraft, Raytheon, E-Systems and other military corporations, this insider explains how images of sky and clouds are sent through fiber-optic cables to "light and durable" Active Matrix Liquid Crystal Display panels bonded to the opposite side of the aircraft – projecting the illusion of looking through the plane.

"Now you know how something as big as a plane can seem to disappear in the blink of an eye," Quinn writes. "All it takes is the flip of a switch."

This could explain what happened when UFO investigator Marshall Barnes witnessed the something strange near Wright Patterson Air Force Base in 1994. Heading south on SR 68, Barnes watched a fighter jet streak across the highway. The plane started to glow, and then suddenly "blinked out". Trying to keep his rental car on the road, Barnes watched to see if the craft would reappear, perhaps been hidden by the glare of the sun. It didn't.

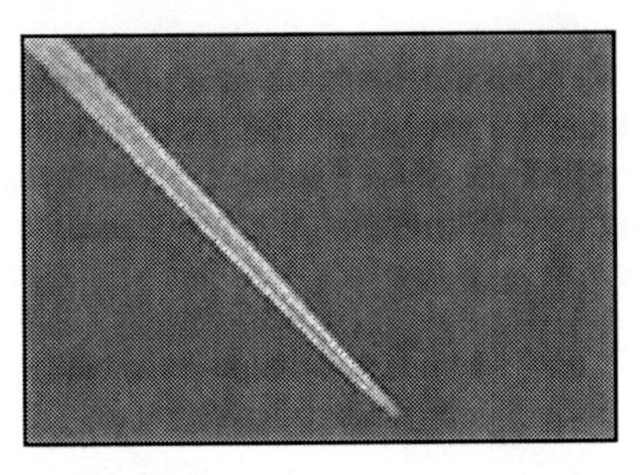

BLACK LINED

A growing number of chemtrail observers – including this reporter – are puzzled by an associated phenomenon we have only seen accompanying chemplanes. If the black line observed ahead of these planes is a shadow cast by the sun, why aren't we seeing it in front of much more prevalent airliners?

In June 2000, while waiting for her car to be washed, a woman "studied the spray planes as they passed as specks overhead. I would guess at around 35,000 feet appearing to be about the same altitude as commercial aircraft cruise 'cross the country."

She "was amazed to see a faint line projected from the nose of the plane directly in their projected path, which appeared to clear the mist or cloud matter that was ahead of them. This faint pathway was constantly projected about a forefinger's length ahead of the jet, as I could watch it become visible at a constant distance ahead of the plane."

Sounds like Sweden. As this Swedish observer relates:

> For about two years, we have had heavy spraying almost every clear day. Usually, you find the same pattern that has been described from all over the world. On the day that this picture was taken, I found a strange dark shadow in front of the plane.
>
> The aircraft followed the dark "shadow-line" in a perfect way, when it all of a sudden made a turn and moved away from it. I realized that this was some kind of line that the plane followed and not at all an illusion created by the plane. I have been watching these chemtrails for a long time, but this was something new.

In early 2002, Judy wrote from Vancouver to confirm similar observations in the U.S. and along Canada's west coast: "Just noticed something. I was eyeing some cloud trying to figure out if it was chemtrail, when a plane went through it leaving a trail of clear sky behind. Hadn't seen that before."

In June 2000 Nancy wrote:

> While driving from Des Moines to Shenandoah, Iowa (rural Iowa), I saw a black line extend out from a plane I was watching. The subsequent chemtrail followed the black line exactly and then continued its formation without further visible black lines. When I saw the chemtrail following the black line, I thought to myself: "This must be how they are able to create the patterns."

A radio listener wrote in:

> The last massive "Spray Day" here was Sunday about two weeks ago. As I was waiting for my car to be washed I studied the spray planes as they passed as specks overhead. I would guess at around 35,000 feet appearing to be about the same altitude as commercial aircraft cruise 'cross the country.

> I was amazed to see a faint line projected from the nose of the plane directly in their projected path, which appeared to clear the mist or cloud matter that was ahead of them. This faint pathway was constantly projected about a forefingers length ahead of the jet as I could watch it become visible at a constant distance ahead of the plane. As it flew it flew directly on or just to the left of the line.

SKIN FLICS

When Gene Willis visited the Nashville airport, he found to his surprise that terminal radar coverage extends only 50 miles. By the time a controller could click her cursor on a blip to determine flight number, altitude and call sign – then run over to the Flight Data system to request a flight strip with additional information on that particular flight number – "the a/c [aircraft] would be out of range and any info requested would get a response of 'Aircraft no longer in the area.'"

For frustrated chemtrail watchers who call their local airport tower only to be told that criss-crossing aircraft they are seeing are not on the radarscopes, Willis explains "Unless an a/c is being 'controlled' locally for either arrival, departure or overflight, they are basically ignored unless they are causing a problem."

Reflected skin tracking – reading radar returns directly from the wings and fuselage of passing aircraft – "is hardly ever done," Willis went on. "Depending on how the individual controller has his/her display set up, they may never even see that there is anything in the area that isn't 'squawking' a [transponder] code – or planes they are not directly controlling."

Military aircraft are often invisible on civilian radars.

Military aircraft using different transponder frequencies would be invisible. Once their pilots declared MARSA (Military Assumes Responsibility for Airspace Separation) civil controllers would ignore their formation flying. Willis wonders, "It would be interesting to see if the airspace at the altitude these guys are flying had been cleared for some reason."

Is a cover-up underway?

Hank wrote from Lake Tahoe to relate how he:

> Called our local airport control tower last week when they were really at it and asked, what all that "stuff" in the sky was about. They advised me that there was a significant increase in the air traffic in our area and that they were just contrails. I asked why said air traffic kept flying in X patterns and all the other odd patterns that appear? He then advised that he was busy with local air traffic. Not so! As I had the scanner on for our local airport. Geez!

A METEOROLOGIST QUESTIONS CHEMTRAILS CONTENTIONS

David Jones, a well-known Meterologist for Environment Canada, wrote to me from Vancouver TV with questions or those suffering chemtrail hallucinations:

> How much time do you spend watching the sky? Have you logged your observations? Have you studied patterns of wind and moisture in the upper atmosphere and linked them to formation or persistence of contrails? Why are trained weather observers who take observations of the sky condition 24 hours a day, 7 days a week and who are intimately familiar with the multitude of natural cloud formations (and contrails), not reporting these so-called weird and unnatural clouds and contrails?
>
> If you think someone is trying to poison us then why would

they be so dumb as to attempt it from the level of the jet-stream? You would waste a lot of poison dropping it from so high in the sky. Do farmers spray their fields from 25,000 feet?

Do I sound cynical?

BEWARE AMATEUR INTERPRETATIONS OF SATELLITE PHOTOS

"The track of large ships is sometimes visualized by a trail of shallow stratus clouds. These clouds, known as 'ship tracks', form in the wake of ships and are remarkably long-lived. They typically are between 0.5 - 5 km wide – that is, wide enough to be seen in visible satellite imagery. Ship tracks are due to cloud condensation nuclei in the ship's exhaust The nature and climatic effect of ship tracks was investigated in a field campaign labeled MAST *shiptracks – not chemtrails – off California* (Monterey Area ShipTrack), which was conducted during June 1994 off the central California coast." – Effects of contrails and shiptracks on climate" by B. Geerts

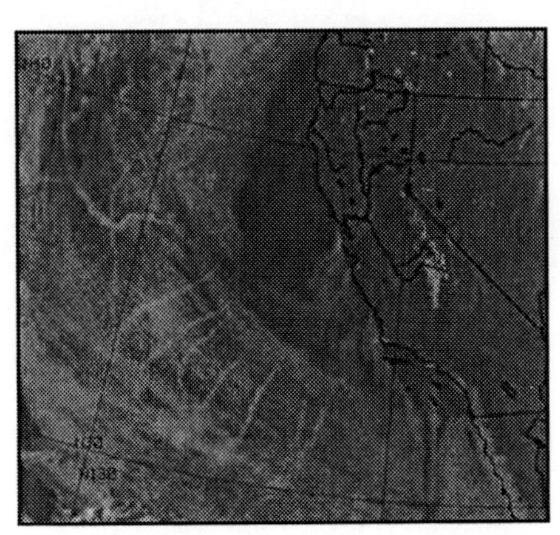

Chapter 7

THE CASE FOR A CULL

It is striking and disturbing that a government so adamantly opposed to the drugs it routinely trades for arms expends so much effort persuading Americans to take various experimental vaccines. Ostensibly developed to relieve symptoms of flu, migraines and pneumonia, these experimental vaccines continue to be widely advertised in areas subjected to heavy chemtrail spraying and concurrent epidemics of "flu-like" ailments, extremely severe headaches and life-threatening pneumonia.

Though there is no evidence that intensive high and low-altitude chemtrail spraying over North America and other countries over recent years are part of a planned "depopulation" campaign, the pathogens found in our samples of low-level spraying are hitting the elderly and those with weakened immune systems the hardest.

LOSING MOM

The following excerpted letter relates an increasingly distressing and common experience among families across North America. It also explains why so many Americans are not buying the "weather modification" explanation for chemtrails. The writer offers his letter for publication here in the "hope everyone who reads this report is awakened to new possibilities for the 'silent' extermination of our elderly and loved ones."

For the record, her doctor gave my mother an excellent health report back in 1994 at her hospital. Her doctor said: "Well Jack, you have a remarkable mom. She has the best respiratory health I've seen in years with a person her age of 76. It must have been all those years in the professional opera and movies she was in. Because she never drank or smoked has paid off now. Her other health is pretty darn good overall. You should have a mom around for a long time Jack. She should go for another 15 years easily."

On Mar. 22,1998 a police vehicle pulled up to my driveway. A single officer came to the front door. He said: " I have very sad news to tell you. Your mom has passed away."

I made a call directly to the care home. They said mom didn't die at the care home but up at the main hospital. They were very unclear as to why mom had really died. I begged them to tell me what time she died and then received the greatest shock of my life. The nurse at the hospital said she died at 5:07 am on Mar. 14, 1998. I asked why I wasn't called and the nurse said the doctors didn't know for sure if I was her son or not.

After 90 years in the area, our family name was well known. It had taken the police dept. and hospitals over 11 days to come to my front door to give me the terrible news. No attempts were made to contact me by telephone. I had left my phone number with both the hospital and care home but nobody tried to call me. The hospital informed me that: "We didn't know who to call."

"I noticed that most of the locals in town became drowsy, sleepy, tired – and a lot of unexplained headaches."

When Jack checked around the neighboring counties, neither the court assistant to nor the judge remembered his mother's name. There was nothing on file at all.

> During the late months of 1996 and 1997 I was seeing strange jet exhaust trails being exuded by highflying commercial and military aircraft over our mountain town and over the entire region. I have now come to realize why I was so tired after riding my racing bike in the fallout from those chemtrails.
>
> Mom was also exposed to them while she did yard work. She loved the outdoors and always produced a beautiful landscaped garden wherever she went. It became apparent that the chemtrails were affecting both of our health.
>
> I saw the brown residue on the Lincoln's windshield several times and it smelled awful. I noticed that most of the locals in town became drowsy, sleepy, tired – and a lot of unexplained headaches. Children seemed to be coughing and sneezing. General store workers looked very slow and tired on chemtrail spray days.

In May 1998, "a friend remembered seeing strange jet trails over the Owens valley in the eastern Sierras during the three days prior to mom's death." He and his wife were outside preparing to enter some hot pools "when out of nowhere came this C-130 Hercules flying low down the Bishop/Owens Valley."

> His wife saw another set of jet trails coming from other higher-flying jets expelling long whitish trails that turned brown while drifting to the ground. When the descending clouds began to pass over their hot tubs they began to feel sick and tired all of a sudden. His wife began coughing and both their eyes burned profusely. They abandoned their tubs and jumped in their truck and left the area.
>
> Both saw the same jets and C-130 continue to expel more and more of this whitish cloudlike exhaust right over the same location as the care home my mom was in. It made at least four passes over that locale [care home] then began moving south leaving at least nine criss-cross patterns all the way down the Owens Valley.

> Their other friends who lived in that town said many locals there became very ill that evening. They said they saw this operation several times, but didn't know at the time what to make of it. Both of them had tremendous headaches that evening when they got home.
>
> I have since learned that the care home staff always put most of their patients outside for fresh air each day for at least a couple hours in the shade under the trees. I was told mom was outside on the days prior to and the day of her death. I heard many of the care home residents incurred a high degree of respiratory difficulties at the same time mom passed on. The staff said she died of a "heart attack." But her previous medical reports showed her lungs and heart were way above average. So, you decide what killed my mom. In my mind and heart I feel it *was* the chemtrails that extinguished my mother.

"I awoke after a couple of hours of sleep with a migraine headache and a racing heart. I experienced such severe dizziness and nausea."

HOROWITZ LINKS MYSTERY PANDEMIC TO ELITIST AGENDA

In December '03, Len Horowitz responded to an interviewer, noting that the 1998-99 epidemic was back, with people "hacking and coughing with this bizarre illness that does not seem to follow any logical viral or bacterial onset and transition period."

Bacterial and viral infections cause fever. This doesn't, Horowitz noted. Lasting weeks, even months, even those not severely stricken suffer fatigue and general malaise.

"Call it a fungus related to a flu." Horowitz said, labeling the '04 pandemic a "pathogenic mycoplasma".

Developed and patented by the Armed Forces Research Institute of Pathology, this manmade illness has apparently entered the world population through contaminated vaccines and blood supplies.

Deliberately contaminated? Horowitz doesn't say. But he does not related this AIDS-derived germ to chemtrails.

"I don't believe that this particular organism could be suitably spread that way," the Harvard trained researcher explained. But immune suppression caused by chemtrail exposure, "would then allow people to become susceptible to opportunistic infections, such as this mycoplasma and other opportunistic infections."

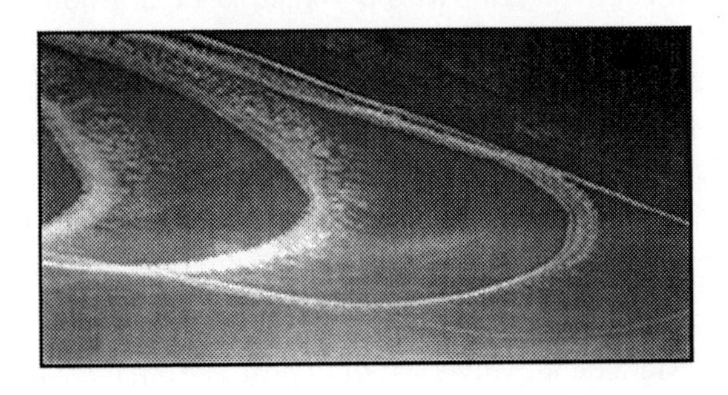

The author of *Healing Codes* and *Emerging Viruses* began investigating chemtrails after photographing spray planes over his northern Idaho home. After the usual run-around, a chief toxicologist at the Centers for Disease Control wrote back saying ethylene dibromide in jet fuel could be making people sick. In fact, health statistics show that living near an airport is an excellent way to become chronically ill.

"When you examine who owns the fuel, who are the fuel company directors, suddenly you enter into the realm of the Rockefeller family and the royal families - Standard Oil and British Petroleum." Horowitz told the interviewer, named Redden.

In his books, Horowitz convincingly documents the historic funding by these parties of eugenics – a euphemism for genocidal depopulation. These big banksters also run the blood banks, and fund massive vaccination programs.

The agenda behind chemtrails, Horowitz believes, is to completely deplete and weaken entire populations so that people are not too sick to work, but too waster to do much else – like protest chemtrails, fraudulent presidential "selections", illegal and immoral wars, and the hijacking of America and its Constitution.

"Weakened populations are easily to control," Horowitz observes.

EUGENICS MEANS EXTERMINATION

The scientific investigation of genetic differences between races examines the genetic predisposition for disease to which various peoples are susceptible. The Rockefeller Foundation's eugenics program of the 1920s called for the mass sterilization and elimination of minority populations in America.

In 1929, the Rockefeller's chief executive in charge of their eugenics institute was the fascist Swiss psychiatrist Ernst Rudin, assisted by his protégés Otmar Verschuer and Franz Kallmann. The monster Mengele was directed by Verschuer Kallmann, who went on to create the American Society of Human Genetics – which later organized the "Human Genome Project". This $3 billion effort to map the genetics of humanity, is paying special attention to each race's specific disease susceptibilities.

Chaitkin continues:

> The Merck company's windfall profits from the Nazi war chest was specifically arranged to help actualize Hitler's proclaimed "vision of a thousand-year Reich and world empire" – outlined in *Neuordunung,* New World Order. The partners decided that a world chemical and pharmaceutical monopoly was necessary to eliminate undesirable populations, while making money to most effectively create a "master race". Lucrative drugs and chemicals could be used to control minds, dull the senses and insidiously eliminate unwanted people.

NATIONAL SECURITY MEMO 200

On April 24, 1974, the re-elected President Nixon ordered a comprehensive study to determine the "Implications of World Population Growth for U. S. Security and Overseas interests."

Serving alongside Litton's Roy Ash as National Security Adviser, Henry Kissinger drafted "National Security Memorandum 200". Warning of a worldwide population crisis "more dangerous than nuclear war", NSSM 200 pointed out:

> Reduction of the rate of population in these States [Third-World nations] is a matter of vital U.S. national security. The U.S. economy will require large and increasing amounts of minerals from abroad, especially from less-developed coun-

> tries. That fact gives the U.S. enhanced interests in the political, economic and social stability of the supplying countries. Wherever a lessening of population can increase the prospects for such stability, population policy becomes relevant to resources, and to economic interests of the United States."

Kissinger added that ethics might have to be put aside in calling for a cull in 13 Third World countries through lowered birth rates, or increased death rates, or both.

Immediately after Kissinger requested an overview on U.S. biological weapons capabilities, Dr. MacArthur told the secret 1969 Defense Department Appropriation Hearings that 24 years of biological warfare research was about to develop the ultimate stealth weapon.

With 76 biowarfare labs in operation, McArthur asked congress for more funds on top of the $31 million already allocated for CB warfare, pledging that "within a period of five to 10 years it would be possible to produce a synthetic biological agent, an agent that does not naturally exist and for which no natural immunity could have been acquired."

In 1970, Congress paid $10 million to let the AIDS jinn out of germ warfare's bottle. Newly emergent Chronic Fatigue outbreaks followed the hepatitis B vaccine program, which either deliberately or inadvertently triggered the AIDS pandemic in the seven U.S. cities where 200,000 doses of that monkey-derived vaccine were administered.

AIDS researcher Dr. Robert Strecker says the new HIV immunodeficiency disease agent appeared out of nowhere. Displaying characteristics of animal viruses not normally adapted to humans, the codons in the DNA of the AIDS virus do not exist in primate genes.

AIDS deaths subsequently peaked at 50% of the New York gay population – as well as in many central African villages. The U.S. Census Bureau reports that AIDS has claimed more than 11 million people since its first outbreaks in the late 1970s. Current estimates of people infected with HIV/AIDS worldwide are around 40 million people. The census report predicts that the spread of AIDS in Asia will account for more infections than in sub-Saharan Africa.

But this may not be enough to protect the profits of an exploitative elite. According to the U.S. Census Bureau's "World Population Profile", while the rate of increase is slowing, the population of our planet will increase to eight billion by the end of 2026 in the developing regions of Africa, Asia and Latin America. In more developed countries, by early in the present century death rates will exceed birth rates.

SPLITTING GRAY HAIRS

On January 25-26, 2000 a little-publicized high-level working group met at the Center for Strategic and International Studies Washington, D.C. Their purpose – and the urgency of their impetus – was to be found in the conference title: "Assessing the Economic, Political, and Strategic Implications of the Simultaneous Aging of the Major Industrial Nations".

President Clinton was invited to give a key address. Also in attendance were such aging luminaries as former Vice President Walter Mondale, former Japanese Prime Minister Ryutaro Hashimoto, former National Security Advisor Zbigniew Brezinski, former Secretary of Defense James Schlesinger and former Chairman of the U.S. Federal Reserve Paul Volcker.

Big money also showed up in the personages of the Chief Economist of Deutsche Bank, the Chief Economist for the International Monetary Fund, as well as representatives from Barclays, Goldman Sachs, the World Bank, the head of CSIS (Canada's equivalent to the CIA), the Minister of Labor and Social Affairs, Federal Republic of Germany, and the U.S. Secretary of the Treasury. Working panels formed among these heavy-hitters discussed the "wild card" of biomedical research that threatened to greatly increase old age dependency. Even scarier for the controlling elite: "Defense budgets are shrinking in response to fiscal competition from old-age benefits and the rising cost of recruitment and retention. Meanwhile, population trends in the developing world may increase the prospect for crisis."

What to do about penurious pensioners? Give them pneumonia? Many chemtrails commentators are convinced that this secret aerial spray program is directly aimed at eliminating the weak, the sick, the elderly and similar "useless eaters" – while jacking up already outrageous pharmaceutical profits.

There is no evidence that chemtrails are deliberately spreading mycoplasma or other "biologicals". There are not enough b/w agents stockpiled to fill fleets of tankers for five years. Bioweapon organisms are never spread in sterilizing sunlight from high altitudes.

AERIAL VACCINES?

Could widespread aerial spraying be a clandestine attempt to inoculate us against an undeclared biowarfare threat? After looking at the evidence, one MD decided: "Aerial spraying of a vaccine would be exceedingly inefficient. Cost would be prohibitive. That is why I do not think the mass secret immunization theory is plausible."

The leading expert on low-level spraying, Erminia Cassani continues:

> The organisms contained in the samples I collected are not viruses and they are not capable of becoming antigens to any viral-based disease. The bacteria contained in the samples are not of the type and caliber to create any type of bacteriological immunity against such killer attacks as anthrax. Besides, the size and volume of the dropped material [show that they cannot be] part of any mass inoculation program involving inhalational organisms – they were not of respirable size, i.e. too big to be breathed in by any human pulmonary system.

Because bioweapons can be quickly genetically altered against all known antidotes, effective inoculation is futile. As Ken Alibek, former head of the Soviet biowarfare program pointed out in a recent interview, "In many cases it's impossible to vaccinate the entire population of the country against all possible agents. It's absolutely impossible."

What to do about penurious pensioners?
Give them pneumonia?

THE SECRET AFFLICTION OF PLANTS

Withered and dying plants have often been observed in the wake of heavy chemtrails – including stunted plant growth in once-healthy gardens and wilderness areas in Santa Fe and Aspen. Similar plant problems are commonly associated with chemtrails in other regions of the U.S. Weird weather patterns and toxic fallout are the primary suspects. No *el Niño* or *la Niña* events were underway when this account was written:

> The plants in my area are all crossed up. Some think it is spring and started their spring growth. As I write and look out into my back garden I see my lawn showing through approx. 1/4 inch of snow, which is melting – I have not seen this in the 31 years that I have resided here.
>
> We have just completed three days of *rain*, unheard of at this time of year at Tahoe. Temperatures have been quite warm approx. 37-degrees F. Very strange! Had been having some severe "gut" problems that I am unable to explain, about a week now. Storms start and then for some reason just fizzle out? 'Tis a very strange winter in the high Sierras of California.

Chemtrails are no friend of tomatoes:

> No one seems to have the answers (at least not that I'm aware of). I can also tell you that my family is not feeling 100% lately. My neighbour's tomatoes turned black and rotted from the inside out. (Something that, he tells me has never happened before). Last night I also observed an unidentified white plane with absolutely *no visible markings* fly at an *extremely* low level right over the roof of my house, on a totally out of whack flight path, that I have never observed here before in my six years of living here.

None of the immune-weakening pathogens identified in samples of air-delivered powder or gels can be used as antidotes to germ warfare.

OUR FURRY FRIENDS

Animals also suffer from the aerial spraying. From Oakville, Washington where 15 barn cats died following repeated "gel" storms, to the deaths of William Wallace's cats and dogs in the remote mountains of that state, and a report from Oregon where "sheriff deputies come down sick from a goo" that fell from the sky and "cats and dogs died" from something "like Jell-O" – our furry friends may be trying to tell us something. A comment from Atlanta is typical: "My little kitty cat has been coughing since we lived there and he still suffers from a respiratory problem. The vets I have seen say they don't know what is wrong with him."

In Santa Barbara, Paulette recounts how she:

> Just got back from a walk with Elmo and ran into my neighbor, who is a nurse at a hospital here. She said that the hospital is so overloaded with sick people with flu-like symptoms. The hospital is offering nurses time and a half pay for coming in and a half of a day off along with the regular days off.
>
> She says people are really sick. Ever since we had a rain a few weeks ago, my dog and I have not felt right. Or I should say, worse than usual (from chemtrail poison). A lot of people are "feeling trashed, pain at back, pain at neck, headachy, etc."

Chemtrails are no friend of tomatoes and chickens.

Gary writes from Santa Rosa, California where

> Spray has continued in northern California off and on since December, (1999) with one really heavy day just a couple of weeks ago. Here, one vet my wife works with in the MRI says that he has never seen so many carcinogenic tumors and deaths with small animals in his entire career and does not know why. I explained to you once how our horses, our dogs and us, all have the same smell in our feces after a spray day. My wife consistently complains (and is much aware of the spray days)

that about two - three hours after a medium spray, her tongue starts tingling, almost a 'sting'. Also sudden onset of diarrhea, totally out of the blue. A lady across the street mentioned that her family of six has been going through toilet paper like crazy suddenly.

Deb's son raises chickens. One evening in the late summer of 2000, I went out to check my birds before bedtime and found one of my birds with her neck twisted sideways and her beak pointed skyward and walking in circles. I straightened her head and as soon as I let go, it would contort again. She was gasping. The vet was dumbfounded. He'd never seen anything like it.

He gave her a shot to reduce swelling and inflammation but didn't offer much hope for her survival. Said the brain and throat were swelling causing the neurological symptoms and breathing problems. I sat up all that night holding her head and neck in an upright position. The next two days were hideous trying to get food into her and keep her from choking. The vet called and said he'd been doing research and the closest he could come to her symptoms would be botulism. Told me to look for moldy food. There was none.

It took a month of intensive care, a slow recovery and walking circles and backwards before Sidney could keep her head straight and finally eat. Today, you'd never know anything was wrong with her. Others weren't so fortunate. If it were a disease common among chickens, the entire flock would have symptoms real close together. Two others got it and died.

A few days ago, chemtrails were being sprayed above us. We now have another one sick. Not head twisting, but lethargic, sleepiness, tremors, and definitely sick. I don't know what this is; neither does the vet, but it isn't something any experienced people I've talked to have ever seen. Maybe those ice crystals from the contrails didn't melt and just kinda clunked them on the head.

Westchester, Pennsylvania

In South Dakota last year: "For the past say 3-4 weeks I've seen strange looking big jets on flight paths overhead that we do not have! And last week my dog and horse came down with sudden digestive problems. Really acute. And as you know, everyone has had the respiratory crud – even me."

This same writer watched the planes come over and described what happened next:

> They come through hourly: three to four every hour in the morning, and one or two in the afternoon. During rush hour they are all over the skies, every 3-5 minutes or so. It is pretty easy to see here, because we have very little air traffic. Immediately on flyovers, my horses stop eating and look lethargic, my cat stopped running round and lay down. After about 35 minutes, the animals activate again. And I can feel my skin start to burn 10 minutes or so after I've been outside."

In what might be a description of artificially induced glanders, a chemtrail correspondent wrote in the spring, 1999 of incidents eerily similar to a Kentucky horse kill in May 2001:

> We are experiencing a situation in Ashfork, Arizona. Numerous local residents have lost livestock – the death of 17 horses and numerous wildlife in the immediate area. The federal task force has interrogated us and there is military presence throughout the area. The symptoms are always fatal and we have been told this is caused by "an unnatural toxin".

> Numerous residents have observed late night unmarked helicopters flying low over the area. Toxic waste disposal trucks being driven by uniformed military personnel have also been seen on rural residential streets. A fine "mist-like hairspray substance" was observed on the backs of many of the animals. One rancher has lost three horses to whatever this is.

A California correspondent corroborates chemtrails and animal illness:

> A client of mine called this morning. Her dog has a terrible skin condition and when they did testing of a skin sample found Pseudomonas Aeruginosa, and two forms of staph. *Everyone*'s dog is itching and scratching *and* has ear infections that are found to be PA caused. The vets are attempting to say it is scabies. *Except* they cannot find any scabies. She is in Southern California. The skin problem is epidemic in animals down there.
>
> We have been swamped with chemtrails the past few days. Mark had it in spider-web form on the back of his car. He didn't realize, until he got home and told me what he had. My friend's car had dried white crusty things on her car window that shined like a rainbow. While we were observing them, more droplets appeared. Last week Rex, the dog with the skin problem in Malibu has another skin test. E-coli was found. Kledsiella pneumoniae, E-coli, staphylococcus epidermidis are the new three things found on skin. What the hell is going on? And there are white dots on her car and my car and my friend's car – white dots that eat glass and metal on car.

"Immediately on fly-overs, my horses stop eating and look lethargic. My cat stopped running round and lay down."

Just weeks before the millennium, I received this message from heavily sprayed Sallisaw, Oklahoma: "Hi Will, I found out from a vet that many small animals are suffering around here from upper respiratory problems. Julie's cat was sick Saturday. The vet told me he is seeing many small animals being brought in for treatment with this condition."

Why is animal illness important to humans? Because they could be serving as involuntary chemtrail canaries, confirming sickness in the air.

Kanab, Utah July '03

SPACE PRESERVATION ACT OF 2001

107th CONGRESS
1st Session
HR 2977

To preserve the cooperative, peaceful uses of space for the benefit of all humankind by permanently prohibiting the basing of weapons in space by the United States, and to require the President to take action to adopt and implement a world treaty banning space-based weapons.

IN THE HOUSE OF REPRESENTATIVES
October 2, 2001

SEC. 3. PERMANENT BAN ON BASING OF WEAPONS IN SPACE.
The President shall—

(1) implement a permanent ban on space-based weapons of the United States and remove from space any existing space-based weapons of the United States; and

(2) immediately order the permanent termination of research and development, testing, manufacturing, production, and deployment of all space-based weapons of the United States and their components.

SEC. 7. DEFINITIONS.

(ii) Inflicting death or injury on, or damaging or destroying, a person (or the biological life, bodily health, mental health, or physical and economic well-being of a person)—

(II) through the use of land-based, sea-based, or space-based systems using radiation, electromagnetic, psychotronic, sonic, laser, or other energies directed at individual persons or targeted populations for the purpose of information war, mood management, or mind control of such persons or populations; or

(III) by expelling chemical or biological agents in the vicinity of a person.

(B) Such terms include exotic weapons systems such as—

(i) electronic, psychotronic, or information weapons;

(ii) chemtrails;

(iii) high altitude ultra low frequency weapons systems;

(iv) plasma, electromagnetic, sonic, or ultrasonic weapons;

(v) laser weapons systems;

(vi) strategic, theater, tactical, or extraterrestrial weapons; and

(vii) chemical, biological, environmental, climate, or tectonic weapons.

(C) The term `exotic weapons systems' includes weapons designed to damage space or natural ecosystems (such as the ionosphere and upper atmosphere) or climate, weather, and tectonic systems with the purpose of inducing damage or destruction upon a target population or region on earth or in space.

Chapter 8

OWNING THE WEATHER

Brampton, Ontario May 25, 2002

Forget that old complaint that no one is doing anything about the weather. The U.S. Air Force is doing plenty. Despite *la Niña* forecasts calling for a considerably *drier* climate was forecast across the USA for late 1999 through early 2000 – just the opposite occurred. The desert town of Bakersfield hosted an unusual snowfall after heavy springtime spraying coincided with jammed emergency rooms there.

"Can it be that the contrails reported in the Bakersfield area are related to the 6" of snowfall in Bakersfield?" one resident wrote. "If not, it's an interesting coincidence."

Whether accidental or intentional, spectacularly lousy weather often follows chemtrail gridding – which often takes place in clear blue skies *ahead of approaching fronts*.

Another Californian reported, "Since my initial message to you, we have had two severe storms pass through the San Francisco Bay Area, one of which passed over Lake Tahoe and dumped eight feet of snow! Also, I have experienced some respiratory difficulties and some stomach upset."

On April 8, 1999, Channel 3 KCRA reported that Sacramento was in the middle of the wettest and coldest storm yet, with hail and snow forecast for the San Francisco Bay area. In the Sierra foothills, Interstate 80 was closed in both directions east of Sacramento and Reno. According to one area resident, "It is snowing so hard in the Sierras that the snow is coming down sideways. They continue to spray this area. When there are breaks in the clouds, you can see the tell-tale signs of what the chemtrails look like as they spread further and further out."

Another correspondent described how in Arkansas on January 19th and 20th, 1999: "There was heavy spraying. On the 21st, Arkansas had the worst outbreak of tornadoes on record, killing many people. The spraying has continued. I spent eight years in the military and was around many different kinds of aircraft and I have never seen anything that left contrails such as those in these photos."

In Utah that month: "I did not know of the impact of such things until a 4-line grid was made over the Cottonwood Utah Area and David John Oates and myself fell ill. Three-line grids were seen three days before. The temperature in Utah was 62 degrees and dropped to 10 degrees; 90 mile-an-hour winds took place and clouds rolled in dropping six-inches of snow."

"It is snowing so hard in the Sierras that the snow is coming down sideways. They continue to spray this area."

In Rockford, Illinois:

> The City of Rockford, metro area 650,000, has experienced last week on a Wednesday XXX patterns in the sky. The next day Thursday it was a record 65 temp, then it dropped to about 20 temp same day with violent thunderstorms and winds of 60 mph plus damage to property. The contrails continue with the black helicopters unmarked and I called a friend who is an Air Traffic Controller he did not know anything about the choppers – six going crazy around the city. It appears the weather, plus numerous flu-like symptoms, and choppers are not coincidences.

"Arkansas had the worst outbreak of tornadoes on record, killing many people. The spraying has continued."

In West Virginia an item on the 6 o'clock news on WSAZ channel 13:

Hospitals are full with flu bug. Doctors say "near epidemic", "schools closed". People have "sinus infections to pneumonia". There is a waiting list for people to get into Cabell-Huntington Hospital. Blamed on the weather. By the way, the temp here in Charleston today was 75 degrees. Tonight it will go down to '30' with snow this weekend. The planes are still making waves over the skies

In Pittsburgh, Kansas:

It's incredibly rare that we have a plane come in here. I've lived here for more than 10 years; jets going overhead is a *very* uncommon thing. These jets flew over about three different nights, with a two or three night 'break' between. I've watched the 'contrails' in the sky myself. I remember thinking how 'different' they seemed, wondering why they just hung there, thinking how much it looked like somebody took a thick paintbrush and drew a couple of lines across the sky.

The weather here has been crazy. Literally, during the day walking around with no shoes and a T-shirt. That *very* night, snow, light hail, and ice on the ground. Few days later, comfortable again.

In Houston on January 15, 200:

We've seen the largest spraying operation we've ever recorded over and around Houston, today. Reports coming in from all directions. Started at dawn, will probably continue all day long. Absolutely unbelievable. Extends to small cities as far as 75 miles from here. Dense enough in some cases to produce rainbow colored "sundogs". Weather is warm and beautiful (no natural clouds) and many many people outside, of course.

"Tonight it will go down to '30' with snow this weekend. The planes are still making waves over the skies!"

In Washington state:

Our town, Twisp, has only 600 full-time residents. We are experiencing jets spraying contrails east to west. They have been going at it a few days every week since early spring, some time in February, and all day at least three days this week, but do not seem to fly on weekends. The regular jet flights with normal contrails are above the spraying planes. Those regular contrails disappear, but the lower jet trails spread out and cover the sky with a gray overcast that does not go away for many hours.

We have had X patterns and circles as well. Many people here in the valley are suffering from upper respiratory ailments, the same lung problems as are being noticed in many parts of the country.

I have just finally gotten over a major cold that took a month to go away. I am still clearing my throat very frequently, and I still have a pulled muscle under my left lung, from coughing so hard. It hurts like a broken rib and takes about as long to heal. I sure would like to know the 'who' and 'why' story on these contrails!

I have two grandsons, three and five years, who live with me. They have had a bad hacking cough for months, it seems to come and go, they always have running noses, and are frequently cranky. I know it is because they are ill from the spray.

On the 16th of June we had a fierce thunderstorm that had horizontal lightening, and rained so hard that it felt like we were under a waterfall. It was unreal. Like the worst monsoon rain a tropical island could endure. Yeah, it does rain a lot in Washington State, but not that way, particularly on the east side of the mountains. I have lived here most all my life, and we have always experienced mostly light rain, or drizzle. Never monsoon, waterfall deluges like the one we had Wednesday night.

I spoke to a number of friends up and down the east side of the Cascades, three of them said, it was the same in Idaho, and Oregon all along the Cascades. A huge line of storms that really dumped massive water in a short time in Bend, Oregon, Chelan and Twisp Washington, and Caldwell, Idaho simultaneously. If this has anything to do with weather modification, and rain was the desired result, it is obviously working!

Temperatures dropped from 62 to 10 degrees after chemtrail grids were laid.

Storms in the southern United States turned vicious in January 1999, spawning 150 tornadoes and killing 18 people during a time of year when summertime twisters are rarely seen. In Tennessee, former Raytheon missile technician Tommy Farmer filmed complex chemtrail patterns the day before 90 tornadoes struck three adjoining states.

NOAA meteorologists ruled out any direct link between the freakish weather and the cooling of Pacific waters known as *La Niña.* When David Letterman asked Al Roker last September why they were not having any sunshine this summer in NY and Roker said – "It's *la Niña* which is Spanish for *government controlled weather*!"

"It's la Niña which is Spanish for government controlled weather!"

MAGNETIC STORMS

Another possible explanation for the weird winter weather comes from *Earth Changes* TV. Some scientists say that giant solar flares could be influencing our planet's magnetic field, causing weather patterns to change, sometimes severely.

Accelerating annual magnetic variation from True North indicates that the North Pole is shifting much faster than normal, bending the jetstream and perhaps causing upper atmospheric winds to dip close to the surface of the Earth.

"This may be the cause of the increase of tornadoes, also affecting its wind speed," web TV host Nick Battros writes.

MAKING WAVES

The temptation to tinker is total. According to a source identifying himself as a high-ranking air force weather-tracking pilot, NASA and the U.S. military have long been interested in artificially inducing "atmospheric folding" – a process in which upper atmospheric winds are "folded" down into the weather-forming troposphere.

Air Force weather mod pilots reportedly attended a NASA-sponsored meeting in 1989 or '90 at the NOAA office in Washington, DC.

According to this source:

> The theme was the potential adjustment of large air masses. NASA wanted to be able to move or stall some of the systems in order to ensure a reasonable or enlarge the launch window at the Cape. Because of the financial consequences, there was an *oh! la!* amount of money available for the information and application. Our team, with some of the best Weather Mod people, concluded that it was not possible to accomplish such a large-scale rearrangement, because of the lack of a focal point and the general energy distribution parameters. After we were dismissed from the meeting, there were at least two other groups (modelers) still engaged in the discussion. One of my former colleagues has again reminded me of the stratosphere folding work that we started in the mid- to late 70's.

Weather experts like Atmospherics Inc.'s Tom Henderson insist that the amount of energy needed to influence weather is beyond human means. But Chaos Theory teaches that in systems as dynamically unstable as weather, even the beat of butterfly's wings in Taiwan can cause a hurricane in the Caribbean.

Smaller-scale weather modification involving the seeding of clouds with silver iodide and similar compounds has been routinely conducted for many years under license in most states. In Fresno, California in 1960, Thomas Henderson founded Atmospherics Inc. with a vision of taking commercial weather modification global. An internationally known authority in weather modification, Henderson has conducted and applied cloud physics research for government and private industry.

North American Weather Consultants, also seeds rain clouds with silver iodide to enhance rainfall for reservoirs supplying irrigation, power and drinking water around the world.

In 1994 this leading weather modification company filled rainmaking contracts in California, British Columbia, Utah, Wyoming, Idaho, Colorado, Guatemala, Honduras, Taiwan, Texas, Delaware, Abu Dhabi, Georgia, Oregon, Mexico and Iowa.

Weather mod tracking radar, USA

Both companies use primitive but long-proven "cloud seeding" techniques to trigger rain clouds into selected deluges using silver iodide crystals to attract moisture, tipping humidity into rainfall.

While acknowledging increasing interest in non-conventional weather modification, both companies say they are not aware of weather modification techniques that actually form clouds, or trigger weather change using advanced spraying technologies or "atmospheric heating" techniques.

They need to do some homework

> *Weather modification is routinely conducted under license in most states.*

"KILLER" CONSEQUENCES

On August, 30, 2001 the BBC reported on "Rain-making linked to killer floods" after learning that 35 in the historic Lynmouth flood disaster "came only days after RAF rain-making experiments over southern England" triggered monsoon rains which caused 90 million tons of water to sweep down a narrow valley into Lynmouth on August 15, 1952.

Entire buildings were destroyed as North Devon experienced *250 times* normal rainfall for the month of August rainfall – within hours. In a description familiar to many chemtrails observers, survivors described planes circling before the disaster – and "how the air smelled of sulphur on the afternoon of the floods" as rain fell hard enough "to hurt people's faces."

Uprooted trees dammed streams behind bridge abutments, "creating walls of water that carried huge boulders into the village, destroying shops, hotels and homes. Bodies washed out to sea were never found. Dilys Singleton lost six members of her family, including her grandmother."

Jokingly referred to by those involved in the secret experiment as "Operation Witch Doctor", an operation named "Cumulus" used silent gliders to "seed" clouds with salt and chemicals. A glider pilot named Alan Yates described, "how he flew over Bedfordshire as part of Operation Cumulus, spraying quantities of salt into the air." Scientists later told him his efforts caused a massive downpour to fall from "summery" skies over Staines, 50 miles away

The perpetrators of this drastic deluge drank toasts to meteorology – until a BBC news bulletin caused a "stony silence" to fall on the military contractors.

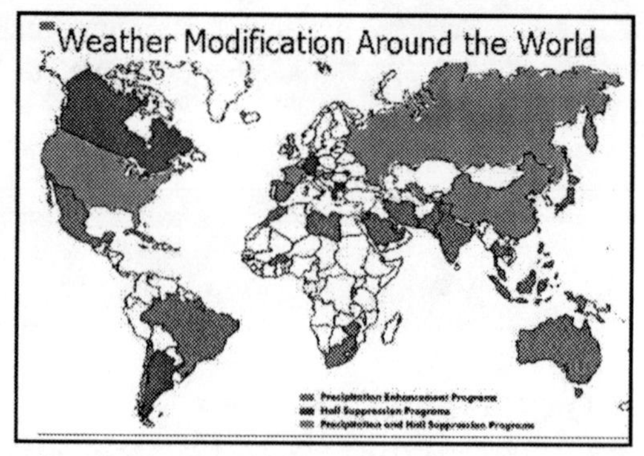

worldwide cloud-seeding = all colored areas (2002)

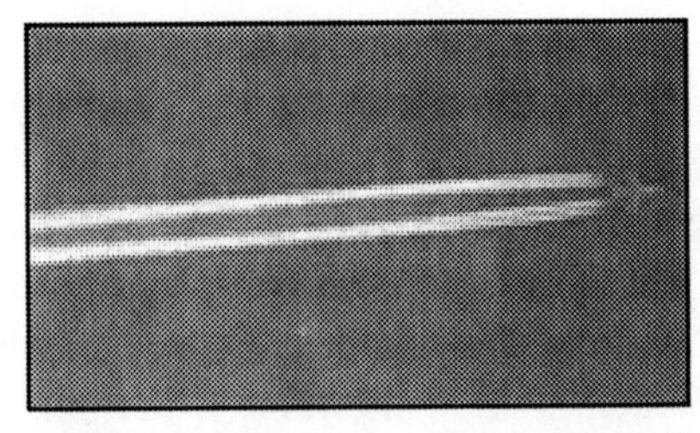

NOT IN MY SKY

Large-scale atmospheric modification is instinctively and increasingly unpopular. It is also illegal. In May 1997, Washington adopted a United Nations "Convention on the Prohibition of Military or Any Other Hostile Use of the Environmental Modification Techniques", which prohibits "the use of techniques that would have widespread, long-lasting or severe effects through deliberate manipulation of natural processes and cause such phenomena as earthquakes, tidal waves and changes in climate and weather patterns."

Citizen displeasure with atmospheric modification intensified in October 1999, when the grassroots group Citizens for Natural Weather collected a mail-in vote in which 252 respondents were in favor and 903 opposed to the Western Kansas Weather Modification Program. The non-binding vote led the Rawlins County commission to pass a resolution opposing weather modification there. Other counties are considering a similar move. Perhaps it is time to declare your community a "Chemtrail Free Zone."

TWISTERS

In early November 2002 a savage series of twisters killed 35 people in nine states in a single day. On Nov. 10, much of the town of Carbon Hill, Alabama was totally destroyed – killing 11 people and injuring 50. An intense band of tornado swept across Tennessee. In Crossville, 40 miles west of Knoxville, seven died and 28 people were injured when a dozen homes were reduced to rubble. Also that day, more deaths and destruction were reported from more twisters in Tennessee, Mississippi, Pennsylvania and Ohio.

The previous month, a sudden tornado touching down in Chataignier, Louisiana one morning blew a mobile home 200 yards, crushing it into junk. Two occupants were killed, another five injured. At Corpus Christi, Texas, three tornadoes injured 30 people and left 100 homeless. A math prof. was killed in a college library when the roof peeled off and a wall collapsed.

Were chemtrails involved? Recall that former Raytheon technician

Tommy Farmer videotaped massive chemtrails over Tennessee in the winter of 1999 – just before dozens of tornadoes ripped through Tennessee and three bordering states.

On the Friday before the November 2002 onslaught, ***Columbus Alive*** reporter Bob Fitrakis witness chemtrail spraying by at least six aircraft working the Ohio skies. On Saturday and Sunday, 70 tornadoes struck the area. On Monday, temperatures in wintertime Columbus were a bizarre 75 to 80 degrees.

"OWNING THE WEATHER"

On Nov. 23, 2000 the *Times* of London reported renowned scientist Dr. Rosalie Bertell's confirmation that "US military scientists are working on weather systems as a potential weapon. The methods include the enhancing of storms and the diverting of vapor rivers in the Earth's atmosphere to produce targeted droughts or floods."

The air force admits to deploying its jets to spray weather-altering chemicals. A U.S. Air Force study, *Weather as A Force Multiplier: Owning The Weather In 2025* describes how jet tankers flown by Weather Force Specialists are being deployed in "aerial obscuration" missions that spray chemicals to form "cirrus shields".

Marc Filterman, a former French military officer, told the *Intelligence Newsletter* of several types of "unconventional weapons" using (RF) radio frequencies. Referring to an ongoing "weather war", Filterman stated that the U.S. and the former Soviet Union have already "mastered the know-how needed to unleash sudden climate changes" by the early 1980s."

Tightly beamed ELF (Extremely Low Frequency) have been used to bend the jetstream and alter weather patterns over entire regions since the Soviets' first fired up seven transmitters arrayed around a place called Chernobyl in the late 1970s. Hammered by successive crop failures from frosty weather, the Soviet "Woodpecker" chirping disrupted HAM radio bands around the world – and ushered in unprecedented warm winter temperatures from Vladivostok to Anchorage, Alaska.

The Russian harvest rebounded.

Indulging a planet-threatening impulse to turn the environment into a weapon or war, the U.S. Air Force admits that it now deploys "Weather Force" specialists to upset the weather "by adding small amounts of energy at just the right time and space."

Chapter 9

PULSES, PRECIPITATION AND PERSUASION

You won't be seeing this on the evening news: the Air Force and Navy have for years been conducting atmospheric engineering experiments known as the High Altitude Auroral Research Project. Using phased-array antennas situated near Gakon, Alaska, HAARP is steering the most intense beams of tightly-focused radio waves generated on this planet "to stimulate," heat and steer sections of the upper atmosphere.

"The name of the game is, can you accelerate electrons?" HAARP's inventor Bernard Eastlund told me. Capable of being operated remotely in concert with similar smaller "ionospheric heaters" located in Puerto Rico, Germany, the Soviet Union and other far-flung locations, HAARP's 72-foot antenna arrays will be able to bounce beams off the ionosphere strong enough to "penetrate" deep underground, peering for command bunkers or missile silos hidden by the "bad guys" – who know their countries would be flash-fried if they dare launch a single nuke.

These new beam weapons of mass destruction are all about unrestrained curiosity and control. Oppenheimer and other nuclear enthusiasts went ahead and detonated a weapon brighter than the sun for the first time at Alamogordo, knowing as the countdown clicked toward zero that the entire atmosphere might ignite in the ensuing chain reaction. Oppenheimer later repented. And more than three million people died at Hiroshima and Nagasaki, the Marshall Islands, Nevada, Kazahkstan and many other locations as lethal fallout rained down, accumulating in teeth, breasts and bones. That legacy of plutonium pollution, spit-second incineration and lingering death haunts us still.

What hazards will HAARP unleash? Instead of melting cities and killing kids with cancer, the new idea is to heat up 30-mile patches of an already highly charged ionosphere until "the air glows". Why? In the immortal and immoral words of one HAARP researcher to a reporter: "To see what will happen."

WEATHER VANDALS

The first of three patents awarded to MIT physicist Bernard Eastlund describes his *Method and Apparatus for Altering A Region of the Earth's Atmosphere, Ionosphere and/or Magnetosphere* as focusing on weather modification. Issued on August 11, 1987, commercial patent #4,686,605 claims that directed energy beams of more than *one-billion watts* can be used for "altering the upper atmosphere wind patterns using plumes of atmospheric particles as a lens or focusing device" to disturb weather thousands of miles away.

Writing in *Nexus* magazine, Dr. Nick Begich and Jeane Manning – authors of *Angels Don't Play This HAARP* – note "leading-edge scientists are describing global weather as not only air pressure and thermal systems but also as an electrical system." Scientists say "there is a super-powerful electrical connection between the ionosphere and the part of the atmosphere where our weather comes on-stage: the lower atmosphere."

Calling HAARP, "vandalism in the sky," Begich and Manning report that:

> Weather modification is possible by, for example, altering upper atmosphere wind patterns by constructing one or more

> plumes of atmospheric particles, which will act as a lens or focusing device. As far back as 1958, the chief White House adviser on weather modification, Captain Howard T. Orville, said the U.S. defence department was studying "ways to manipulate the charges of the Earth and sky and so affect the weather by using an electronic beam to ionize or de-ionize the atmosphere over a given area.

"I had looked at using this intense beam, which can be angled, to do some experiments in terms of guiding the jetstream, moving it from one spot to another," Eastlund told me.

Paul Schaefer has a degree is in electrical engineering and used to build nuclear weapons. Shaefer says, "The unnatural level of motion of highly energetic particles in the atmosphere and in radiation belts surrounding Earth is the villain in the weather disruptions."

Fire up giant transmitters like HAARP, and Shaefer's computer models show how Earth discharges this sudden heat buildup, relieving stress and regaining balance through storms, earthquakes and volcanic eruptions. Commenting on HAARP-related experiments, Schaefer says, "One look at the weather should tell us that we are on the wrong path."

Scalar clouds could indicate HAARP activity.

NEED TO KNOW

Did you agree to this?

Have you been officially notified of a February, 1990 Plans and Activities report RFP N00014-91-R-0001 jointly issued by the U.S. Air Force Geophysics Laboratory and the Office of Naval Research?

Perhaps not. Its circulation was "restricted."

RFP N00014-91-R-0001 declares with emphasis, that HAARP will go "beyond basic research" to "*controlling* ionospheric processes" by "significantly altering" regions of the ionosphere at a range of 1,200 miles or more. "What is clear," this formerly classified study notes, "is that at one gigawatt and above effective radiated power...a variety of instability processes are triggered" in the ionosphere.

Weather is all about energy transfer and the distribution of heat. One recipe for intensifying regional weather calls for adding iron oxide or carbon black to the atmosphere and allowing the sun to heat those particulates.

Aimed at doffing Earth's ionospheric cap, HAARP's high-energy beams pass right through the atmosphere without heating it. Unless you add something to the atmosphere for HAARP to heat. Putting iron oxide into the atmosphere similar to the particles found in chemtrail fallout in Washington State, Tennessee and Ontario, would help HAARP heat the weather-forming troposphere.

Alternately, strands of extremely fine polymers could be sprayed into the upper atmosphere to be heated by HAARP. Wafting slowly earthward in thousands of gossamer strands to drape porches, power lines and police cruisers across the United States, this "cobweb-like" material would tend to disintegrate rapidly from moisture, handling and abrasion on the ground. After the *Environment News Service* carried my story on advanced weather modification worldwide, HAARP's inventor, Bernard Eastlund wrote to say, "The experiments described by Thomas seem technically feasible. Recent work on polymeric additives for microwave absorption has been done for commercial curing applications so the polymer fibers are available."

Trying to imagine polymers sprayed aloft to hold heat, Eastlund said, "The choice of the polymer for high altitude heating experiments would be based on the ability to make low weight filaments that have aerodynamic properties that would allow them to stay in place for long periods of time."

HAARP's inventor supplied addresses for two producers of polymer capable of being heated by intensely focused Radio Frequency beams. "The heat generation occurs by adding magnetic iron oxide powder to the polymer," Eastlund explained. FREQUON-B-20 and F-5 PPS polymers "are sensitive in the 1-50 MHz regime. Note that the HAARP is between 2 and 10 MHz."

POLYMER POWER

On August 24, 2001 Margie was walking down her driveway when her path was blocked by an "extremely long strand, shimmering in the sunlight." Anchored near the top of an oak tree on one side of the driveway, the strand ran to the ground on the opposite side.

It looked synthetic.

Suspecting aerial antecedents, Margie ran back to the house to fetch a pair of microscope slides. After collecting slide samples, two very long pieces remained. Heedless of health hazards, "I grabbed both and they flowed behind me as I walked up the driveway."

When she examined her finds under the microscope, the snipped strands had recoiled into corkscrews and matted together. After teasing it apart, she found that what looked like a single submicron strand was really composed of two or more strands woven together.

In November, she wrote to Professor Brian Spratt at the Department of Infectious Disease Epidemiology, Faculty of Medicine, Imperial College, St. Mary's Hospital, London after reading about his work in a newspaper story.

"Dear Professor Brian Spratt," Margie wrote, "All across the country we are experiencing dense amounts of spider silk, whether natural or synthetic, falling from the sky and draping itself over everything I have collected a number of samples and had sent one off for an Infrared Analysis.

> The Institute that I sent it to concluded that it was natural spider silk. They compared the Infrared A of my sample to one of known spider silk done by some company in Japan. The two spectrographs were similar but not identical. I got a second opinion from a biology teacher who worked in a lab and he stated twice that he thought the sample was synthetic. He pointed out to me that the spectrographs were not identical.
>
> In trying to be rational about all this, I thought to myself, I know they are making synthetic spider silk so it follows that they would use similar components to the real thing. I would assume this would also mean that the spectrographs would also be similar. There are never any spiders seen clinging to these strands from the sky.

> My sample has a very artificial looking corkscrew quality. I looked at it under my microscope and compared it to known spider webs and there was no similarity. My strands were much thicker and were composed of what appeared to be many sub-micron strands bundled together.
>
> People are reporting sickness after touching these strands. I myself became strangely ill about four days after playing with it under the microscope however it could have been coincidence. I would be very much appreciative if you could share any knowledge you may have on this subject. I feel that all the different types of experimentation that are taking place at every level of our atmosphere, must be affecting our health and the public has a right to know what they are breathing and also how they are being affected electromagnetically.

An intrigued Spratt replied the same day, wondering if she was "referring to experiments that were carried out using spider's threads to test the survival of bacteria in the environment by the military in the 1960's and 1970's." The idea behind the experiment was to use spider threads as a convenient matrix for bacteria to be sprayed on "and left in the air to see how they survived."

Allaying his questioner's concerns over biowarfare on her driveway, Spratt pointed out. "The silk thread technique is of no use for spreading bacteria as a BW attack as far too few bacteria will stick to them to get any significant exposure."

But what about an "Open Air" test gone awry? It turns out that it was Spratt who disclosed the secret military tests of biowarfare agents carried out over Britain between 1961 and 1976. According to one news report, "Prof Spratt's report focuses on a series of tests by Porton Down on the transmission of biological agents released by sprays from aircraft and ships in Dorset and east Devon. A number of tests used the 'microthread technique' where "bacteria were attached to the threads of a spider's web."

Prof. Spratt stated that the spiders' thread tests "posed no conceivable threat to human health". But he added that other "open air" biowarfare trials "did expose a large number of people to clouds of bacteria that would have been breathed into the lungs."

As we have seen, the bacteria Serratia marscesens and Kledsiella aerogenes were supposedly "attenuated" or killed before being released over jolly old England.

ARE YOU GETTING THE PICTURE?

Could chemtrails be part of mind and mood-modification experiments employing chemical processes activated by the deliberate beaming of discrete radio frequencies?

Or could the inability to concentrate, sudden anxiety attacks and indefinable depression among some chemtrail sufferers stem from the inadvertent interaction of chemtrails with sporadic HAARP experiments and incessant "electronic smog"?

In a report echoed in Michigan and other parts of the U.S., Jan wrote from San Francisco during the first month of the new millennium: "We have an outrageously high incidence of plane and helicopter coverage in our little valley area, and intense electronic disruption with television for periods of 10-20 minutes at a time."

Another Bay area chemtrails researcher noticed the same thing:

> My sister called this morning to report that large jets were flying low over her area and that one had a "big thing" on its tail. About 20 minutes later I heard jets, got my binoculars and there were two jets flying low (for this area). One had a large device off the tail, facing away from the plane at right angle to the tail, extending beyond the body of the plane. A few minutes later there was a mid-sized plane that appeared to have something extra on the tail.

More recently, on May 20, 2000 at 1600 hours:

> I was sitting with my wife talking when we heard a loud noise. She asked if that was thunder and a few minutes later were heard it again, only this time it sounded more like a large jet, but sort of rolling like thunder. It's totally overcast but not thunderheads as the clouds are bright, with patches of blue, meaning not too thick. A few minutes later I went into the hall and heard an alarm going off. It was the ELF meter. I have it set on "high" so the meter said 4.25 milligauss. Not a big

move as its generally around 3 1/2 but high enough to trigger the alarm.

Now sometimes if I turn on a large air purifier or pick up the probe it will go off. Also when first starting the TV with the remote a burst of ELF will set it off for a moment. This time *nothing* was running in the room and I just stood there saying, "This is scary!"

SCORPION'S TAIL

In Michigan, in the summer of '99, Christine watched a plane spreading chemtrails. Through her Bushnell binoculars, she could make out no identifying markings. Suddenly, the trail stopped – "as if he'd run out of chemicals." With the obscuring chemtrail emissions halted, she then saw a "scorpion tail" apparatus fixed like a crooked index finger below the aft fuselage of the plane. It was clearly visible through the Bushnell's, "pointed right down."

Christine later noticed a strange white fungus on the ground – "stiff and springy". When she carefully collected a sample; it felt like "water-logged stiff cotton." She put it under her microscope and saw that it was apparently "not living."

INTERRUPTED SIGNALS

In early October 2000, what one resident described as "a rare cloudless north central Florida day" brought no thunderstorm and no clouds in the afternoon. With his father-in-law complaining that his ball game on the Dish Satellite TV had just winked out, he walked outside "expecting to see a big thunderhead in the signal path."

Rain-blocked signals rarely blackout reception longer than a few minutes. But this time, "Much to my surprise the sky was perfectly clear – except for one greatly expanded airplane trail right in the signal path. It was about 50% blocking the blue sky behind it." Even more revealing, "In a few minutes the prevailing winds moved it out of the signal path and the satellite TV system resumed working."

Addressing this investigator, the signal-savvy sleuth suggested, "It seems to me that if you are correct about aluminum being sprayed into the atmosphere this would be one way to detect it. There are a lot of small satellite dishes in use. I was really quite surprised that a white trail in the sky could reduce the satellite signal that much."

HARASSED

Some chemtrail activists have been virtually monkey-wrenched. Vicki's photo-filled "purplehaze" website was hacked shortly before Christmas, 1999. A vexed Vicki reports, "All the info from all the files (34 pages at the time) was deleted. The files themselves were left intact, all showing 0 bytes of info."

Clifford Carnicom's "carnicom.com" website offers frequently updated chemtrail news and photos. It has been knocked off the Internet three-times by extremely sophisticated viruses that this professional computer consultant says could not have been devised by amateur hackers.

Some official responses are even more intimidating. After William Wallace went to Channel 2 television news with his claim that odd-acting contrails were making him and his wife sick, "two jets buzzed me and left a contrail" over their yard. Two days later, after returning to channel 2 with this new complaint, a small airplane over flew the Wallace's remote homestead. When it reached their property, Wallace says the prop plane emitted a chemtrail from its tail. The plane passed directly over their house, shutting off its valve as it exited their property.

"After that," Wallace relates, "we started getting really sick. We got horrible headaches and backaches and bone aches and we felt nauseous and sick and we felt very sick. We felt we would get cancer and die. Ann got shaky and achy and went upstairs to bed."

The propeller planes were "white planes with blue on the tips. I call them UN planes. They fly by all the time. And out of its tail came a spray and we got real sick and that was tellin' me to shut up."

On New Year's Day, 1999, when Wallace was outside splitting wood, "It started up again. The jets came over about three times." That evening another jet flew over their remote mountain home and William Wallace showed Ann chemtrails woven in a silver tracery against the moon. About six in the morning, Wallace became sick with diarrhea. He suffered from diarrhea all day – "the worst I ever had it." But Anne, who had remained indoors when the jets were working overhead, suffered no ill effects from maneuvers many observers liken to high-altitude "crop-dusting".

The plane passed low over their house, closing its valve as it exited their property.

After asking for an explanation from the FAA's Arthur Jones in Spokane, William Wallace received a letter stating in part:

> Dear Mr. Wallace:
>
> The contrails viewed in the video all appear normal and shows a variety of shapes, which are dependent on atmospheric conditions such as temperature, wind speed and direction, and relative humidity. While your hypothesis is doubtful, we have taken the liberty of forwarding the material to Ms. Margaret Gidding, United States Air Force, Environmental Public Affairs, Pentagon, Washington D.C. You may expect a direct reply.
>
> Sincerely, *Arthur Jones*

That reply, says Wallace, was delivered at 1045 on January 22, 1999 when two jets broke the sound barrier over the Wallace home. William and Ann "thought that they had dropped a bomb on us."

According to Wallace, at 1430 that afternoon, a CH-53 "Black Stallion" Marine helicopter "painted all black" flew over their home at treetop height (about 200-feet), flying north to south. The next morning, after a twin-turboprop aircraft flying east to west laid a single fat chemtrail overhead, William and Ann Wallace became "very sick and ill with headaches."

MAKING WAR ON AMERICANS

If there is nothing to chemtrails, why are American taxpayers being harassed by the military they pay to defend to their skies? On Sept. 8, 2000 aerial interlopers followed Kim Weber home. As the head of CACTUS (Citizens Against Chemtrails U.S.) relates:

> Today I returned home from dropping my husband back to work after lunch – it was around 1:45. I was followed by a helicopter part of the way home. I reached the parking lot of our apartment complex and got out of the car.
>
> I literally stood there nearly five minutes leaning against the car with my legs crossed looking up as the helicopter hovered over me. A neighbor sitting outside on her stoop smoking saw the whole thing. Her jaw was hanging down around her chest. I just sent out yesterday beaucoup announcements about Blue Skies Intl. to radio/shortwave, webcasts, patriot groups, etc., some even overseas.

Ohio

On Sept. 26, Weber wondered why.

"We once again had a helicopter hover directly over us for a long period of time about 4:00 pm. in the parking lot of our apartment complex.

"We are carrying cameras at all times in an effort to catch this on film. As far as I know this is still the U.S. of America. If something should ever happen to us {and we will *not* go quietly into the night}, assume foul play."

The next day she elaborated on the intimidation tactics she experienced since forming the grassroots chemtrails group, CACTUS:

> We're carrying our cameras full time. I know I should probably be scared, but Will, I am not. Our telephone has been bugged for two years. The Army National Guard from VA tried to hack into my computer the last week of June and did a little damage to my start up. We've had helicopter flyovers now for about a year and two hover incidents. It just gets me angry. And when I get mad I work all that harder.

Yikes, I thought. Then I rec'd this letter in June 2003:

> A friend of mine, told me today, you were one of the people to talk to about this, and that you are either involved in one of the biggest organizations for investigating or researching chemtrails, or would know people that are heads of the best orgs in the nation.
>
> Well, we are involved. In fact, one my very top contacts for us, has just informed me, he is being harassed by the military. He had two black choppers fly over his house, and hover there, and fly away. Shortly after, a F-117 fighter jet flew in within 1000 feet above his home, and turned on the sprayer, and sprayed his area, and closest to his house the jet could. As soon as the jet made its pass, it quickly turned off the spray, and sharply turned, and went straight back towards Edwards AFB. I know this is for real! This one of our top men, and he has given us 100% reliable information for close to two years, so you can see why I am upset, worried and angry for!

HAARP SOLD TO PIMPS

As this 3rd revised edition of *Chemtrails Confirmed* goes to press, Britain's biggest arms producer has purchased HAARP and all other divisions of Advanced Power Technologies for $27 million in cash.

Constantly in the UK press for scandals involving its $33 million slush fund financing "prostitutes, gambling trips, yachts, sports cars and more for its most important clients the Saudi royal family and their intermediaries" – as well as hefty bribes to secure lucrative weapons contracts – BAE Systems enjoys annual death-dealing sales of $20 billion in just about every country on Earth, according to the *London Sunday Times* CorpWatch and KPFA Pacifica Radio.

A partial list of BAE's "corporate crimes" includes bad business in Indonesia Saudia Arabia, Turkey, Zimbabwe, Qatar and Algeria [CorpWatch]

Formerly known as British Aerospace, BAE Systems is treated as a US domestic arms company by the Pentagon. Arms sales to impoverished dictatorial regimes, environmental havoc and political corruption are hallmarks of Harps new owners, which took possession of Eastlund's invention in Feb. 2003. [BAE press release Feb. 17/03]

Though the Pentagon will continue running HAARP "experiments", BAE has yet to announce what tunes it intends to play on its new toy. The deal also muddies accountability in the USA for an increasingly controversial program now run by a private British firm notorious for accepting bribes in return for spreading violent upheaval.

EASTLUND'S LATEST PLANS FOR HAARP

In a direct contravention of EU protest, Eastlund says that his company ESEC has recently signed a contract with the European Space Agency "to review the weather modification potential of the HAARP facility in Alaska."

Eastlund is also looking to hit budding tornadoes with HAARP – and turn them off before wind speeds reach destructive force. Neither Eastlund nor Dyn-O-Mat – which sprays tons of gel into forming hurricanes to dry up the moisture that drives them – has satisfactorily explained where excess energy equivalent to hundreds of hydrogen bombs is "dissipated" to in the closed recirculating system of Earth's atmosphere.

Eastlund says the extremely high power required to zap tornadoes will come from "high power electromagnetic radiation produced with solar power satellites." At a time when even low-power cellphones are being shown to have detrimental health effects, the Texas inventor has yet to describe the effects on wildlife and humans of beaming extremely intense energy through the atmosphere from HAARP or orbiting satellites.

Eastlund says that his present preoccupations with HAARP include its application as a "missile shield antenna" – using a *one-trillion-watt* phased array antenna. The unpredictable consequences of hitting the highly fluctuating ionosphere with a beam of energy never before radiated on Earth include wild weather, blown-our power grids thousands of miles from the Alaska transmitter – and the holing or possible complete destruction of the ionospheric shielding that protects all life from lethal cosmic rays – including the gamma and X-rays pouring from the biggest sun flares ever measured.

If destroying Earth as a habitable planet is not ambitious enough, Eastlund's "current project menu" also includes extracting North Slope gas to power a souped-up HAARP "for weather modification", "high power solar satellites" and "ozone hole mitigation" using electromagnetic processes some scientists fear could destroy the remnants of Spaceship Earth's tattered radiation shielding.

HAARP TO QUADRUPLE POWER

Then came word that HAARP is heading for hellacious power levels. The ARRL amateur radio newsletter of Oct. 31, 2003 reported that their technical specialist had attended the 2003 High Frequency Active Auroral Research Project meeting on September 24 at the HAARP site near Gakon, Alaska.

At the meeting, Richard Lampe learned, "Joint funding through DARPA will allow HAARP to quadruple in size from its current 960 kilowatt output to 3.6 megawatts." That's nearly four-and-a-half million watts of power tightly focused on Earth's electrically unstable ionsophere – already under relentless pressure by high-energy bombardments from unprecedented solar eruptions.

NORTH AMERICAN POWER GRID CRASH – CAUSED BY HAARP?

On August 14, '03, the biggest blackout to hit North America left large swaths of the United States and Canada without power – just weeks before a similar blackout affected large parts of Europe.

In the USA, the Associated Press reported on August 16 that three rickety, "privatized" transmission lines in northern Ohio triggered the massive blackout just 10 seconds after alarm systems failed. Almost a half-million miles of aging transmission lines directed by more than 100 control centers carry high voltage electricity throughout the country.

But what caused the sudden power surge in parts of the system not normally prone to problems?

At a "public meeting" announced by a little-publicized Dept. of Energy news release held in Cleveland, Ohio on December 4, Michael Kane told the Electric System Working Group's nine task force members that HAARP had been turned on at 4pm on August 14 - just 11 minutes before the blackout occurred. Kane urged the task force to insist the Air Force turn over all documentation pertaining to HAARP's mission that day.

Describing the aerial aerosol spray operation he witnessed the night of the blackout, Kane also wondered at the timing of the "Determined Promise '03' national military drills announced the day after the blackout. Suggesting that the blackout was a planned military drill, Kane said he had received a report that the Canadian border was militarized in the Mohawk River Valley region just three hours before the blackout. Why?

Senior Policy Advisor James Glotfelty reportedly nodded his head up and down as Kane spoke. [www.prisonplanet.com/120803blackout.html]

HAARP

RUSSIANS WARN HAARP ENDANGERS THE WORLD

Kane's comments came seven months after the Ukrainian parliament raised renewed concerns over HAARP's "global threat".

Carried on the front page of the Jan. 15/03 edition of *Pravda*, an article by Duma deputy Yuri Solomatin explained that the Russian Federation State Duma spent nearly a year considering the global threat posed by HAARP.

The first of two documents prepared by the Duma was sent to President Putin and the UN, as well as to international organizations, parliaments and governments worldwide and the global scientific community. The second info sheet was sent to the mass media.

Calling HAARP a "weapon," Solomatin warned, "The operators of such a weapon are able to program floods, tornados storms and even earthquakes in any region of the planet. It is also possible to paralyze civil and military electronic surveillance systems, and even to affect the psyche of entire nations."

According to the parliamentarian charged with handling another techno-calamity called Chernobyl, the Russian government suspects that "unusual natural phenomena and cataclysms, technological catastrophes in 2002 were caused by HAARP transmissions. This techno mayhem, charge the Russians, includes the otherwise inexplicable crash of a jet SU-27 "Flanker" at the Ukrainian Skynliv airshow on July 27 of that year, which left 83 dead an 199 people injured.

As described in my book, *Scorched Earth*, high-performance fighters like the Flanker depend entirely on electronics for their flight-control and fuel systems. The US Air Force earlier launched a major study the effects of electromagnetic pulses on high-performance aircraft after bombs were inadvertently released and fuel systems shut down, causing crashes. Other aircraft exposed to electronic emissions have exploded in flight.

"APATHY" OF RUSSIAN POPULACE BLAMED ON HAARP

Even more alarming was the Russian government's allegation that "the scientifically incomprehensible apathy of entire peoples in the post-Soviet territories, can be connected to testing by the USA of such geophysical weapons at low power."

"Apathy" is a widely reported symptom of North American chemtrail exposure. Do high levels of HAARP-conducting barium found in chemtrail samples could point to a deliberate policy by Washington to control the moods and emotions of people subjected to relentless travesties of their rights and freedoms? Or are these symptoms another "unintended consequence' of chemtrail spraying that serve its perpetrators well?

Yuru Solomatin is a deputy in the Ukrainian parliament, and Secretary of the Ukrainian committee for economic policy, ecological management and the cleanup of the consequences of the Chernobyl tragedy.

Referring to the 1970 convention signed by the USA prohibiting atmospheric modification, the Russian parliament is seeking a global banning of all HAARP tests.

DOING SOMETHING ABOUT THE WEATHER

In March 1997, Arnold Barnes Jr., of the "Star Wars" Phillips Laboratory described a key element of "Full Spectrum Dominance" at the U.S. Army's Tecom Test Technology Symposium. In his address this consultant on the Air Force study, calmly outlined the history of the U.S. military's weather modification programs and what would be needed for future "integrated weather modification capabilities," reported Bob Fitrakis for *Columbus Alive.* [May 16, 2002]

- In Operation Popeye, USAF aircraft intensely seeded clouds over Vietnam in order to produce heavy rains along the Ho Chi Minh Trail through Laos which carried supplies from North to South Vietnam.

- USAF weather modification was also allegedly carried out during Desert Storm.

- USAF projects conducted using the HAARP transmitter are, according to inventor Bernard Eastlund, primarily aimed at "weather modification".

- Air Traffic Controllers across the USA say they are being told to direct civilian airliners below US Air Force tankers engaged in spraying chemicals for the purposes of "weather modification" and "climate modification" experiments.

- A secret 1967 memo from the Joint Chiefs of Staff to President Johnson: "Authorization requested to implement operational phase of weather modification process previously successful tested and evaluated in some area". (*US Senate, Subcommittee on Oceans and International Environment*; 26 July 1972; p. 5).

Chapter 10

SUNSCREEN

When Dr. Edward Teller stood to address an International Seminar On Planetary Emergencies in 1998, the Earth's lowest temperatures had just been found by worldwide NOAA observatories to be heating up more than *2 degrees* Fahrenheit per century. Frightening forecasts called for even more rapid heating over the coming decades.

Bellwether Antarctica was warming *10-times* faster than this global rate. Adele and Chinstrap penguin colonies were going extinct on the Antarctica Peninsula, where stunned scientists clad in windbreakers strolled in unprecedented rain showers marveling at a first-time profusion of wildflowers.

While corporate-controlled media scoffed at the inevitable outcome from trapping more solar heat in Earth's enclosed greenhouse, top scientific advisers to governments from Tuvalu to Washington were freaking out.

Just the year before, while the father of the H-bomb was busy co-authoring a quick techno fix to reduce global warming without reducing greenhouse gas emissions, our space colony was hurriedly heating up.

Even as malaria invaded the continental United States and tropical Dengue fever spread as far north as South Carolina, melting Arctic tundra threatened to burp megatons of heat-trapping methane gas into an already overheating atmosphere. Canada's northern boreal forests were sweating out a warming trend that threatened to add their dying mass of carbon to the greenhouse, as well.

World oceans were also heating up, altering climate-moderating currents, changing pelagic patterns of food fish and other sea life, and triggering massive storms. As Teller described his sunscreen solution, the strongest *El Nino* ever recorded was seeing tropical marlin and mahi-mahi caught off the coast of Washington state. Swordfish were beaching in Scotland, and torrential rains resulted in "once-in-500 year" flooding in Germany.

The year before similar "Superstorms", droughts and floods killed 50,000 people. Also in 1997, the first "Category 6" hurricane ever recorded packed sustained winds of 200 mph.

As long-lived CFCs, bromines and other industrial chemicals continued to devour Spaceship Earth's solar shielding, ground level radiation levels were also rising alarmingly. U.S. farmers alone were losing more than $3 billion a year to crops damaged by rapidly rising rates of solar radiation, as an epidemic of sun-induced cataracts was sweeping North America. The U.S. EPA sharply revised its estimated skin cancer deaths from 9,300 to *200,000* sunshine-related fatalities over the next 50 years.

Global warming threatened to bankrupt global insurers. Bigger than big oil and the international trade in arms, insurance companies handling more money than many once-sovereign nations are one of the world's largest sources of investment capital. Losses from Extreme Weather Events and related damages were hitting a record $92 billion a year – three-times the annual dollar cost of the Vietnam War

Reeling from catastrophic storm losses up *1,500%* over the previous decade, this powerful lobby pressed Ottawa, Washington

and Whitehall to turn down the heat on global warming. If global warming bankrupted insurers, the resulting "domino effect" would take out the money markets and the banks that backed them.

Flagship Lloyds of London was already nearly foundering after losing almost $11 billion in just four years. Insurance claims from Hurricane Andrew alone "totaled" $15.5 billion.

Over many millennia, Earth's climate has cycled between extremes. But there is nothing natural about the unprecedented warming we are now experiencing. Tree rings from a 10,500 year-old Tasmanian pine show that the last 30 years have been the warmest in 2,000 years.

No question carbon levels are climbing steeply within our space colony's closed, recirculating atmosphere. For at least 220,000 years prior to industrialization, CO2 did not exceed 300 parts per million; methane never exceeded 700ppm. Today, CO2 is at 358ppm and methane is over 1,700 ppm! If this trend continues, our unconscious "Climax Civilization" must soon collapse.

What happens when Chaos kicks in? Robin A. White writes in *The Flight From Winter's Shadow*:

> There was a zone of uncertainty, a chaos zone where small perturbations had large effects...very soon after, a breaking point was reached. The world's climate shifted suddenly and dramatically from the familiar to the utterly hostile. How long would it take? The journey from the zone of shadows to utter collapse was a matter of decades; perhaps as much as two. The climate was already in the shadow zone. Ten years sounded like a long time, but it wasn't. Every five weeks you lost one percent of the time remaining until, until what?

In 1998, the choice appeared stark. Lawrence Livermore National Laboratory calculated that cutting back fossil fuel burning 20% to 1990 levels would cost the U.S. economy $100 billion a year. But other scientists reported that carbon emissions must be slashed by 80% to curtail runaway global warming. Either way, global warming threatened to be a real showstopper.

In the midst of deepening environmental crisis, Teller offered a quick affordable fix. Dusting off a proposal first suggested by scientists in the 1960s and '70s, Teller urged the conference on planetary emergencies to adopt his updated magic bullet.

Everyone present listened intently to one of America's most prominent scientists, whose last horrific invention had held half the world hostage while spreading radioactive fallout to mingle with Soviet plutonium over every square mile of Earth. Long enamored of massive engineering projects, Edward Teller had once proposed detonating "peacetime" atomic bombs to carve harbors and canals out of U.S. coastlines. Now he presented an even more grandiose geoengineering scheme. Why not, Teller urged, spray a protective chemical "sunscreen" into the upper atmosphere?

Computer simulations conducted at Lawrence Livermore showed that if enough reflective particles could be suspended in the atmosphere to deflect just 1% of incoming sunlight, runaway "greenhouse" warming could be stopped in its tracks. This chemical cloud cover would also greatly reduce levels of potentially lethal ultraviolet rays at the same time.

It could be done. With the Cold War officially over and nearly 700 air-to-air refueling tankers in its active inventory, the U.S. Air Force had the planes and the personnel to conduct a sustained aerial spray campaign.

But climate modeler Ken Caldeira was in a quandary of conscience. As the Lawrence Livermore scientist later told *New Scientist*, "My hope was to show that it wouldn't work, so people would give up on it."

Cutting back fossil fuel burning could cost the U.S. economy $100 billion a year. A chemtrail sunscreen could be put in place for just $1 billion a year.

That didn't happen. When Caldeira and his colleague Bala Govindasamy crunched the temperature and weather numbers with a resolution of 200 square kilometers, their three-month computer simulation showed that instead of a 1.75°C temperature rise in 40 years, doubling CO2 emissions beneath an aerial screen of sunlight-reflecting particles would result in *no net warming* over at least 85% of Earth's surface.

And it was cheap. The models showed that greenhouse warming

could be averted – and petroleum-derived profits and pollution continued without cutbacks – at a chemtrail cost of just $1 billion a year.

But Caldeira was worried. Not enough is known about the "Chaotic" processes of a complex and constantly changing atmosphere to predict what cascading and possibly catastrophic events might follow such drastic tampering.

Caldeira told a California conference of geophysicists that massive aerial spraying of reflective particles would further cool the stratosphere by diverting incoming sunlight. This cooling would create more CFC-accreting ice-clouds just like those already eating continent-size holes in protective ozone over both poles. Further concentrations of spray-induced CFC ice-clouds, Caldeira warned, "could destroy the ozone layer."

Caldeira's caution was seconded by a Lawrence Livermore press release. Issued on Dec. 19, 2002, the lab noted, "There are many reasons why geoengineering is not a preferred option for climate stabilization." Among these reasons, the lab lamented, are risks of global "system failure" and the unpredictable responses of Earth's climate system to large-scale human intervention.

"Geoengineering schemes impose a variety of technical, political and economic challenges," says Bala Govindasamy, who worked with Caldeira on the chemtrails computer modeling. "International consensus to develop and maintain the schemes would be difficult," and failure of a scheme "could be catastrophic."

UV SUMMER

Ozone depletion is a true planetary emergency. In 2001, alarm bells rang throughout our spaceship as a record ozone hole larger than the combined area of the United States, Canada and Mexico opened above the entire Antarctic. [*USA Today* 11/24/02]

When that happens, plankton are toast. And if these tiny sea critters go extinct, so do we.

Plankton *anchor the entire marine food web – while acting as bigger CO-2 scrubbers and oxygen suppliers than all the forests ashore.* We've already seen disaster around Antarctica in recent years, when the krill die-off from solar radiation streaming through an Antarctic-wide ozone hole was followed by the starvation and extinction of entire penguin colonies. And a lot of hungry whales.

DEEP DO-DO

The latest ozone hole measurements coming in from Antarctic weather stations operated by Argentina, Finland, Italy, Spain, Australia, France, Germany, Japan, New Zealand, Russia, the UK and USA – augmented by data streaming from TOMS, TOVS, SBUV/2 and GOME satellites – shows we are still in deep do-do.

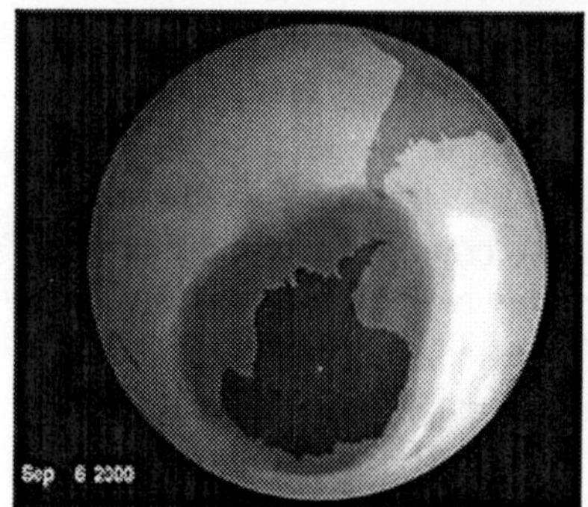

Antarctic ozone hole Sept. 2000

Natural regeneration of the ozone layer is being short-circuited as stratospheric temperatures low enough to form huge high-altitude ice-clouds of frozen CFCs are "continuing to be much below normal" according to the World Met Org. According to the WMO, the most recent measurements of the ozone over the Northern mid- to polar latitudes show "strong ozone deficiency" persisting from Northern Scandinavia over the Russian Arctic and Northern Siberia.

After a brief pause, last year's ozone decline has accelerated, with a 20% drop in normal ozone layer levels appearing "for a short time, over the Canadian Arctic, and nearly continuously over Northern Siberia where, in early March, they exceeded 30%."

These are big numbers. A 30% decline in the ozone layer = 60% increase in skin cancer.

Chemtrails over croplands and populated areas offer a dangerously daffy shield against increased solar radiation *caused in part by the ozone-destroying chemicals they contain and the jets that lay them down*. In Lausanne, Switzerland, whenever the sun passes behind a contrail, atmospheric researchers B. Geerts and E. Linacre measured up to a 5% reduction of solar radiation.

They also noted that the reduction of the diurnal temperature range in the Midwestern USA during the last 50 years "is partly attributed to the increase of contrails along the main flight corridors."

Taking Earth's pulse at McMurdo

"Interactions between global warming and ozone depletion could delay ozone recovery by more than a decade," the United Nations Environmental Program now says.

One increasingly sophisticated climate model predicts differences in ozone recovery patterns, "with larger ozone depletions being expected in the Northern European sector."

If some 14 nations are attempting to secretly shield their citizens and crops from fluctuating solar radiation levels with chemtrails, they must be prepared to carry out this program for many years to come.

Which would seem to point to Antarctica's incredible shrinking ozone hole as part of this early recovery. Until, that is, we recall that last year's split ozone holes over Antarctica were caused by freakish weather conditions – not a recovering levels of stratospheric ozone.

Stay tuned.

CHEMWEBS BLOCK UV RAYS

According to Mike Castle, aerosol polymer filaments dropping from the sky in long, web-like strands have – as Eastlund earlier intimated – been "clearly identified" by "individuals employed by the US Air Force National Atmospheric Lab at Wright-Patterson Air Force Base in Dayton, Ohio" as a "polymer technology used in UV radiation mitigation strategies."

The Ohio-based patent-hunter says he has viewed US Patents assigned to corporations working as federally approved contractors. These patents describe "the use of encapsulated Ultra-Violet absorbers" – including "Mannin and other organic compounds" that absorb UV or reflect solar radiation.

According to Castle, the original chemtrail patent holder, "Hughes Aircraft Corporation is also very involved in the development and articulation, experimentation and deployments of some of these technologies."

Referring to "the chemtrails debacle", Castle adds that barium, aluminum [oxide], and similar compounds "can be easily sprayed into the atmosphere, are chemically stable and reflect UV and may carry a specific electronic charge. This is the model aerosolized platform."

HOT TIMES

Just what is going on with all these chemtrails? A major clue came in late summer 2000, when this reporter was handed a leaked draft document prepared by the International Panel on Climate Change. As the BBC put it, the IPCC "represents the best consensus the world's leading climatologists have been able to achieve."

Governments listen when IPCC projections call for atmospheric heating from a disastrous 3°F to a catastrophic 7-8°F by the year 2100.

In fact, Vostock ice core sampling shows the present levels of heat-trapping atmospheric CO2 to be the highest and hottest in the last 220,000 years. Since the 17th century, methane – an even more powerful greenhouse gas – is up *150%.*

The Inuit of the far north do not need oil company "scientists" to "debate" global warming. They are too busy trying to find words in their 12,000-year-old language for the robins and mosquitoes appearing there. They will also soon need a new way of life as the ice no longer supports their hunters' snowmobiles. In winter!

No wonder. Since the 1970s, as Arctic temperatures have risen a balmy *11 degrees*, the thickness Arctic ice cap has shrunk by nearly *half!* At this rate of melting, it will be gone within 50 years.

Already, the giant influx of cold fresh Arctic melt water is drastically slowing the warm water Gulf Stream essential for moderating British and northern European winters and year-round weather of England and Europe. Together with its Southern Ocean counterpart, the Arctic ice sheet also balances our spinning gyro of a planet. When its high reflectivity switches suddenly to the deep heat sink of open Arctic water – and the methane from all that melting temperatures jacks temperatures up another 10 degrees or so – worrying about the sex lives of movie stars is not going to seem much of a priority.

IPCC-WGIII TAR SOD

Issued for peer review on May 15, 2000, Chapter 4 of the GOV-

ERNMENT / EXPERT REVIEW IPCC-WGIII TAR SOD report is all about geoengineering.

"Geoengineering" means the deliberate, large-scale, manipulations of Earth ecologies. It includes the calamity-inviting hubris of attempting to "manage" the atmospheric circulations of the entire planet – even though we know little about such dynamic and complex interactions, and have no control whatsoever over the vast oceanic processes that drive weather and climate.

Intended to advise policy makers around the globe on ways to anticipate and perhaps ameliorate the catastrophic effects of global warming, the IPCC report points to the plausible "potential" of Caldeira's computer models and Teller's sunscreen Scenario.

The IPCC points out that the "mean effect on the Earth surface energy balance from a doubling of CO2 could be offset by an increase of 1? to 2% in the Earth's albedo, that is by reflecting additional incoming solar radiation back into space. These later concepts offer a potential approach for mitigating changes in the global climate."

In agreement with a 1992 National Academy of Scientists study, Teller and his cohorts found that *10 million tons* of sunlight-reflecting chemicals spread in the atmosphere "would be sufficient to increase the albedo of the Earth by 1%."

Recent computer analysis by Govindasamy and Caldeira "suggest, however, that a 1.7% decrease in solar luminosity would closely counterbalance a doubling of CO2 at the regional and seasonal scale."

Yippee! Fire up the lawnmower, the barbecue and the SUV…

But hold it.

The IPCC adds, "Two of the key problems with earlier proposals were the potential impact on atmospheric chemistry, and the change in the ratio of direct to diffuse solar radiation and the associated *whitening of the visual appearance of the sky.*"

Additional concerns include: "unexpected environmental impacts, our lack of complete understanding of the systems involved, and our concerns with the legal and ethical implications."

GOING FOR IT

The IPPC report followed a weighty 1992 NAS study. Rivaling a Stephen King horror-fest in its length and frightening scenarios, the hefty $80, 944 page report on "Policy Implications of Greenhouse

Warming" includes entire chapters on "mitigation" – including geo-engineering schemes later championed by Teller and others.

Produced by an ominous-sounding "Committee on Abrupt Climate Change", comprising heavyweight oceanographers and atmospheric scientists from the USA, UK and Switzerland, this massive study opens like a clap of doom, warning: "Large, abrupt climate changes have repeatedly affected much or all of the earth, locally reaching *as much as 10°C change in 10 years.*"

To put this in heart-lurching perspective: the *1°C* warming experienced in the 20th century is a very big deal, triggering Extreme Weather Events, widespread droughts and the movement of some 25 million "environmental refugees". A *3°C* jump in average temperatures will end daily life as we know it, turning weather into Nature's vengeance as rising sea levels drown the coasts where most people live.

The alarming intro continues, warning, "Available evidence suggests that abrupt climate changes are not only possible but likely in the future, potentially with large impacts on ecosystems and societies."

> Surprising new findings that abrupt climate change can occur when gradual causes push the earth system across a threshold. Just as the slowly increasing pressure of a finger eventually flips a switch and turns on a light, the slow effects of drifting continents or wobbling orbits or changing atmospheric composition may "switch" the climate to a new state.

We are on the threshold of climate Chaos. "Roughly half the north Atlantic warming since the last ice age was achieved in only a decade," the National Academy of Science notes. Further "climate surprises" await us.

One key problem with spraying sunlight-reflecting particles, says a leaked scientific study, is "the associated whitening of the visual appearance of the sky."

What to do?

Immediate and drastic reductions in fossil fuel consumption come to mind. Freaked out scientists now say that a 60% reduction in CO_2 is necessary for meaningful climate change abatement. But Big Oil has installed their own puppet President. GW Bush has dismantled the Environmental Protection Agency and air pollution regulations with equal alacrity, placing a low priority on alternative energy research in a country responsible for 25% of the world's global greenhouse emissions."

Which has the remaining 95% of the world's population hopping mad.

QUICK FIX

In 1998, the year the father of the H-bomb began calling for a sunscreen to be placed over the planet (or at least over the countries that could afford it), the Stanford Environmental Law Journal January published a paper by Jay Michaelson calling for a geoengineering effort commensurate with the Manhattan Project that spawned the first U.S. atom bombs ever dropped on cities.

The big selling points for a quick geoengineering band-aid, Michaelson mentioned, are that it's cheap, fast and doesn't call for anyone to change their habits.

> Geoengineering is less contentious than regulation. Geoengineering avoids any form of behavior modification. Geoengineering, in contrast to regulation, leaves powerful actors and their interests relatively intact. It may yet be the cheapest available strategy in terms of political economy because it carries almost no social costs whatsoever.
>
> No one need change lifestyles, take a bus instead of a car, or pay more at the gas pump to combat climate change, if geoengineering can offset the climate effects of business as usual. Consumptive patterns of life, which the majority of Westerners seem to enjoy, can continue unabated. Unlike reducing automobile use in the United States, for example, with its avalanche of economic effects and perceived interference with Western consumptive patterns, seeding iron filings in the sea and layering particulate matter in the sky carry very low social costs.

He means "political costs". Imagine what would happen to a president telling people to stop driving their cars so much. Or introducing taxes on high fuel consumption to ensure that happens. Instead, with a sunscreen in place, it's petroleum profits and pollution as usual! "Geoengineering avoids the institutional problems of collective action. There would be no more discussion of clean coal versus dirty coal or (re)forestation versus hydrogen cars."

Coal? In the 21st century? Reforestation? Zero-emission cars? Given the mass extinctions already well underway, what's to debate?

KILLING KYOTO

"The physics of carbon dioxide and other gases absorbing and subsequently transmitting heat is not a matter of theoretical fancy but is a scientifically measured property," Michaelson warns.

With fossil fuel burning releasing some five billion tons of heat-trapping carbon into Earth's attic, and deforestation releasing another three-million more metric tons of carbon dioxide every 12 months, it's urgent that we somehow prevent a doubling of atmospheric carbon dioxide levels from pre-industrial levels within the next 50 years.

It would be nifty if the U.S. would join the rest of the world's nations in implementing the Kyoto Accords for carbon emission reduction, Michaelson says. But climatologists agree that Kyoto is but the first step on the road toward seriously addressing the problem.

With atmospheric carbon dioxide levels presently around 360 parts per million, stabilizing future emissions at 450 ppm "would likely keep temperatures from rising more than 2 to 3 degrees Fahrenheit over the next century."

> *"Given today's political and economic climates, emissions reductions alone cannot do the job." – "A Geoengineering Manhattan Project"*

But according to Patrick Huyghe, author of *Geoengineering Our Way Out of Trouble,* "It is extremely unlikely to be attainable, given current rates of growth in emissions. Cutting back to a 550 ppm increase would likely yield a temperature rise of between 3 and 8 degrees Fahrenheit, depending on which climatological model is to be believed."

"Because the social and economic costs of conservation are very high," Michaelson continues, "a periodic program of distributing particulate matter in the atmosphere can be cheaper than simply conserving fossil fuels." Geochemist Wallace Broecker believed the "sunscreen" proposal would cost around $50 billion.

Salt Lake City under attack from global warming, Aug. 11, 1999

DOWNSIDE

There are a few glitches on the way to a second (and final) century's petroleum pig-out. Michaelson derides "soft" provisions in the Stockholm and Rio eco-declarations, "which encode into international legal understanding precautions about intentional disruptions of the Earth's natural processes."

Michaelson admits, "Geoengineering has a checkered history, at best, from the Army Corps of Engineers' choking of the Everglades to the Soviet Union's attempts to reverse the flow of Siberian rivers to grow cotton and melt part of the Arctic ice cap." Check out Chernobyl and the dried up Aral Sea for a look at megaprojects gone awry.

Focusing on geoengineering also subverts other efforts to attain sensible reductions in greenhouse emissions. During the 1992 National Research Council panel on climate change policy, scientists worried that the notion of offsetting inadvertent climate modification by deliberate climate modification "could be used as an excuse by those who would be negatively affected by controls on the human appetite to continue polluting and using the atmosphere as a free sewer."

"Essentially," Michaelson agrees, "a Climate Change Manhattan Project seeks to cure lung cancer with the latest technology, when really the smoker should just quit smoking…Economists believe a sizable amount of GHG emissions can be reduced quite cheaply."

He adds, "Surely, it is better to just get used to the idea of 'living lightly' than to scatter dust in the sky or seed oceans with iron, especially when living lightly is good for all of us anyway.

But that's not going to happen, Michaelson insists. Not in time to save our spaceship from foundering on the shoals of sheer human numbers, desperation and greed. A year before chemtrail spraying began in earnest, one of geoengineering's biggest advocates urged, "We have to do it now."

IRON OOPS

A big fan of seeding the oceans with iron pellets to explode the growth of carbon-removing plankton, Michaelson enthuses, "This relatively large "bang for the buck" results from the fact that only one iron atom is needed to stimulate enough plankton to consume approximately 10,000 carbon atoms."

Just 430,000 tons of annual iron seeding "is likely to be required to offset the three billion tons of carbon that humans release into the atmosphere each year."

Sounds promising. But giving a big shove to unpredictably "Chaotic" systems can result in…chaos. As Jessica Tuchman Mathews of World Resources Institute says, "Technological fixes can turn around and bite you."

Josh Tosteson, curriculum coordinator for the abortive Biosphere 2 project which failed to artificially maintain a miniature Earth habitat draws on bitter experience when he writes: "Do we have the capacity intellectually to understand complex systems at the level of the globe well enough to make intelligently thought through conscious perturbations that result in only the consequences that we want, and nothing else? My intuitive answer to that question is: No, we don't."

"Iron Ex" once again proved this point. Michaelson doesn't mention what happened after the second "successful" ocean-seeding experiment caused proliferating plankton to gobble tons of atmospheric CO2. The giant plankton blooms also devoured all available sea surface oxygen, killing the sea life that came to eat them, and leaving "dead zones" of oceanic desert in the wake of the iron pellet-dispensing ship.

GOING FOR IT ANYWAY

"What if the Big Fix leaves us worse off than we were before?" Michaelson asks. "If 'Nature knows best'...human interference with the Earth's climate is both unethical and profoundly unwise."

Then there are more practical matters. "How will geoengineering be funded? How will it be monitored? Who will be ultimately responsible" in case geoengineered disaster ensues. These are questions, says Michaelson, "we have barely begun to ask."

Nevertheless, this terraforming technician speaks for many policy makers when he decides, "The need to mitigate climate change may simply outweigh the aesthetic valuation of the natural world."

Aesthetics? We're talking biocide here. By our own hands.

CHILL OUT

Lighten up, urges Jay Michaelson, chill out and have another Prozac:

> It is time for environmentalists to learn to stop worrying and love the Big Fix. The addiction is firmly in place. Conspicuous consumption is deeply entrenched in American self-conceptions, and in conceptions of Americans by people in the developing world who want to be like them. It is unwise to bet the planet on changing people's deeply held practices.
>
> We need an alternative A geoengineering project may be expensive, unreliable, dangerous, ugly, and unwise. [But] when the Damocles' sword of massive biotic disruption is hanging over our heads, we should choose what works. We need a Manhattan Project.

"SUNLIGHT SCREENING"

Chapter 28 of the massive NAS study looked at various geoengineering schemes. One brainstorm was to launch 50,000 100-square-kilometer mirrors to reflect incoming sunlight. Placing enough parasols into orbit would cost $5.5 trillion.

The scientists also discussed using 16-inch naval guns to fire enough sulfur-filled 1-ton shells 20 km into the air to maintain a permanent sulfur dust cloud in the stratosphere to increase sunlight reflection. The dust would drastically heat up the atmosphere, while raining sulfuric acid on the planet below.

Another brainwave they considered was placing "billions of aluminized, hydrogen-filled balloons in the stratosphere to provide a reflective screen."

Or seeding the oceans with iron "to stimulate generation of CO2-absorbing phytoplankton" and remove 7 billion tons of CO2 while suffocating all sealift in those regions.

Or using lasers to break up ozone-eating CFCs in the atmosphere. Even if the technology existed, which it doesn't, the electric power bill would exceed $10 billion.

Of course, carbon cutbacks remain the surest, cheapest, long-term antidote to cracking up our space colony. According to the experts' best guess, "the United States could reduce its greenhouse gas emissions by up to *40%* of 1990 levels *at very low cost."* The results of increased energy efficiencies and the creation of many new clean technologies "could be net savings if the proper policies are implemented."

POP GROWTH

Pesky population growth must also be addressed. Developing countries that currently account for just 23% of commercial energy consumption "are expected to account for about 40% by 2030." Billions of new consumers aspiring to North American standards of consumption and waste could doom the rest of us unwilling to cut back on either activity.

CHEMTRAILS CONSIDERED

But wait, said these top atmospheric scientists the year before chemtrails took off. "Another option for mitigating a global warming would be to try to control the global radiation balance by limiting the amount of incoming radiation from the sun."

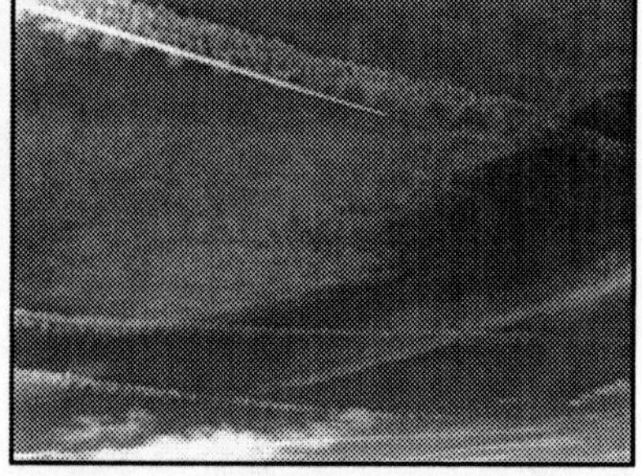

Using airplanes to make clouds, the scientists said, could remove a whopping *4 trillion tons* of carbon from the greenhouse. Or any amount desired. *Cloud stimulation* by spraying cloud condensation nuclei from high-flying airplanes "appears to be a feasible and low-cost option capable of being used to mitigate any quantity of CO2 equivalent per year," NAS nattered. "Perhaps one of the surprises of this analysis is the relatively low costs at which some of the geoengineering options might be implemented."

NIGHT SPRAYING

A clue to late night chemtrail spraying could also be contained in IPCC's leaked 1998 report. As Project Light notes: "Nighttime temperatures over land have generally increased more than daytime temperatures."

SPRAYING OVER LAND

Spraying a sunscreen over the oceans would protect people from fallout, but would spare people from chemtrail fallout – without shielding them from in-streaming solar radiation. The emphasis on spraying over the continental United States also follows IPCC findings that "the recent warming has been greatest over the mid–latitude continents in winter and spring."

SPRAYING ABOVE CLOUDS

With many chemtrails observers glimpsing massive spraying through broken cloud cover, it might seem redundant to spread sunlight-reflecting chemicals above sunlight-reflecting clouds. But tonnage quotas must be met – that is, enough particulates must be suspended in the atmosphere to make this sunscreen work.

As NAS notes, spraying chemtrails over clouds boosts their efficiency: "One additional side effect of aerosols and dust particulates in the atmosphere may be an increase in cloud brightness, which could increase reflectivity even more."

Of course, the experts add, these particles "would have a visible effect, *particularly on sunsets and sunrises*. These chemicals would also "have an effect on the chemistry of the stratospheric ozone layer," they added. This "may be a serious problem."

The scientists concluded, "These ideas do not now seem worth great effort." Instead, they concluded, "reforestation is a low-cost, ecologically attractive option that could be adopted rapidly as an expanded program."

What a concept! Switch to 40% energy efficiency from clean sources, boost profits from 40% cheaper production costs, and plant trees to remove carbon from our greenhouse atmosphere. No matter what does or does not happen in our emerging Greenhouse World, these and similar "No Regrets" policies will enhance everyone's life.

DO OR DIE

Though Europe has just announced an immediate transition from petroleum to an economy powered by hydrogen and even cleaner energies such as windmills and tidal power – the options of leaving remaining forests intact, planting more trees and slashing personal and corporate oil consumption were no more politically palatable in the USA in 1998 than they are now.

But something had to be done to reduce the mounting economic impacts of greenhouse-driven Extreme Weather Events and solar radiation. Even as the U.S., Canada and Japan were busy blocking reductions of their own greenhouse gas emissions at a crucial conference at the Hague, the *Independent* reported, "Fish in the seas around Britain are suffering sunburn and blisters caused by the thinning ozone layer, symptoms of a drastic change in environment that threatens to wipe out species once common to these shores."

Dover sole, cod, mussels and oysters were being hit, along with freshwater fish, newts and frogs as the sun's less filtered rays blistered skin and stunted fish growth. Oceanographers at the Plymouth Marine Laboratory found that "The UVB rays also react with pollutants in the water to produce toxins up to *10,000 times* more potent than normal."

The costs of climate change will exceed the world's entire economy by 2065.

INSURERS ON THE BRINK

Who will insure the insurers? In late November, 2000 environment correspondent Michael McCarthy reported from the Hague that a leading insurance expert had warned the international conference on climate change that the damages incurred by global warming will exceed all insurance industry resources by 2065 – when the cost of the damage caused will exceed the value of all the world's resources.

Andrew Dlugolecki is a straight-talking Scot who directs one of the world's six biggest insurance groups, CGNU – and advises the United Nations Environment Program.

"Climate change will have an effect, our studies show us, in new areas and new intensities, and we know in insurance that new intensities can produce accelerating damage at an exponential rate," he said. "A 10% increase in wind speed can increase damage by 150%, so that is why I feel so uncomfortable about people who say, "Let's wait and see what happens", because once it begins, it will happen at a very, very frightening pace.

With property damage already rising 10% a year, "Already we're beginning to run out of money in the insurance industry," Dlugolecki declared. "At the current rate of growth of damage...by 2065, the damage curve will cross over the GDP curve" – exceeding our collective ability to pay this particular piper.

TELLER TALKS

Identifying myself as a journalist, I wrote to Dr. Teller, reminding him "In 1998 at an International Seminar on Planetary Emergencies you recommended placing a 'sunscreen' above the Earth to reflect a small percentage of sunlight and reduce global warming. Were any experiments carried out to test this idea?"

Recently chosen to join the prestigious Congressional Policy Advisory Board, the since-deceased Teller replied: "To my knowledge, the answer is negative. Indeed, my recommendation was a tentative one depending on further evidence whether expecting global warming is realistic."

Not quite. Press accounts show that Teller pushed hard for an atmospheric sunscreen. An article in the July-August, 1998 edition of *Science and Technology Review* points out:

> Teller was the lead author of a paper presented at an international conference in Italy last year that outlined technological responses to drastic climate changes. He argued that current technology offers much more realistic options for addressing global warming than proposed drastic cutbacks in carbon dioxide emissions. One attractive approach, he suggested, "involves diminishing by about 1% the amount of sunlight reaching the Earth's surface, to counteract any warming effect of greenhouse gases."

In a subsequent special report by CBS News Reports, Edward Teller urged tackling global warming through geoengineering. "The simplest solution is to put into the high atmosphere small particles which scatter away 1 or 2% of the sunlight...the sooner the better," Teller testified.

The patent described "light scattering pigment powder particles" dispensed from jets "for any desired purpose."

PATENTLY OBVIOUS

That technology exists. A U.S. Navy "Contrail Generation Patent" issued in 1975 described a "Contrail generation apparatus for producing a powder contrail having maximum radiation scattering ability."

Noting "some details unavailable", the classified invention was intended to produce an easily observed powder contrail behind target drones used to simulate "aerial threats" for anti-aircraft missile tests. The patent described how "light scattering pigment powder particles" are dispensed from jets "to produce a powder contrail having maximum visibility or radiation scattering ability for a given weight material."

But the patent added that the Navy's invention is also suitable "to generate contrails or reflective screens for any desired purpose."

WELSBACH SEEDING

Environmental consultant Mike Castle discovered the primary purpose behind chemtrails when he came across a practical patent for "Stratospheric Welsbach Seeding for Reduction of Global Warming".

Filed by aerospace giant, Hughes aircraft company in 1991, the patent points out that in addition to reflecting incoming sunlight, Welsbach materials are oxides of metals capable of converting heat trapped by greenhouse gases near the Earth's surface into far-infrared wavelengths, which then radiate into space.

Cautioning that the resulting *white skies* may be unpopular, the Hughes patent nevertheless suggests that these very tiny metal flakes could be "added to the fuel of jet airliners, so that the particles would be emitted from the jet engine exhaust while the airliner was at its cruising altitude."

Aluminum oxide can withstand temperatures far higher than jet engine exhausts. While highly abrasive in larger sizes, a former engineer for Alcoa aluminum says that aluminum in the 10 to 100 micron sizes called for in the sunscreen patent would simply polish jet turbine blades without harming them. (A human hair is about 100 microns across). The engineer added that this "very fine, talcum-like" aluminum powder would appear as a ***"pure white plume"*** in the sky.

UNFRIENDLY SKIES

Could commercial planes possibly be involved? While obviously not involved in back-and-forth gridding, with *millions* of flights over North America, Canada, England, Europe, Australia and New Zealand every year, the sheer volume and air mileage flown by daily-scheduled point A to B commercial flights offers convenient opportunities to augment the task of the tankers.

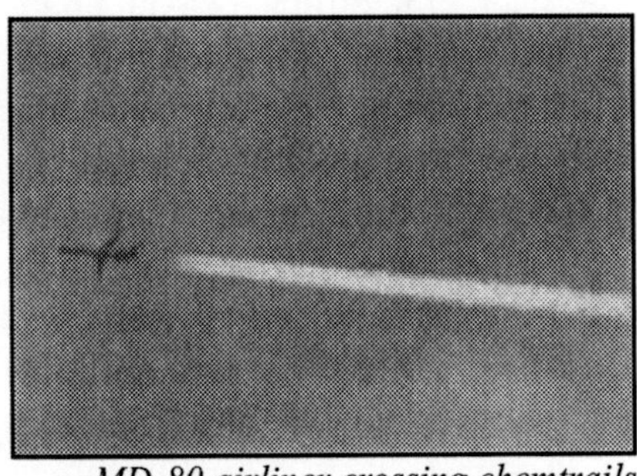

MD-80 airliner crossing chemtrails

Easily identified MD-80s alone currently log *4,800 daily flights*. A disturbing clip in my co-produced video documentary "Chemtrails:

Mystery Lines In The Sky" clearly shows an MD-80 jetliner laying a thick white chemtrail beneath two equally prominent and persistent parallel plumes.

The phenomenon observed above more than a dozen nations fit the patents, studies, proposals and computer models calling for a "sunscreen".

All that remained to prove this theory was a scientific lab test of chemtrail fallout. As we have seen, that "smoking gun" was found in the same samples analyzed by the Ontario laboratory. In addition to weather-altering mica and quartz, the lab turned up large amounts of aluminum in rainwater falling through chemtrails over Espanola. The lab recorded the presence of aluminum at *7-times* government-permissible safe levels. Then came Edmonton.

EDMONTON'S EVIDENCE

Dave Dickie's World Landscapes company performs contract landscape work for the City of Edmonton. "Some contracts require us to utilize the services of environmental labs for soil tests," says Dickie. "Recent soils analysis have come back with a high EC rating 4-7 (toxic) and we've had some soil sources rejected of course because they did not meet specifications."

In an interview with me on Nov. 23, 2002, Dickie explained that his city landscape crews were finding widespread nutrient deficiency in soils could cause severe problems for plant life – including trees.

"Wait," I interrupted. "Aluminum sucks nutrients from the soil."

"No question" answered this soil expert. Moreover, added Dickie, when measuring the electrical conductivity in Edmonton soil samples, "city specifications call for a reading no higher than 1."

Dickie's crews are now finding readings from 4.6 as high as 7.

The "chlorosis" condition resulting from this drastically high electrical conductivity in soil was impacting their landscaping business, Dickie explained. "We were not able to determine the cause of the high EC [electrical conductivity], and many reasons are possible."

Presuming that unusual metal content in the soil could be causing the high readings, Dickie obtained samples of a fresh snowfall in sterile containers and took them to NorWest Labs in Edmonton. As he explained, "Our most recent snowfall was tested for aluminum and barium and we were not surprised with the results. You've said it all along and this just substantiates some of your claims."

In Nov. 2002, lab tests of snow samples collected by the city of Edmonton, Alberta between Nov. 8 - 12, confirmed elevated levels of aluminum and barium. Norwest Labs lab report #336566 dated Nov. 14. 2002 found:

- aluminum levels: 0.148F milligrams/litre

- barium levels: 0.006 milligrams/litre

Because aluminum is ubiquitous in the environment, and its chemistry depends on soil pH and mineralogical composition, it is difficult to provide generalized estimates of natural background concentrations.

But according to Dickie, the NorWest Lab techs told him, "That's interesting. Elevated levels of aluminum and barium are not usually found in Alberta precipitation."

"It may not prove that the aluminum came from atmospheric programs," Dickie admits. "However we are going to sample precipitation from various areas within a 40 mile radius of the City of Edmonton to determine Aluminum/Barium within precipitation."

Dickie says it's simple to test for aluminum and barium in soil samples. Labs typically charge about $15 for these tests. I suggested he add quartz to the list of chemtrail fallout components to check for. In Espanola, quartz predominated rainfall samples, which also showed hazardous levels of aluminum.

Though it must be emphasized that neither Dickie nor NorWest labs are making any claims regarding these early test results, the correlation of known chemtrail chemistry with Edmonton's soil samples is compelling.

This was hot. But imagine my shock when Dickie told me that he regularly visits Air Traffic Control at the Edmonton municipal airport and watches the chemplanes making repeated passes over the city!

"I've been a plane spotter all my life," Dickie explained. Blessed with good friends at work in the tower, he has watched radar-identified KC-135s "on many occasions."

Last Father's Day (2002), Dickie and an excited group of 12 year-olds watched two sorties by two KC-135s. Petro 011 and Petro 012 were tracked by radar as HA (High Altitude) targets flying at 34,000 and 36,000 feet – "one to the south, and one to the north of the city."

"The signature is significant."

Both USAF tankers had flown south out of Alaska. As Dickie, the kids and the controllers watched, the big jets began making patterns over Edmonton – "circuits" the controllers called it. The Stratotankers were working alone in "commanded airspace" from which all other aircraft were excluded.

And they were leaving chemtrails.

"The signature is significant," commented one radar operator, referring to a trail clearly visible on the scope extending for miles behind the KC-135. In contrast, a JAL flight on the display left no contrail.

Going outside, Dickie and several controllers scanned clear blue skies. They easily located the KC-135 leaving its characteristic white-plume "signature". Visibility was outstanding. They also clearly saw the JAL airliner at a similar flight level. It left no contrail at all.

On other occasions, Dickie has watched KC-135s on Edmonton radar leaving lingering trails as low as 18,000 feet.

"We see these guys up here a lot," Dickie says radar techs told him. The tanker flights originate in Alaska, grid the Edmonton area, and continue on into the States. "You should have seen it when they had the big summit up in Calgary. It was exciting to watch them."

Perplexing, too. Was the US Air Force practicing weather modification over the G7 leaders to keep protestors out of the surrounding woods? Or were they spraying barium to enhance radio and radar surveillance – or for some other purpose?

But there was no doubt about the particulates left behind the tankers. On radar, these reflective particles showed up as "birdie feet" – triangles in the radar-tracked plume. They also appeared "as a concentration of dots" in the radar-visible 'trail. Focusing in and out on each plane with the click of cursor, "we could see different contrails," Dickie added. Some were short, and quickly vanished from the scopes. Other trails were thick, long and lingering – not contrails at all.

Especially exciting was watching head-on passes between KC-135s and commercial airliners. Flying directly at each other with a closing rate of nearly 1,200 mph, the huge jets appeared destined to become briefly one. But the controllers were never concerned, Dickie relates, because both planes always adhered to the 1,000-foot vertical separation rule – recently reduced from twice that distance. What would happen, if the "top" plane suffered a sudden decompression and had to dive to lower altitude?

THINKING ABOUT ALUMINUM

Seeing reflective tanker trails on radar – and finding inexplicably elevated levels of highly reflective barium and aluminum in soil samples – is sparking concerted efforts by Edmonton officials to probe deeper into this chemtrail conundrum. Watching plants die, Dickie and others are concerned about possible human health risks. More snow and soil samples are being taken, and questions are being asked of senior transport officials as this book goes to press.

Concern is warranted. For aluminum oxide does more than impact the atmosphere. The BBC reported a furor among Italians complaining of chemtrail-like illness after allied warplanes dropped radar-scattering aluminum over nearby Yugoslavia during intensive air strikes there.

The Italians had their medical facts right. Aluminum is a neurotoxin capable of dulling concentration and reasoning ability. By blocking nerve impulses from being properly conducted to and from the brain, dizziness, memory loss, impaired coordination, involuntary tremors, speech disorders and a loss of balance and energy are also cited in medical texts as indicators of aluminum poisoning.

Linked to Alzheimer's and osteoporosis, calcium-leaching aluminum ingestion also results in gastrointestinal problems, weak and acing muscles, headaches, lethargy, fatigue and flu-like symptoms that leave the body vulnerable to opportunistic infections.

In early spring, 1999 NASA insisted there were "no health risks" from spraying trimethyl aluminum into the ionosphere to experiment with radio wave propagation.

Unlike aluminum, aluminum *oxide* is a mineral almost as common and inert as sand. And sand, as residents of Kuwait and Saudi Arabia and veterans of other desert storms can attest, can trigger radical responses from afflicted respiratory and immune systems.

Dr. Dan Woodard calls aluminum oxide a "nuisance dust". The MD points out that prolonged exposures at very high concentrations (showing as visible dust in the air) "can produce pulmonary fibrosis, somewhat like the silicosis formerly seen in miners."

Woodard continues: "At one time it was thought to precipitate Alzheimer's disease, but more recent research has shown it is almost certainly unrelated. There is little evidence for chemical toxicity, or for effects at levels below the nuisance dust limit."

It does not take chemical toxicity to make people exposed to chemtrail fallout very ill indeed. Basing recent conclusions on more than 3,000 new health studies published since 1997, the EPA has concluded that there is a strong link between the tiniest particles and thousands of premature deaths each year. "There is a veritable deluge of new research," Dr. Lester D. Grant, director of the EPA's national center for environmental assessment told the *New York Times*.

EPA Air Quality Management Rule 402. NUISANCE

A person shall not discharge from any source whatsoever such quantities of air contaminants or other material which cause injury, detriment, nuisance, or annoyance to any considerable number of persons or to the public, or which endanger the comfort, repose, health or safety of any such persons or the public, or which cause, or have a natural tendency to cause, injury or damage to business or property.

Two key studies from the early 1990's by the Harvard School of Public Health and the American Cancer Society found strong links between high levels of small particles and a rise in death rates. In an article headlined, "Tiny particles can kill" the Aug. 5, 2000 *New Scientist* pointed to findings among 8,000 adults in six cities over 16 years, which found that "city-dwellers in Europe and the U.S. are dying young because of microscopic particles in the air."

According to the '*Times*, "microscopic motes – composed of metals, carbon and other ingredients – are able to infiltrate the tiniest compartments in the lungs and pass readily into the bloodstream."

Particles in the lower size range called for by the Hughes aluminum oxide spray patent are *"most strongly tied to illness and early death, particularly in people who are already susceptible to respiratory problems."*

Welsbach "chemtrail" patent = 10 microns aluminum oxide

Particulate fallout 10 microns or smaller = 5% increased death rate within 24 hrs.

On April 13, 2001, the U.S. Environmental Protection Agency released the second draft of its "Air Quality Criteria for Particulate Matter" document for public review and comment.

It will be up to concerned citizens to question chemtrail fallout in regards to proposed stiffer regulations prohibiting particulate pollution. Chemtrails activists can now point to a Dec. 29, 2003 *Los Angeles Times* article reiterating that hearts – as well as lungs – can be damaged by ultra-fine particles small enough to get into the bloodstream and inflame tissues and cells.

When these microscopic particles are inhaled into the lungs, "they are able to penetrate into the cells themselves," says Dr. Ralph Delfino, an epidemiologist at UC Irvine, who helped conduct the latest study. "In addition, they can go in through the blood vessel walls and get into the bloodstream." The *LA Times* reported, "After they reach the heart, the particles are thought to cause a stress reaction in cells, producing inflammation that contributes to heart disease. The particles also may cause blood clots."

On this threat alone, chemtrails must be immediately banned.

The space bugs were eating aluminum.

SPACE BUGS

What about the fungal and possible viral components of chemtrail contamination? If not deliberately introduced into a climate modification program, could malevolent microorganisms be piggybacking on the plumes?

A surprising series of balloon flights made high above the U.S. during the 1960s collected stratospheric samples swarming with live bacteria and fungi – as well as viruses bigger than any known at the time.

If viruses fall from the sky, most would land in the sea. And seawater is brimming with bugs. One study found that coastal seawater contains as many as ten million large virus-like particles per quart. As one researcher said: "No one knows where they come from or what they do. Their size and shape matches the virus-like particles found in the upper atmosphere."

Other life forms, even tinier than bacteria, are thriving in our atmosphere. The discoverer of nannobacteria describes the most populous organisms on Earth as "dwarf forms of bacteria, about one-tenth the diameter and 1/1000 the volume of ordinary bacteria."

FOLK LORE

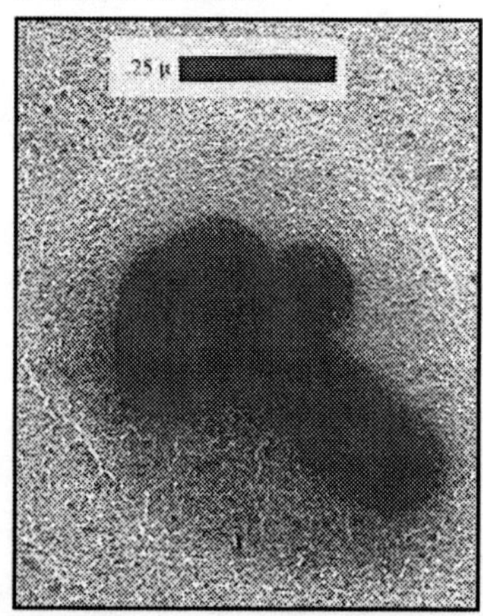

Aluminum-loving nannobacteria

Dr. Robert Folk is Professor Emeritus in the Department of Geology at the University of Texas at Austin. Folk figures that these ultra-tiny critters are "possibly an order of magnitude more abundant" than normal bacteria that swarm everywhere.

Though everywhere underfoot, nannobacteria have gone undetected for decades by myopic microbiologists who have long insisted that bacteria invisible under optical microscopes could not exist.

Since chemtrails are commonly spread over populated areas where sun shading is most needed, it is reasonable to conclude that these particulate-laden plumes are bringing airborne viruses, bacteria and fungi down into human lungs and respiratory systems unable to recognize or resist the alien invaders.

This possibility was further strengthened by Folk, who chose a lightweight metal as a matrix to grow bugs too small to be seen by optical microscopes. Viewed under electronic magnification, Folk found many diverse kinds of swarming nannobac. The bacteria were feasting (he called it "metabolizing") on aluminum.

Strato-bugs also influence the weather. After discovering as many as 1500 bacteria in each milliliter of rainwater collected on the summit of Mount Sonnblick near Salzburg, cloud-catcher Birgitt Sattler says,

"We have so far just proved that there is life up there and that it can reproduce. Now we want to know who is up there."

Reporting in the August 26, 2000 *New Scientist,* the meteorologist believes that these microscopic cloud-dwellers *could play an important part in triggering rainfall and altering climate.*

Translation: Inadvertently precipitating these living nuclei out of the sky with large quantities of free-falling chemical aerosols could cause drought.

> *Tiny aluminum particles could serve as a matrix and culture medium for piggybacking fungi and/or viruses suspended in the stratosphere.*

A May 28, 2002 press release from the National Climate and Atmospheric Research center in Boulder, Colorado announced an 18-month project "to discover whether airborne microbes play an active role in forming clouds and causing rain to fall."

Led by Dr. Bruce Moffett, atmospheric scientists are using a "cyclonic cloud catcher" based on airborne vacuum cleaner technology to sample cloud moisture. The same high-tech PCR (Polymerase Chain Reaction) equipment used to identify mycoplasmas will be used to discover "the composition and activity" of equally tiny atmospheric microbial communities.

Preliminary PCR analysis has already found ammonia-oxidizing bacteria.

"It is known that bacteria, fungal spores, algae and other micro-organisms survive and possibly reproduce in the harsh conditions of the atmosphere," said the NCAR bulletin. Researchers hope to find that "an active, self-sustaining ecosystem exists in the clouds."

These microscopic bacteria and algae apparently "play a key role in the processes that create clouds and trigger rainfall."

As Dr. Moffett remarked, "We know that the balance of gases in earth's atmosphere has been generated and sustained by microbial activity during the 3.5 billion years since life evolved. We are looking for evidence that microbial metabolism could have a major influence on patterns of climate and weather today."

A "really exciting possibility" added Moffett, "is that microbes have evolved ways of triggering cloud formation and rainfall to facilitate their own dispersal and reproduction – in other words, *they could be controlling the weather*."

So what happens when megatons of airborne aerosols laid down by big jet refueling tankers precipitate these microorganisms out of the atmosphere? If airborne bugs act as mobile nuclei for forming clouds and precipitation, the result is another "Unintended Consequence" called drought.

Still gambling with the sky over Las Vegas, 2003

Flathead, Montana Jan 5, 2002

DE NADA

3/12/02

"After fairly diligent search I am unable to find any information on this in the atmospheric science literature. Sorry. The literature I refer to is the published refereed literature in atmospheric science."

Stephen E. Schwartz, Senior Scientist
Atmospheric Sciences Division
Brookhaven National Laboratory
Upton NY 11973-5000

Chapter 11

WE ARE NOT ALONE

Turkey 2002

While most chemtrail reports originate in the USA, many other sightings are swallowed by time and distance and are rarely recorded outside their anxious communities.

Thanks to instant electronic messaging and an exponentially expanding worldwide web, this U.S.-centric viewpoint is changing. With a Croatian observer reporting chemtrails, and a story of cattle-sickening filaments dropped from a passing plane instantly flashing onto computer screens everywhere, the biggest breaking story of the decade can now be viewed and verified with a few keystrokes from any "news" agency in any country.

A friend named Hendrik chronicled a visit to Holland in late 1999:

> The first chemtrails I saw were over Deventer, a town of perhaps 80,000, on Oct. 17. At least five spray planes, one making "dotted line", the others crossing the short stripes in the middle to make X's. At one point at least 10 at once. They worked against the setting sun, totally whited out the sky. I saw two

black helicopters (my first), a round deep black object, stationary for a while, and an ovoid silvery 'drone', spinning around its axis, traversing the sky east to west at the height of the spraying.

I stood on my brother's balcony, went inside when I smelt the acrid, sourish smell associated with the phenomenon. I was shocked and amazed. Even more so, because neither my brother nor sister would come to the window to even look, saying that I was just looking at planes going to Schiphol (A'dam) airport. Whatever I could say, no avail. That surprised me, because my siblings were always pretty smart and curious.

My brother interpreted my excitement at the sighting as a form of mania, to be corrected with the appropriate pill. My second witnessing of the trails was on Oct. 25, from the town of Heemskerk, 30 km NW of Amsterdam. The lines were very long and parallel, almost N-S, covering a good part of the peninsula of North Holland. The spraying lasted all day long, with nary a let up. There were a few trails crossing; the wind was from the west, and the planes [four or five] were working east to west, ending up over the North Sea, which I watched from a high dune, having gone to the seaside. Striking was a huge S-rune, like the one used by the Nazis.

I spoke with a woman who saw me watching in town, and she said this had been going on for at least two months, on most clear days, and the result was a milky white sky. She had complained to Schiphol [airport], but was referred to the Air Pollution Control Branch, which took note but no follow-up. Myself I went to the (now languishing) NGO called "Enviro-Defense" [Milieudefensie] in A'dam, but they had never heard of aerial spraying like this. They were aware of bad air quality around the airport, from conventional sources. They evinced no curiosity about chemtrails, did not even take down your website.

On the streets the Dutch looked very uniform, or fashionable. All had black or dark gray overcoats, black shiny shoes, mostly jeans; they walked very fast, many carried cell-phones, they hardly looked at anything, let alone at one another. As a visitor, I walked a bit slower, and looked around, and when I caught someone else looking around, there was almost a sense of recognition, as of people among robots.

It was definitely a bit eerie.

I spoke with several more awake Dutchmen, and they shared my concern. They said the conformity was of the last few years, and seen as the price for economic prosperity. The economy is booming there, with virtually no more serious challenges to the growth model in the press.

After my return to BC, I heard from a recent visitor to Geneva, that he had been struck by the same extreme conformity; same story about Denmark. The speed limit is now increased to 120km/hr in Holland; the youth is smoking tobacco like there is no tomorrow. I can't draw any definite conclusions, but I am surprised how fast a progressive population can be controlled.

In Feb. 2002, Nick noticed a marked change in "jet trails" over Holland:

Amsterdam 2003

> Some time ago I wrote to you about trails near Schiphol Airport and over Amsterdam. For years – three, four, or more – trails which persisted up to hours at a time and eventually became more like clouds have appeared on most clear days – at least several times a week whether it was summer, winter, fall or spring. But for nearly two months now I have not seen a single trail, which has persisted for more than a few minutes. Amazing how established natural weather patterns of many years' standing can suddenly just stop completely, isn't it?

"Fine dining" magazine ad, 4 Seasons Hotel, Istanbul May, 1997

ITALIAN CHEMTRAILS

On the first of June 1999 Kitty wrote from Italy to report:

> While on military duty in Naples I saw chemtrail grids laid out over the bay of Naples, just off shore. My hotel balcony faced the Bay. Many streaks laid when I came out at noon. Sat and watched them form grids all day. Billowed out. Stayed all day. Bus ride in from base in Cappadicino had many sailors with hacking coughs. Said bronchitis that would not clear up. Very irritable folks. Spoke of the USA chemtrails. They had not heard of them.
>
> That was on the 29th of May. Next day saw the contrails. People coughing all over Naples. I was aghast to see them there. When I returned June 22 they were over my town, a small rural town. Had read of them for a year on the net so knew what they were.
>
> I take good dietary supplements that support my immune system. Have not been sick like others whose immune system compromised. Friends have had pneumonia like illnesses over and over, can't heal. My nervous system seems affected though: short-tempered all of a sudden, low tolerance for this slow burning gal.

March 28, 2002
Luogo della segnalazione:
Provincia di Ancona

Il tempo era buono. L'attivita' si e maggiormente concentrata su una zona che e' state solcata da piu' aerei; risultato: creazione di una nube artificiale a partire dalle singole scie che via via si sono expanse e fuse insieme (ma solo in una zona limitata). Ad un certo punto dopo il passaggio di un grosso aereo e'comparsa una scia isolata molto spessa che si espandeva in modo molto vistoso. Dopo poco e' passato anche un altro aereo proprio attraverso la scia singola (quasi sopra il punto di osservazione); notare l'aereo in uscita (frame 11) porta sulla sua rotta una quantita' di "nube". Da notare come il secondo produca una scia di condensazione molto evanescente.

Translation:

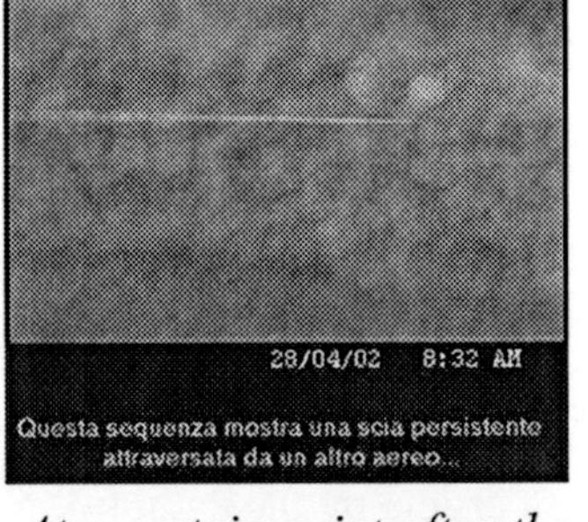

Place of the signaling: Province of Ancona. The weather was good. The activity was mainly concentrated on one zone that had been furrowed from [the aircraft].

Result: creation of a cloud artificial left from the single wakes that gradually expand and fuse entirely (but in one limited zone). At a certain point after the passage of a large airplane appeared an isolated wake – very thick one – that expanded very slowly. After a little time had passed, also another airplane [flew] just through the single wake (nearly over the observation point). Notice the escaping airplane, on its route, a quantity of "nube". Notice as the second [plane] produces a wake of effervescent condensation.

ITALIAN FILMMAKERS HUNT US-CANADIAN CHEMTRAILS

In the fall 2003, concerned countrymen dispatched two Italian documentary filmmakers to document chemtrails on the other side of the Atlantic. After flying in from Rome.

Earlier this week, Vincent Gambino and Duce (du-shey) interviewed me on Hornby Island hideout and were interviewed in turn.

Vincent and Duce showed recent video filmed from their 3,500 year old village in northern Italy. Located 500 meters above the sparkling Mediterranean, the descendants of Roman Legions look out on air traffic departing and landing at a major airport to the south. Arriving airliners sometimes scrawl brief contrails in otherwise flawless skies. But most often, the predominantly low altitude aircraft leave no contrails at all.

But that doesn't save the town's airspace from becoming completely obscured by jet trails.

"We wake up some days and the whole sky is filled with trails, and there is no good explanation of this," Vincent said.

The pair showed excellent-quality digital footage of extensive criss-crossing plumes coalescing and spreading out over the Italian sky – the unmistakable signature of chemtrails. Pointing to the extensive sky grids, Vincent said simply, "Impossible."

Vincent also related how last year, a protest among airport workers at Fiumicino received prominent media coverage after a "famous white plane" belonging to the USAF landed at a cordoned off part Rome's big international airport. "No one was allowed close for two or three days," Vincent explained. Airport workers were angry at the secrecy, he said, and the fact that they "couldn't do their jobs."

Working closely with *Nexus* Italy, Vincent has been investigating chemtrails since becoming aware of them two years ago, after reading an article by the author in *Nexus* magazine.

Hoping to spur awareness and action across a country intensely interested information overlooked or censored by the mainstream press, the two filmmakers are producing a one-hour documentary on chemtrails for Italian audiences. They were especially interested in the experience of Espanola, a tiny Canadian community west of Sudbury, Ontario that was the first to petition a national government after being hammered by photo-identified US Air Forcer tankers spraying sick-making plumes affecting a 50 square mile area in the spring and summer of 1991.

More recently in Italy, a village located in a valley north of Venice has undergone a similar experience. In Fletre In Val Belluna, "People started complaining," Vincent said, after many took ill following heavy chemtrails there.

In Italy, a "Parliamentary interrogation" - or investigation – into the purpose and composition of chemtrails is also being sought.

Italy's Democratic Left - the country's former government and now the official Opposition – the Democratic Left – is demanding a Parliamentary investigation into chemtrails and their possible connection to HAARP. Although barium is two as reflectant as glass – and thus serves well as a sunlight reflector called for in the late Dr. Edward Teller's "sunscreen" scheme – this common electrolyte is also an excellent conductor of electricity.

Vincent says that his group is currently raising money for more extensive tests on chemtrail fallout. But after collecting "white material" from the chemclouds, the Italians have already found "barium salts". While many barium salts are non-toxic, other barium compounds have been used as rat poison. While the filmmakers did not know the type of barium identified in Italian chemtrails, we wondered just who are the lab rats in this ongoing secret experiment?

Vincent reported widespread health effects following chemtrail spraying – including sudden nosebleeds suffered by his mother, sister and father in Florence after "many trails" there a year-and-a half ago 18 months ago.

In other new developments, video of small white orbs observed near Italian chemtrails – and also filmed near U.S. chemtrails – have been identified as robot drones originally developed by the Italian military's "Project Cipher" – and later sold to the U.S. military after funding ran out in the cradle of Western Culture.

Duce and Vincent also said that they have excellent, high-resolution photos of spray coming off the entire trailing edge of sprayplane wings – "*not the engines,*" Vincent emphasized.

THE VIEW FROM PARIS

Oct. 12, 1999

"Again, heavy activity from all directions, X upon X. The pilots here seem to like to play chicken; they fly right at each other and then one will swerve, their trails forming pitchforks and Xs. The

Train to Calais 2002

fork I witnessed was in the southern sky. Plane was flying E to W. The other plane was flying W to E, coming at each other.

"The southerbound made the full turn around, forming the sideways U-shape while the other intersected the rounded part and continued on with the other plane. Then both trails stopped at the same time. The activity is incredible over here. Normal planes were present, no trails being made by these."

Chemtrails or contrails? France July 11, 2002

Oct. 13, 1999 (Paris): "This is incredible. By far the worst I've seen! The planes are flying from all directions. Four planes fly in exact tandem from south to north. The sky is obscured by Xs by afternoon, yet they continue into the evening."

HEADING FOR THE THOLTANS

On Dec. 8, 2001 Michael wrote from the Isle of Man - "A smallish island at the very centre of the British Isles, midway between England, Scotland, Ireland, Wales."

When he returned here in 1995 after a 22-year absence, Michael found "a terrific amount of illness. Very bad viruses, colds, pneumonia."

South Wales, UK June 2003

"Certainly," Michael wrote, "a lot of people died. It seemed that this 'epidemic' had started around 1993. Since 1998, there seems to have been a huge increase in asthma. Strange considering all the sea air we get here, with virtually no industry."

> The Isle of Man is right beneath main airliner routes. Often, you can pick out three or four jetliners in the sky at once, laying down, usually, very long trails. The long trails, in classic Chemtrail fashion, tend to merge and create the wispy and messy 'cloud cover'.
>
> The Isle of Man is way behind the times. A very sleepy place. Maybe it's time it woke up. We have a population of about 80,000 – with about a 40% connection to the Internet rate. So a lot of people have Internet access.
>
> If Island people see something happening, with a little delay, they might get going. If we get the Isle of Man more interested, we may be able to get news items to the main TV channels 'across the water'. I'd prefer if you didn't mention too much too soon on possible alarming connections to Chemtrails – for a while – or we might scare the locals off to hide in their tholtans. (A 'tholtan' is a traditional small, rough-stoned house).

THE "RAIN IN SPAIN" IS PROBABLY CHEMTRAILS

In Spain, and other countries, tourists can buy chemtrail postcards. On April 27, 2000 John Hendricks dashed off a quick Email from El Cafe de Internet:

> We are on vacation in Spain, and were we surprised to see that the chemtrails are as bad here as they are anywhere, both in Mallorca and in Barcelona. We took plenty of pictures. Then we noticed a postcard we bought which has the location printed below a beautiful picture in which a chemtrail is visible!

ADD SWEDEN TO THE LIST

> I saw chemtrails over here 5 days ago (and yes, I've had my first flu in 4-5 years the past 4 days) but couldn't believe my

> eyes at the time. The sky was clear (no clouds, very hot day) apart from 8-10 parallel chemtrails. As I was watching I saw a plane making the first trail orthogonally to the already existing ones. I know the commercial routes, and we have a bunch of them, but not where these trails were. Also, because of the weather conditions any plane passing outside of the normal routes shouldn't have made any trails. So, whatever the conspiracy is, it's bigger than just the U.S. Add Sweden to the list.

Two months later, on July 29, 1999, Ulla-Britt wrote from Henån, Sweden:

> I live on the west coast of Sweden. There is planes spraying the sky with long white contrails. The contrails goes up vertically and after a couple of hours they are very thick and stays in the sky. I have been watching this since November 1998. But then when it was cold the contrails did not stay in the sky. I have also watched this airplane hovering for about 5 minutes. They stand vertically on the contrail. And today when it's clear and sunny the sky looks like milky. They fly over this area all day almost every day.

Chemtrails are being reported over at least 15 nations – including Australia, Belgium, Britain, Canada, Croatia, France, Germany, Holland, Ireland, Italy, New Zealand, Scotland, South Africa, Sweden and the United States – and recently, South Korea. The timing of the Croatian chemtrails is particularly suggestive of an "allied" operation.

CROATIAN CHEMTRAILS

On June 5, 2000 Jeff Rense posted the following letter from Izakovic Rolando on his *Sightings* website [www.sightings.com]. On May 26, 2000, Croatia entered NATO's 'Partnership for Peace.'

> Immediately, the *next* day, Saturday morning 5-27-00, heavy aerial spraying of Croatian main port town Rijeka commenced. Being the first time-ever, foreign aeroplane pilots had the worst luck in guessing the direction of local, constantly changing winds, which they partially-compensated for, in a typically Western way, by working hard all day long.

Pressed by the forces unknown to us, they had to come again second time next Tuesday afternoon, 5-30-00. They start spraying just one hour after the skies have cleared from the daylong rain.

Third spraying, starting Thursday morning, 6-1-00, was shambles. It had all gone wrong right from the start, when the ' X' marking the centre of the chemtrail-laying effort, suddenly found itself downwind. Even the transfer of spraying to the opposite side of the town, at the time upwind, did not help because the wind had swiftly changed direction again.

So, during the next Saturday night, 6-3-00, they had to increase their efforts dramatically, and the town of Rijeka woke up with a low, thick chemtrail cover. Operations continued all day long, resulting with incredible chemtrail fog cowering everything from the sea level up to the heavens, if there were any. It was really spectacular because, in these parts, anything remotely resembling fog occurs only during the winter, once in a ten-fifteen year period, or so. Locals are totally unaware of the origin, state and ramifications of this whole affair and are content to be a joint member of the Brave New World.

Wuerzburg, Germany Oct. 2002

SOUTH AFRICAN FALLOUT

In early July 2000, Jess Miller wrote from South Africa with a translation from an Afrikaans newspaper account in Karoo. This "extensive high desert sheep/cow farming area" is located three to four hours drive northeast of Cape Town en route to Johannesburg. Writing in the Cape Edition of *Rapport Newspaper* on June 25, 2000, journalist Maryna van

Wyck wondered what "are these sticky, spider web-like materials that are falling on to the Karoo areas from the air and forming a blanket like appearance across the vegetation, telephone poles and barbed wire"?

A farmer found fibres up to two meters long hanging over the telephone poles on his farm. "When it is rubbed between the fingers the texture of the substance becomes fragmented and even disappears. It appears to have no smell whatsoever," van Wyck reported.

> Two of my best cows have fallen ill this past month, ever since the debris started falling on to my farm. These cows showed the symptoms of the illness by large bumps appearing on their hides. They became extremely listless and even became blind," says a farm worker for Mr. Du Toit, who first noticed these strange sticky fibres. He maintains that he saw bundles of these fibres falling out of an aeroplane crossing above the area.

TROUBLE DOWN UNDER

In the first days of 2000, a woman wrote from Down Under:

"I have just returned from a two-day bout in hospital with pneumonia. Small town, a whopping 7 in hospital, 5 of which had pneumonia, the rest had lung problems of various sorts.

"Spraying has occurred so we can see it for the past 8 weeks nonstop, including at night, even on full moons. The moon turns green in a sea of fluorescent green mist. I'm mad as hell. Sick as a dog, as are my 3 kids. I can see how this could bring down the populace all in one hit. My local doc is also mad as hell, as he can't do anything about it for fear of losing his license."

On Aug. 2, 2000, environmental consultant Gary Opit wrote an open letter to the Senior Environmental Health Officer and the Byron Shire Council in Byron Bay, Australia. Opit advised that local residents were concerned after watching "unusual sky patterns" over their community. The chemtrails being laid down in "criss-cross" or "single matchstick" patterns made clear skies overcast.

They also appeared to be making many people sick:

"A great many members of our community feel that this Chemtrails spraying could pose the most serious public health disaster in the history of Australia. We have already received reports from people suffering from symptoms commonly associated with the Chemtrail spraying," Opit wrote.

> At least one health professional has informed us that he has had an increase in patients complaining of these symptoms. Dr. Mark Abriel of Byron Bay has observed and photographed many of these Chemtrails (as have I) on several occasions, and he is also very familiar with the medical symptoms. He is currently researching natural herbal cures for Chemtrail toxicity and we would advise that you to consult him too.
>
> The spraying appears to be a planned operation occurring in many different parts of Australia. Ms. Julie King and her children, as well as many others in her home town of Pingally, [Western Australia] became very sick with symptoms leading to pneumonia shortly after spraying took place 3 days before the Easter holidays finished. The local school's entire complement of students were unable to attend for some period of time because of the epidemic of respiratory complaints and the hospital was filled to capacity by patients all suffering from pneumonia.
>
> Symptoms include continuous mucus discharges in the nose and throat, with patients repeatedly coughing up green material with blood, followed by short-term memory loss, lethargy and fatigue continuing for several months and pneumonia in those patients with a less than extremely healthy immune system. Of interest is that there is generally no increase in normal body temperature during the infection. Local Doctors in W.A. have found that only extremely heavy doses of certain antibiotics provide relief, though fatigue will remain a symptom for extended periods of time. We have the urgent responsibility to

> alert the community to the extreme dangers these illegal high altitude spraying operations may have on the health of the population.
>
> Over the last few weeks we have received reports of practically daily Chemtrail spraying over Byron Shire. In the last few days, the usual "lines in the sky" are not always visible. Instead, the spraying seems to be done over the hills to the west in the early morning or night, and it is slowly drifting to Mullumbimby and Byron Bay during the day. This is turning our normally blue sky in the morning to an unnatural "flat carpet" of clouds and haze, which does not raise any suspicions to the untrained eye, and we never have rain. Also, council employees have alerted us that while we have only one flight path, south-north, from Sydney to Brisbane, which we are all familiar with, many Chemtrails are east-west!

A few months before, on July 6, 2000, chemtrails were sprayed over Brunswick Heads near Byron Bay during a music festival. According to an Aussie eye-witness, the mayor of Byron Bay and two members of parliament were giving speeches on the beach "when a very large airplane flew overhead at low altitude spraying Chemtrails, with precise parallel lines that started and stopped abruptly next to each other and at about the same length."

Trees blocked the view of the festivalgoers – and "in a few minutes, with the wind, they covered all Brunswick Heads in a form of clouds and haze that did not raise any suspicions."

> A business-woman friend whom I discussed it with today, who was aware of both the chemtrail spraying on July 6 and today [July 19], suggested that this may be the reason she has a "flu" that she "cannot shake". She also suggested that this might be the reason why "half of the people in town have "flu" or respiratory problems recently.

QUEENSLAND COAST "CHEMTRAILED"

On July 6, 2000 during a festival on Australia's Queensland Coast, low-flying airplanes were reported spraying chemtrails on the beaches

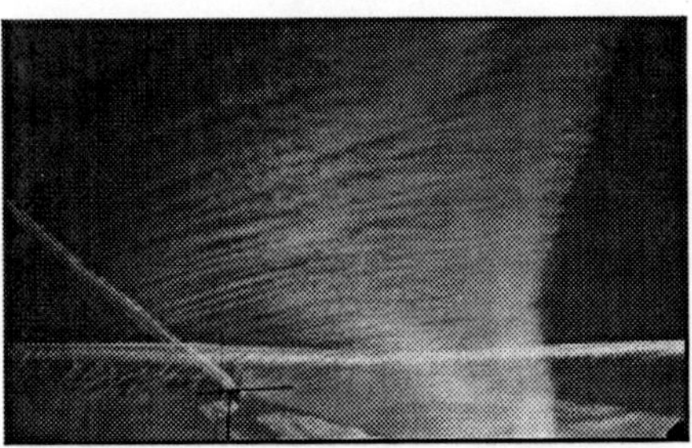
Daylesford, Australia Aug. 2000

at Brunswick Heads, a port city about 200 kilometers south of Brisbane.

Nearly two weeks later, on July 19, "starting at 7:00 AM several large aircraft flying at low altitude crisscrossed the sky in all directions spraying chemtrails. Within a few minutes, the famous clear blue Australian sky turned cloudy and hazy," Diane Harrison reported. "For the first time in history here, it was almost impossible to see the beautiful mountains to the west."

Byron Bay was the target of this renewed spraying, Harrison wrote.

> To our astonishment, the clouds did not disperse, and they were very long, all the way down Australia's Gold Coast. People stopped on the side of the road and got out of their cars to watch the incredible spectacle. I know of a few people who took photographs.
>
> The event resembled a war, as airplanes 'attacked' Byron Bay from all directions. The 'contrails' were 'turned' on just before Byron Bay and 'turned off' after the planes passed over us. The sky "resembled a load of match sticks that was dumped on the floor. These 'contrails' did not behave as ordinary contrails. While one side of these contrails remained straight, the other side dispersed, resembling a comb or a feather."

"DANGEROUS EXPERIMENTS IN GREEK SKIES"

On Dec. 22, 2002 an American named Wayne wrote from the Greek Island of Aigina:

> There has been aerosol spraying in recent days over Athens, Greece. For a couple of months I guess. But I was up on Mount Pendeli yesterday with a couple of boys who wanted to play in the first snows of winter and I saw four planes systematically going back and forth. One of them was white and unmarked and later descended to a lower altitude, without spraying. I don't want

to get involved with this subject myself. I am a member of ATTAC-Hellas and we are concerned with economic problems and more lately with the European constitution. This chemtrails issue is for ecologists and medical doctors, but I haven't seen any ecologists here taking an interest in it.

Here in Greece where I am we're having the wettest weather anyone can remember. The drainage system in Athens is not very efficient and we have had bad floods five, six or more times in the last six months, including twice last summer when it usually doesn't rain much.

The consistent bad weather for the last weeks has meant that the aerosol sprayers have been largely invisible until the last days. But now the weather has cleared up, and this morning the sky is a total mess. I was very much looking forward to the opportunity of getting out of the stifling atmosphere of Athens for the Christmas break and at first felt relaxed and liberated on the island of Aigina, amid the fresh air.

But then lo and behold the next morning at about ten o'clock the clear morning sky was decorated by the first approaching jet trail. I thought it might have been jets that operate over Athens, on their way to work, but no. Back and forth they went, up and down the Saronic Gulf, at least seven jets, for hours, leaving among other things two gigantic plumes right over the town of Aigina and thoroughly messing up the sky. How many places in Greece is this going on? Everywhere I go: three locations in Athens, and now here, they are operating directly overhead.

Wayne noticed similar 'trails, over central Athens, the northern and southern suburbs, Mount Pendeli and the Saronic Gulf. "The trails these planes leave behind often remain visible for a long time. They gradually disperse and become clouds, which again do not look like the natural cumulus clouds we see at lower altitudes in the sky. Often on clear days a few hours of the these planes flying backwards and forwards is enough to spoil the whole appearance of the sky."

On Christmas Eve a huge chemcloud was laid over the town of Aigina. "It was unlike anything I have ever seen before in my life," Wayne commented, "and it got me wondering what we would be breathing when the contents of that cloud got down to ground level."

Chemtrailing the Greeks turned out to be a major mistake. On Sunday Feb. 16, 2003, the mass circulation Greek newspaper *Ethnos* headlined its lead story: "Scientists Uneasy: Dangerous experiments in the Greek skies".

The story's subheading must have turned a few heads: "American aircraft are spraying the atmosphere with chemicals with a view to creating an artificial cloud as an "antidote" to the Greenhouse Effect."

The story by Giannis Kritikos described a vote by the Aigina Island town council to ask the Greek government to explain what is happening in the skies over Greece.

A picture taken from *Chemtrails Confirmed* was used to illustrate similar phenomenon observed over Aigina "without any warning" two months previously.

The translated caption read: "The white trails left behind by this tanker plane which is used normally for aerial refueling, is not smoke but a cloud of chemicals which provide scientists with the ability to control the climate in an entire geographic region."

Aigina town meeting considers chemtrails

A photograph of Leonidas Kardaras, an environmental chemist with a master's degree in environmental technology was paired with a shot of Katsaros from the Democritus research centre in Athens, with the inscription: "The two scientists point out to our correspondent the dangers to public health entailed in the specific experiments."

A third photo showed former parliamentarian Tasia Andreadaki asking, "Who gave permission for this spraying?" The story noted that Katsaros had been invited to speak about chemtrails on Greek national television a few mornings later.

CROWDS AND CHEMTRAILS

When air force tankers spread chemical plumes over rock concerts, race tracks, and other major sports events and outdoor gatherings, people on the ground looking up feel they are being deliberately targeted.

CACTUS (Citizens Against Chemtrails U.S.) organizer Kim Weber reported from Ohio on Oct. 14, 2000 that large gatherings appear to be spray targets:

> Started bright and early. By 9:30 a.m., as folks started coming into town for the home football game at OSU and morning parade down High Street, it was quite obvious that *people*, yes, *people* were the target. TV sports news even showed heavy chemtrails right over the freaking stadium. We also had military jets fly over. By mid-afternoon, the sky was milky opaque and smelled to high heaven. We stayed indoors.

EARTH DAY SPRAY

The previous month, a California correspondent wrote:

> I have watched chemtrails for a long time. I watched them for over a year before William broke the story. I have seen it all as far as chemtrails go. They sprayed very heavy right over my head September 5 and 6, and right after that I got laryngitis. I watched a silver jet spray low over my head and poof it disappeared. They sprayed heavily during Earth Day in Balboa Park in April; they sprayed over a national soccer tournament in the spring.
>
> The worst day of chemtrails I witnessed was over Disneyland in March of 1999. On Friday, October 20 there was a strange chemtrail "circle" near my work in La Mesa, which is 8 miles inland from me.

Two years later, the Houston chemtrail trackers sponsored a "Chemtrail Awareness" booth at the Earth Day festival held on Saturday, April 20, 2002 in that Texas city.

Heavy chemtrail spraying has been reported over the Daytona 500 auto race, and the Rose Bowl. A Toronto music promoter also notes the prevalence of spray planes over outdoor concerts. On July 30, 2003 the

Rolling Stones headlined a the biggest rock concert in Canadian history. Intended to help Toronto overcome the economic fallout of a 2003 SARS epidemic, *Science Daily* reported that the concert was attended by an estimated 450,000 people. But the online publication did *not* quote concertgoers reporting heavy chemtrail spraying directly over the outdoor event.

TARGETING CHILDREN?

On November 6, 1999 KJ wrote from Oakland:

> Yesterday as I left work I noticed in the sky that they're spraying round circles that stayed there for an hour at least and they grew wider. As they grew wider the sky became real hazy (milky) and after awhile it appeared as though the sky looked like a fire had been burning. It was smoky looking thru the trees, a low smoggy blanket and above that it was a milky sky, with patches of blue, weird huh? I work at a school and I, as a concerned parent and humanitarian have noticed alot of activity going on above our skies on Thursday the 4th and Friday the 5th of Nov.1999! I've also noticed that it seems like the sprayers know when the children are at recess, especially lunch recess since that's the longest.
>
> My point is that I've observed their targeting our children especially! Thursday and Friday I observed at lunch recess at least 9-12 small white planes and three – four jet planes above head. God only knows what in the world they're doing to us!
>
> I also observe the illness that my children and I are experiencing as well as the other children and adults of the school. Now you see a sore throat, now you don't.
>
> Just like that!

Hampton, England Nov. 12, 2002

TEMPER FI!

U.S. Marines who jammed field hospitals following CBW attacks on their desert positions know the signs of chemical-biological exposure. In July 2000, a former marine wrote - ***Semper Fi:***

> Keep me posted on this, my mother is very ill in the hospital with bacterial pneumonia and atrial fibrillation. This occurred 48 hours after chemtrail spraying, she was fine before and perfectly healthy, and now she is coughing up blood. What the hell is this shit? What the hell have these bastards done now?

CHEMTRAILING COMDEX

From Las Vegas 12 months later, a Registered Massage Therapist named Annette wrote, "We have been getting 'hit' hard here in Las Vegas, Nevada! We were 'sprayed' almost every day during one of our largest conventions of the year (COMDEX) which brought over 250,000 extra people to our town a week and a half ago!"

BROWN RAIN

From Australia to the Caribbean and across the USA, inexplicable brown and black rains are falling without warning or explanation. On October 15, 2000 Tricia wrote:

> Have seen all of this with my own eyes. Watched two white planes laying down parallel chemtrails directly overhead about 5 p.m. this evening, after a day of large X trails starting this morning. Also goes along with the brown rain we saw driving

> home from Oregon on the 10th. Looked like it was raining mud. Never had that before!
>
> As we left Oregon and crossed the Columbia River on 395, it was raining heavily across the low hills, and it was *brown*. Just reported on CNN Headline News that brown rain is falling in Idaho! Other reports of the black rain in Australia.

Also on the 15th from upstate New York:

> We have an Escort, just a couple of years old. Washed regularly. No garage, so it is parked outside. Yep – clear-coat is peeling right off. Siding on house – vinyl-coated aluminum. Speckled with black that won't wash off. Same for a brand new year-old vinyl shed on property. Windowsills have had to be washed every couple of weeks, all year, or they'd be deep in the black "fallout." I wonder how much of this we've eaten this summer from our pesticide-free homegrown vegetables. This stuff won't come off!

Hampton, England Nov. 12, 2002

"TERRORISTIC EPISODES" IN ALASKA

Gary called from Juneau on May 6, 2003 to complain of "Salvador Dali clouds" that looked "airbrushed" by the planes laying them down. "I look up I look around," Gary told me. "I've got a boat. I'm a photographer. I see things. I look for things."

Several years ago, he thought a high-flying jet must be in trouble, there were so many emissions." Until, that is, the "stricken" plane passed out of sight, "came back, made more than a dozen passes and created a checkerboard in the sky."

Fishermen and pilot buddies say that the planes only spray over populated areas, always shutting off the 'trails as they exit inhabited areas. The bush pilots are suddenly seeing big military jets "make a wide circle over the ocean or the ice fields" before returning to lay down more chemtrails over this small city of 30,000 souls.

But when the wind changes, which it does on that wild coast Gary says, "the X bends, and the planes shut off their trails in mid-flight."

Now many people in the region are complaining of flu-like symptoms, Gary said. His ears ring, and "nose bleeds come out of nowhere." An MD told him, "It could be anything."

Which was true. But Gary says when he had his hair tested, a naturopath looked at the high aluminum levels and told him, "Sounds like you've been exposed to heavy metals."

"It's real obvious that stuff is falling," Gary said. The area's pristine air quality now rivals California smog on bad spray days. In response, Gary shot "more than four-dozen video tapes" and sent them to city and state officials – some of whose "jaws dropped".

"It's cruise ships," they finally told him. The same ships that have been plying Alaskan waters for years with no lasting air pollution are now lost in chemtrail mist.

Others simply said, "You're nuts."

"Look up there," Gary shot back. "Look at that crap falling. When have you seen that before? How come we're getting lines after lines that make this a hazy sky?"

On some occasions he has watched four planes in two pairs flying in opposite directions, "spraying dozens and hundreds of lines."

Finally he went to the state and Juneau police departments to report "a terroristic episode." That did it! "They sat straight up," Gary related. "They were just freaked."

"I'm a patriot," he reassured the authorities. "If I was reporting a small plane spraying something from low altitudes, what would you do? But if I say there are big planes spraying something at high altitudes, I'm seen as a nut or an enemy combatant."

Yet, he told the cops, "There's no difference. Our air quality is going to shit here. This should not be happening."

You don't have to convince Alaskans that the climate is changing dramatically.

According to Gary, plankton levels are down 50% in Alaska's coastal areas, leaving Nantucket-style "dead zones".

"No plankton, no breathe," Gary remarked. They supply more oxygen than rainforests, "and they're killing both."

"Global warming used to be a snicker thing," the straight-talking Alaskan concluded.

Now, "The tiger's out of the bag."

AN AIRLINE PILOT RESPONDS

Airline pilots are beginning to add their names to the chemtrail convinced. Describing himself as "an airline transport pilot with experience in both propeller driven and high performance jet aircraft" Captain D.A, Wheeler has "flown for more than one airline here in the US and internationally."

Corroborating possible alumina (aluminum oxide) spraying, Captain Wheeler wrote into *Sightings* "to report a strange weather-related occurrence yesterday (6/28/2000), 25 km north of the California town of Santa Barbara."

> Firstly, the chemtrails started in earnest around 10-11am PDT and by afternoon large areas of high altitude cirraform clouds

were observed and did not drift much at all with the upper level winds. Now, the weird part: I went inside and flipped on the Weather Channel to check the radar summary for our locale (central coastal California), and lo and behold, there were strong radar returns exactly over the Pacific where these high altitude "cirrus clouds" were located.

Normally, cirrus clouds are mainly composed of ice crystals at those altitudes, and no convective activity was possible due to very low humidity in the area. Also, I observed two separate jets about 20 miles in-trail of each other, at equal altitudes, one producing chemtrails in short bursts, the other did not produce anything. *Bingo*!

The only other radar returns observed were hundreds of miles to the east over the desert southwest, which is normal for this time of year. Could it be that the strange echoes were some sort of metallic substance contained in the cirrus "clouds" to allow better tracking of drift?

MILITARY METEOROLOGIST MEETS MODIFIERS

On May 6, 2001, a former military meteorologist wrote in:

Just thought I'd report that I have witnessed my first chemtrails over central NH. I have absolutely no doubt whatsoever. I am a former military meteorologist and am familiar with the typical commercial flight patterns over my area. I went out to look at the sky around mid-night and directly overhead stretching east to west was a large fat plume at the midlevels, about 16000-20000 feet I would estimate.

I also noticed two aircraft to my north flying east to west and minutes later another large plume showed up. The moon is nearly full so visibility is good. Again, I have absolutely no doubt whatsoever that these plumes are completely anomalous and in no way are they typical of any contrails I have ever seen, and I've seen many in my 12+ years in the military, observed

> both from the ground and on satellite photos. The aircraft traffic is also non-typical for my area.

PORTLAND HAMMERED

On June 4, 2000 Jeff Rense's popular website began adding updates from Oregon – a "Ground Zero" of US chemtrail spraying.

> The skies in Southern Oregon are clear today. A 'No Spray' day here. I just went upstairs and looked toward Portland, about 300 miles north, and was amazed to see the entire upper sky there was white and dense overcast. I could also clearly see two or three long chemtrail lines at high altitude at the edge of the overcast. They must be getting hit very hard today.
>
> Deborah here. I just got back from Gresham. The city of Portland is completely blanketed with the chemclouds—it is solid. Driving in to Portland it looks like a cloudy day. The spraying is definitely going north/south. The spraying is ending east about Corbett, and west I could not tell because the chemclouds are packed-up west as far as I can see.
>
> When I got home there were three new trails above my house. I'm telling you Jeff, we are socked in with chemclouds. Earlier there was a HUGE sundog around the sun with an oily orange rainbow at the edge of the sundog.
>
> I have never, ever seen it this way. What could possibly be going on? Whoever it is knew it was going to be a hot spring weekend. There is barely a breeze. The stuff will disperse and drop right down on us.

That day a retired marine named Sardar wrote:

> I have been on my local news station like a pit bull and they just blow me off. I even told them I was a former pilot and it still doesn't raise an eyebrow. This is the worst spraying we have ever had; they are just blasting us. I point out the spraying to people and they just say, so what? I called the Duty

Officer at the Air Guard and haven't heard back and probably won't. I called my Senators office in Washington D.C. today and will call Monday and raise hell.

My father was a Colonel in the Marine Air Corp his whole life and he says that he has never seen anything like this in his life and he is now 84.

I don't go outside much and I keep my animals inside to lesson the effects of this spraying. We have had beautiful blue skies in the morning and by 11:00 am we are getting soaked by this shit. Yesterday they were flying a circular pattern later in the day. You know that the weathermen know what's up because they say we are to have a clear day on the news and the next day it is covered with chemtrail haze. Whoever is doing this has really put the clamps on the media and the military, as I can't get even a call back to my questions. My next thing will be to walk around on a spraying day with a bullhorn and shout that we are being poisoned from above. Use old town crier tactics. Keep me up to speed and I will do the same. ***-Semper Fi***

Portland "chemset"

That same day, Derek contacted Jeff Rense's "Sightings" webpage:

> I too have wanted to also report *massive* contrail spraying in Portland, OR. The last two weeks have been horrendous. I finally got my wife to look up and notice—she, like everyone I mention it to, didn't believe me. Two days ago we had one particular contrail that spread mostly across the metropolitan sky. It looked like a huge spine with all the nerve endings shooting out up and down the trail. I too have been sneezing uncontrollably - I have no allergies, and am not sick.
>
> Very strange. I have tried to alert people here, but they are so complacent. I am outraged that we are being dumped on and no one is talking about in government or media circles. I don't remember a clear day from morning to night for at least two years now. If there really aren't "chemtrails" up there, then the planes are dumping more fuel than ever before. And that in itself is deadly to the environment and to US.

Gary described a possible chemtrail monitoring mission the previous day:

> My friend and I are spending the day in the foothills of the North Cascades, at Lake Cavenaugh, about 75 miles north of Seattle. Around noon we see massive "trails" criss-crossing each other and beginning to spread. A couple hours later they have spread to cover half the visible sky (from our vantage point, that is). The huge "rainbow" that is often reported to be seen around the sun through the "trails" was clearly visible.
>
> When we arrived home late that night (about 20 miles north of Seattle in the Everett/Mill Creek area), I noticed a pen and ink sketch on the table. Actually, two sketches. I recognized it as the work of my friend's daughter who is twenty years old. I'll call her "Jane". The one sketch showed two circles, one labeled "Sun" and the one around the "Sun" was labeled "Rainbow". Obviously Jane had seen what we had seen.
>
> The other sketch, however, had me baffled. It was simply labeled with a "?" beside it. She said as she was gazing up at

> the "trails" she saw something emerge from one of them. She kept watching it descend as it floated northward. She could clearly see it was a parachute with a large, orange "ball" attached to the bottom of it. This is what she had attempted to sketch. I asked her if she had any idea how large it was. She didn't but said she thought it must have been "pretty big" since she could see it so well.
>
> Perhaps chemtrail watchers should keep an eye out for orange balls on parachutes coming out of the chemtrails. They could be some sort of atmospheric monitoring devices.

Two weeks later, on June 21, 2000, another commercial pilot reported to Rense:

> Today we got "pounded" with trails. My wife is a bus driver and calls me when she sees them working. I hold a commercial pilot license, but I am not flying much these days. The entire sky, from the major north/south airway (V121 that is predicated on the VOR on the Eugene Airport, just west of town) to as far as we could see east. They were rather high, I am guessing appeared about 25,000 feet, and very heavy. They created an obscured overcast to the east, as the prevailing winds aloft were from the west. There are over a dozen trails, each about a quarter mile apart. They spread out until they met each other.
>
> Most of the spraying stopped after I contacted McChord Air Base last week saying we were filming these trails in the Portland area. They resumed with a vengeance yesterday, 6-20-00.
>
> If these were normal contrails in the north-south flyway, they would happen every day – not just certain days. And from the films we took and sent to LA it clearly shows only 4 planes: three white and one orange. I talked to the CDC yesterday and they said that 'no one in America' has reported these trails.
>
> The Portland Tower also denied any flyovers as I was standing outside watching them spray. Temperatures soared abnormally

> for 36 hours following south latitude strike. My eyes were itching and I had a rough throat for 24 hours after strike. Some other friends that were working outdoors felt abnormally tired and generally lethargic.

SOME OTHER PATHOGEN?

Chemtrail exposure can lead to chills, aches, "spaciness" and other symptoms of chemical, heavy metal or fungal exposure. The fevers of flu are conspicuously absent. But as we head into the 6th consecutive summer of chemtrail spraying, year-round "flu", headaches, allergies and lethargy are increasingly seen as "normal" in the U.S. and other "advanced" countries pursuing biowarfare. Are we being set up for a worldwide "flu" epidemic that may not be the flu at all?

Masked by perennial public acceptance, influenza's extremely contagious nature, debilitating symptoms and propensity to kill the weak and the elderly have led to development of more virulent strains as an ideal population control and culling agent.

In 1970 – immediately after National Security Adviser Henry Kissinger's calls for drastic depopulation sparked secret congressional subsidies into a new generation of bioweapons – Litton Bionetics received a contract to develop *lethal airborne strains "influenza" and "parainfluenza" viruses.*

On Dec. 29, 1999 the London *Sunday Times* warned readers that the WHO was calling on every country to prepare for a pandemic similar to the Spanish Flu that swept the world in 1919, killing 40 million people. Whitehall worried that one in four people could be infected by this "lethal strain of flu" – which has yet to be identified.

On Sept. 14, 2000 every Knight Ridder newspaper in the USA breathlessly reported: "The stage is set for a nasty outbreak that could kill at least 88,000 Americans in one fast season." According to statistics obtained by *Parade* magazine, at least 92,000 Americans already die from flu and related pneumonia every year.

If the point was to panic people – *or prepare them for an outbreak of unnatural origins* – newspapers read by millions of Americans helpfully explained that according to six leading experts, "The world is well due, if not long overdue, for a super-epidemic."

LETTER TO THE EUROPEAN UNION

To Peter Gammeltoft
European Union - Air Pollution Dept.
RE: Chemtrails (Chemical trails) over Europe
Dec. 20/02

Dear Mr. Gammeltoft,

A person who wished to remain anonymous at the European Commission recommended that I contact you by e-mail with my question. I was told that this is how a person living in the European Union poses questions to the E-government.

My questions are about the pollution regulations and standards that are in effect in the European Union, particularly those regarding airplanes.

It was a clear morning in Berlin with a nice blue sky until the "chemtrail" spraying planes got started (early) messing it up. By midday the sky was covered with artificial cloud cover, in some places thick and in some places thin, but covering 70 percent of the sky it was.

These planes are probably emitting aerosol aluminum and/or barium stearate, both of which are toxic to humans and other life forms that still exist in Europe. In any case they are emitting something that disperses into a thin layer that eventually falls to earth - that much is clear.

Certainly you must be aware of the activities and conditions of which I speak.

My question is, what is the position of the European Union on the air pollution being rained down on Europeans from high-flying planes and what is the legal liability of these planes for the impact they cause on the health of the people living below?

I know many people who suffer a number of health and psychological complaints due to these "chemtrails".

Thank you for your prompt response.

Christopher Bollyn
American Free Press (European Desk)

Chapter 12

BREAKTHROUGHS

Victoria, Canada 1999

The crack in the dam of denial erected by officials insisting that sky-clogging, never-before-seen jet trails are "normal airline operations" came in the winter of 2000. A brief message left by a conscientious airport official would eventually travel from a concerned citizen's answering machine to this investigator's tape player. And the chemtrails conundrum would have some answers at last.

According to the city caller and many other eye-witnesses, similar unusual plume patterns had been spread by large four-engine jets over Victoria for the past two years – most often on weekends. The aircraft had been photo-identified as USAF KC-135 tankers – often silver and sometimes all-white in color. A check with the air force found that the official aluminum coloration for its tanker aircraft has recently been changed to an all-white paint scheme.

Similarly spaced sky patterns – disturbingly different than normal contrails – had prompted the December 7 call to the Victoria International Airport. Months later – when the microcassette containing Stewart's call made its way through Internet links, phone calls and Canada Post and began playing on a miniature tape player, the reply from the airport manager for planning and the environment blew me out of my chair.

The following unedited transcript is a recorded message from a Dec. 8, 2000 call by a Canadian aviation authority from the Victoria International Airport to a local resident.

Stewart was responding to a call the previous day demanding to know why intense aerial activity had left lingering X's, circles and grid-like plumes over the British Columbia capitol on Dec. 6 and 7.

"Mark, it's Terry Stewart, Victoria Airport Authority. Just calling you back from your comment. From what I gather, it's a military exercise; U.S. and Canadian air force exercise that's goin' on. They wouldn't give me any specifics on it. Hope that helps your interest. Very odd. Thanks a lot. Bye bye now."

Bye bye "airliners". For the first time, an aviation official at a major airport had confirmed that the chemtrails were coming from a military operation. Since joint US-Canadian military exercises have been going on for decades, I found it intriguing and also significant that an aviation authority at one of Canada's busiest international airports would refer to this particular operation as "very odd."

A call to Leftenant John Coppard at the Comox Canadian Forces air base north of Vancouver elicited a brief official response from Canada's primary air defense base on the west coast. "No such joint operation exists," Coppard claimed.

But it was too late for Coppard to cope. The operation had already been confirmed.

"Chemtrails has become the bane of my existence," Stewart later told the Vancouver *Courier*. "It's caused nothing but embarrassment. My uncle in L.A. even phoned me one night to say that a late night talk show host mentioned my name in his monologue."

The ground-level airport manager was also red-flagged at the U.S. border. "I may be getting paranoid," Stewart added, "but the last few times I visited the U.S., the border guards really grilled me and made me cool my heels, as if they suspected me of being a whacko." Or they wanted to know how much he knew.

A March 20, 2001 Lifeboat News press release sent to news agencies across Canada was headlined: "'Chemtrails' Confirmed As USAF "Military Operation" In Canadian Skies". Instead of investigating this encroachment on Canadian sovereignty and serenity, myopic "news" organizations kept their corporate gaze averted from the skies directly over their heads. But more pieces of the chemtrails puzzle would soon be disclosed from higher-level source.

TIFFANY'S TALE

> I am the "S. T. Brendt" of the e-mails you have been receiving from Parsonsfield, ME. I am a broadcast journalist and a disc jockey for WLKZ, Oldies 105 in Gilford, NH, as well as a free-lance reporter who works with other radio stations in the Mt. Washington Valley and western Maine.

This is what I saw on 3/12/01:

> I'm on the air into the wee hours of Monday so I get up late. Lou Aubuchont (my other half) was already up. I did not know he had already observed something at approximately 11:30 am.
>
> I was sitting at our kitchen table having my first cup of caffeine and just glanced out the window on the door to our small pantry and through that room's window. It was 12:10 pm and a beautiful cloudless crystal blue-sky day.

Until two jets hove into view...

> They were both over 30,000 ft. These were neither landing nor had they taken off from the Portland Jetport (approx. 35 miles SE of us by car). I looked due west and saw "lines" in the sky. Two lines that arched with the horizon, in other words *miles* long. I called Lou outside at that point and, again, moving NE to SW were two more jets.
>
> Now there were four jets that we could see in the sky at the same time. Lou and I watched this from 12:10 to 12:55 and in that time we saw over 30 jets, approx one every 1 1/2 minutes. They were overlapping each other, that is, others were still visible when a new one appeared. I had seen chemtrails and contrails before but never this many jets in such a short time at this altitude. We just don't have that kind of air traffic here.

A series of phone calls finally put Brendt in touch with a senior Air

Traffic Control manager. The government official told her that the nine jets on his scopes represented "an unusual" amount of air traffic.

Brendt continued:

> I thanked him, and Lou and I left the house heading for Limerick, ME, and Ossipee, NH. When we were on Rt. 160 we could see even more jets. We could look in any one direction at a time and see five or six jets, all flying over 30,000 ft. Lou guesstimated they were going…well over the usual commercial airliner speed. As far as your eye could see looking southwest were lines and lines including two huge grids that were quite blatant. No "wind" could do *that.*
>
> *I have never seen so many jets in the sky at that altitude all doing the same thing at the same time, in my life!*
>
> At approx 3:55 we headed home to Parsonsfield. They were *still* up there. What's worse is that these grids were now merging to the point of graying our beautiful skies just to the south and west of us and the "crap" was moving in our direction.

"They counted 370 different lines in the sky."

> The lines over *our* area were now merging. By 5:30 our beautiful day had turned dingy and hazy like air pollution and our sunset was dirty. Lou remembers seeing the last jets at about 5:15 pm leaving chemtrails. They were spaced further apart then the earlier jets.
>
> I had left a message for my "boss" at my radio station who called me back and told me they had seen what we had seen on the 12th and further that they counted 370 different jets/lines in the sky from the time the chemtrail spectacle had started till the time it had ended. They said that was a total, not that these 370 jets were in the air at the same time. The most jets they could

see from where they were (their view is obstructed by trees on three sides of the bldg) at any one time was 17!

That is *incredible* for this area! You just don't see that kind of air traffic in the Lakes Region of NH or in western ME. On 3/13/01, we had lousy weather. The spraying took place just ahead of a front.

Brendt's "Deep Sky" source later agreed to go on record. In three interviews with the radio reporter, the senior Air Traffic Control manager repeated and developed – "for the record" – the information relayed to Brendt in their initial phone conversation.

The following press release went out to all major print and broadcast media across Canada and the USA:

FAA OFFICIAL CONFIRMS AIR FORCE CONDUCTING WEATHER MODIFICATION OVER U.S. AND CANADA

by William Thomas and S.T. Brendt

PORTLAND, Maine (March, 2001) A senior air traffic control manager responsible for commercial aircraft over the northeastern United States has confirmed in a second exclusive interview with radio reporter S.T. Brendt that large formations of U.S. Air Force tanker aircraft are conducting ongoing operations over the USA and Canada.

The sky-obscuring chemicals laid down in criss-cross patterns by the big jets have been observed by thousands of eyewitnesses across North America over the past two years. In a corroborative statement, a Canadian Airport Authority for airport planning and environment at Victoria International Airport confirmed on Dec. 8, 2000 that grid patterns and X's laid by tanker aircraft over the British Columbia capitol on Dec. 7 was "a joint U.S.-Canadian military operation."

When asked the purpose of these missions, the FAA official said he was told "weather modification" after a "higher civil authority" ordered him to divert incoming trans-Atlantic airliners around military formations flying over 37,000 feet on March 12, 20 and 21, 2001.

On Monday, March 12, reporter Brendt and her partner Lou Aubuchont counted 30 aircraft laying down a lingering gridwork of several hundred plumes between 12:05 and 12:55 p.m. Aubuchont, who witnessed many military maneuvers during his stint as a courier in U.S. Navy Intelligence, said he had never seen anything like it.

"It looked like an invasion," he told this reporter. Aubuchont emphasized that unlike aerial battle exercises, the tankers were unescorted by combat helicopters or fighter jets. "It was just tankers."

After being contacted at a major metropolitan airport by Brendt, the ATC manager drove to her home on Monday; March 26 to see for himself how many commercial jets would be visible from her location. The FAA official counted just three jets "off in the distance" between 12:05 and 12:55 p.m.

Of the nine jets on his radarscope during that same time period on March 12, the official told Brendt she should have been able to see only one from her location. Instead, she and Aubuchont counted 30. The flights continued all day.

Such cloudy radar returns are consistent with clouds of talcum-fine aluminum particles released by high-flying tankers in a process USAF Weather Force Specialists term, "aerial obscuration."

The Air Traffic Control manager admitted that the chemicals sprayed by the tankers degraded ATC radar returns. When asked if this posed a threat to flight safety, he replied, "not from my perspective."

> But the ATC manager added that similar military operations have been carried out "on other dates" and "other regions" in the USA. When asked whether the air force jets crossed into Canadian air space, he replied "yes."

In a third follow-up interview, Brendt and I decided to play a hunch. Referring to the mission objectives, the ATC manager had actually said that weather modification "approximates" what he had been told. We guessed that "climate modification" was more accurate.

When Brendt questioned Deep Sky again regarding the purpose of the spray planes, he agreed that "climate" modification was the word used by higher authorities calling for airspace to be cleared for the big military jets.

HOUSTON STUDY COMPARES CONTRAILS AND CHEMTRAILS

Houston 1999

More proof that chemtrails are *not contrails* came from a Houston sky plume study conducted by Mark Steadham in the winter of 2000. As Steadham states, "This report is the result of research into the science of contrail formation and an analysis by observation and measurement of contrail persistence. This research was inspired by the claims of an unnatural type of trail known as Chemtrails as an attempt to detect such trails."

Steadham has his atmospheric science right when he explains that moisture and particulates from burnt and non-combusted jet fuel "play a fundamental role as the basic foundation for the formation of a contrail. The ability of the resultant ice crystals to last is governed by the ambient moisture at flight altitude."

As we have seen, airborne particles serve as nuclei for atmospheric moisture to condense around. The resulting bigger droplets quickly freeze into persistent plumes at much lower levels of moisture than is usually required for normal contrail formation.

This means that the persistence of broad white jet trails at flight altitudes with relatively low humidity (32%-39%) indicates very large quantities of particulates in the air – most likely spread by the aircraft leaving the plumes. To plumb the plumes, Steadham steadily correlated personal observations of jet traffic over Houston with airliner identification provided by a computer program called "Flight Explorer". This consumer software uses "real time" FAA tracking to plot commercial flight paths across the USA. It does not track military flights – which are indicated as unidentified aircraft.

Commercial aircraft tallied in the Houston study included the Boeing 752, Boeing 757, Airbus, DC87, Boeing 733, Learjet and MD80. Airlines included Southwest, Air Canada, Northwest, American, AeroMexico and Federal Express. While altitudes are not given for military aircraft, according to the FAA large military aircraft usually transit commercial airspace around 30,000 feet to ensure safe separation from airliners flying at 35,000 to 39,000 feet. The Air Force confirms that its tankers do not fly at contrail forming altitudes in order to reduce hook-up times for fuel hungry fighters.

So military tankers should leave far fewer contrails in lower, warmer air than commercial airliners. But Steadham's study found just the opposite! The best explanation is that tankers trailing persistent plumes must be emitting heavy concentrations of particulates.

Busy metropolitan airports see nonstop take-offs and landings during peak daily periods. But aircraft descending or climbing far below contrail-forming altitudes do not create contrails over airports. As Steadham points out, "Most contrailing jets observed are just through the area at approximately 31,000 ft. to 40,000 ft."

After using "Flight Explorer" to identify the airliners and military aircraft passing overhead, Steadham timed their respective plumes.

Some examples tell this chemtale:

12/02/00		
11:00 am	~4-8 hrs.	(military)
11:45 am	~2 minutes	(commercial)
12:00 noon	~2 minutes 10 sec.	(commercial)

12/08/000		
8:50 pm	10 seconds	(commercial)
01:00 pm	~4-8 hrs.	(military)
01:00 pm	10 seconds	(commercial)

12/21/000		
8:50 am	20 seconds	(commercial)
09:00 am	~4-8 hrs.	(military)
09:20 am	~2 1/2 minutes	(commercial)
09:40 am	~4-8 hrs.	(military)
10:10 am	20 seconds	(commercial)

Confirmed contrail observations in study (46)	
All confirmed contrails 15 seconds or less	72%
All confirmed contrails 30 seconds or less	80%
All confirmed contrails 2 minutes or less	96%

Confirmed Commercial Airline Contrails
5 seconds to 25 minutes

'Trails from Military Aircraft
~4 hours to 8 hours

Steadham found:

> The highly persistent trail is entirely inconsistent with the trends of identified trails observed this day. These highly persistent trails have a persistence more conveniently measured in minutes or hours, as opposed to seconds. One highly persistent trail was timed at over 5 hours. This particular measurement was limited by line-of-sight visibility, the actual persistence was longer.
>
> The goal of this research was to determine if there was a type of trail that was inconsistent with normal contrails, especially with regard to increased persistence.
>
> Highly persistent trails that last for many hours were seen above Houston., TX on a majority (60%) of observable days during the data collection period. During this time period none of the 46 Flight Explorer confirmed contrails observed persisted for over 30 minutes and most contrails were under 30 seconds of persistence.

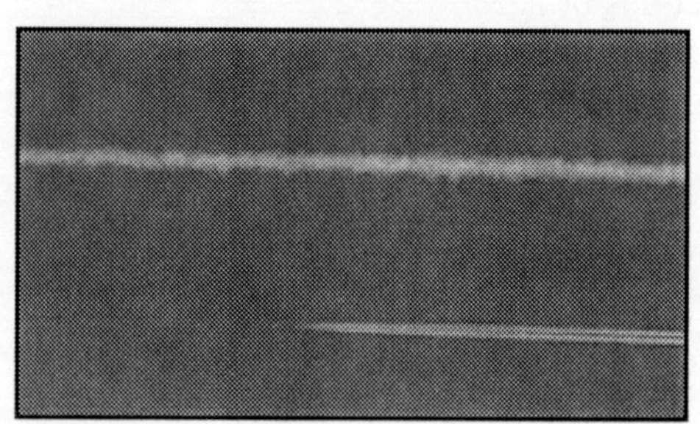

Houston

Houston

BARIUM LEVELS UP SHARPLY IN USA

Clifford Carnicom has been reporting spectrograph readings of sharply increased levels of barium over New Mexico for several years. Then the Chemtrails Central website republished this 2002 official state graph showing a sharp rise in barium in California's atmosphere over the past decade:

- In 1991,the average California barium concentration was 26.7 nanograms/cubic meter.
- In 1999, barium concentrations in the air breathed by Californians suddenly jumped above the two previous "highs".
- By 2002 it had *nearly doubled,* to 50.8 nanograms/cubic meter.

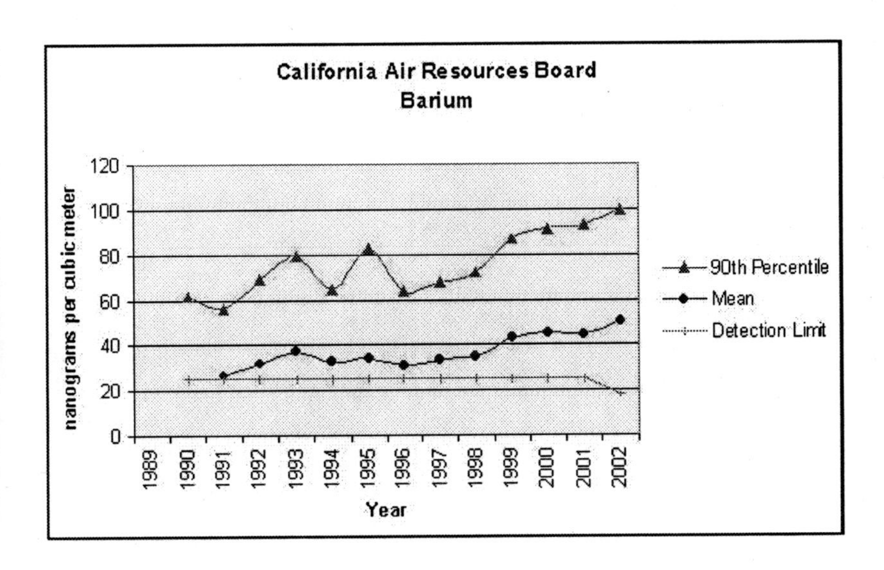

There was no explanation for the sharp rise.

The following information is presented as journalism – not prescription. These reports are in no way advised or recommended as therapy or treatments for any ailment. Severely ill patients should seek the advice of qualified natural and technological medical practitioners.

Chapter 13

TREATING CHEMTRAIL - RELATED ILLNESS

Rx

The good news is that chemtrails – as well as most mystery pathogens currently responsible for chronic allergies, low energy, headaches and year-round "flu" – do not prey on people with fully functioning immune systems. When healthy people do succumb, their illness is usually short-lived and much less severe than among those with weakened immunity.

Stress is the single biggest cause of disease. Because we become what we think, and attract what we fear, the first step in protecting ourselves, our families and loved ones from disease-causing microorganisms is to support and love the heck out of one another.

It is also essential to cultivate a positive mental attitude that distinguishes real concerns from media-hyped threats without succumbing to fear.

The best way to do this is not being attached to the outcome. And by giving thanks for each human- and heaven-sent gift. Instead of putting ourselves down, it's wiser not to do the would-be controller's work by celebrating each victory – from paying the rent or saving a last stream or stand of life-giving trees, to airing chemtrail clips on local TV.

Engaging in enjoyable outdoor exercise, love, touch and a good diet are as vital for staying centered and connected as taking daily time out for contemplation and prayer.

Knowing that fungal infections are the most common culprit lurking behind a complex array of symptoms gives us a further edge in rebalancing bodily chemistry. (For more on alternative healing, including supplementation and longevity, please see my book *Alt. Health.*)

SAY SO LONG TO FUNGAL INFECTIONS

After identifying fungal infections as a primary cause of illness and general malaise, the *Idaho Observer* observed how naturopaths "found great success in treating the illnesses with anti-fungal herbs such as black walnut in conjunction with blood purifiers such as yarrow and garlic."

Dr. Joseph Puleo has successfully treated many extremely ill patients complaining of chemtrail-related symptoms. He recommends that all of us "Detox, deacidify, boost immunity and eliminate dairy products and sugars that form mucus and grow fungus while reducing blood pH."

We can avoid molds in our daily environment by making sure our living and workspaces are clean and dry. Start taking Cayenne capsules daily. Combinations of hot sauce at mealtime also work well to improve circulation and overall health.

It is vital that we eat alkaline foods as much as possible, avoiding acidic "fun foods" – as well as caffeine and alcohol. [See the Dr. Matsen's marvelous book *Eating Alive* for more insight – and helpful lists of acidic and alkaline food groups.] Matsen's program of careful food combining saved my ravaged immune system after I returned from the minefields, oil rain and blazing deserts of Kuwait. So did the highest quality supplementation I could find. With chemically contaminated soils depleted of essential minerals, and factory foods devoid of natural nutrition, quality vitamin, herbal and mineral supplementation is also essential to rejuvenate and shield cells.

> *"Detox, deacidify, boost immunity and eliminate dairy products and sugars."*

HOROWITZ ON HEALING

In an interview with *The Konformist*, Dr. Len Horowitz outlined "five critical steps" in counteracting the new pandemics:

> The first step is detoxification, because we've all virtually eaten of Babylon's harvest, we've all eaten the garbage that comes from Monsanto and Dow Chemical and Archer Daniel and all their genetically engineered foods and the chemicals and the fluorides and the chlorines.
>
> Step two is deacidification, to change your body's chemistry, to become more alkaline. It's only in the acid state that your body gets into that causes the growth of bacteria, viruses, fungus, molds, and cancer cells. They cannot grow in an environment, a terrain that is more alkaline. And what causes your body chemistry to go acidic and become a breeding ground for the bacterial and infectious agents? The main lifestyle risks are caffeine, nicotine, sugar, refined carbohydrates, alcohol, and pharmaceuticals – virtually all of them, including antibiotics. And then, red meats. That, plus stress, are the seven factors that cause your body chemistry to become more acidic. So you want to eliminate those or reduce them as much as possible.
>
> Horowitz also recommends squeezing lemon into your drinking water. (But don't overdo it! Too much lemon can erode the enamel on your teeth.) The reason I did that is because the lemon has a lot of calcium in it, it turns to calcium hydroxide in drinking water. That's alkalizing. It raises the pH of that water from about 7 to about 8. So now I'm drinking pH 8 water instead of pH 7 water. That's step two, deacidification.
>
> So step three, then, is boosting your immune system in every way possible. In other words, step one is detoxification, step

two is deacidification, and now you can go out and spend your money effectively with your vitamins and your minerals and your supplements. You can get the value out of co-enzymes, you know. You can get the value out of the olive leaf extract. Out of the variety of other vital nutrients and botanicals. There's a revolution in that health science.

People think that all they have to do is take those supplements. But if they're throwing those supplements into an intoxicated terrain and an acidified terrain, it's a waste of your dollar. It's so much less expensive to go through an easy detoxification program using fresh squeezed lemonade that you make with maple syrup and fresh squeezed lemons and cayenne pepper.

To heat up the blood and prevent fungal growth, take cayenne pepper in powder or capsule form daily.

Then, if you're sick and ailing, you go on to steps four and five. Steps four and five have both been heavily suppressed by the same Rockefeller-directed international banksters, blood banksters and medical monopolists. They are oxygenation therapies and bioelectric therapies.

There's a product called Body Oxygen, which is one of the products that I have developed. It's an excellent product. What it does is, what most people who are involved in oxygen treatment use 35 percent of food grade hydrogen peroxide, between 4 and 24 drops in an 8-ounce glass of water. That oxygenates the water.

But the problem is, it's really caustic to touch. It burns you skin. And it tastes horrible. If you drink it, it's horrible. We put it into a cold press, organic aloe vera and then we added additional immune boosters, so you're getting your oxygen, you're getting your aloe, which is great for your gut, and you're getting hawthorn berry, Ginko and St. Johns Wart – excellent for immunity.

ELECTRIFIED

Do not neglect the new bioelectric therapies. Horowitz refers to the realm of electromagnetic healing as "God's technology". He's talking about sound, color and light therapies when he notes that over the last decade, Nobel Prize winners in medicine have shown how DNA functions as an electromagnetic receiver and transmitter that literally delivers God's healing vibration to all the cells and tissues.

Puleo and Horowitz were guided to a series of six repeating codes in the Book of Numbers that correspond to the six missing tones of the ancient Solfeggio scale used in early hymns and Gregorian chants. The resonant frequency of the third note is the exact frequency used by genetic biochemists to repair damaged DNA – using sound to mend rips in the genetic blueprint upon which life is based.

"So are you doing Colloidal Silver?"

DE-TOX FORMULATIONS

A person who used a detox herbal formula to remove suspected chemtrail chemicals from her body that were causing her to feel sick says of Quit For Life:

> It's all completely herbal. This is the product that I took that reversed my contrail-illness that nothing else would touch (not colloidal silver, nor Aerobic 07, nor Microhydrin – had it been viral or bacterial I'd have knocked it out in a day.)
>
> I didn't get anywhere fast until I used this detox formula. Other people I talked to were flat in bed for two weeks with continued weakness and other symptoms. I was flat in bed for only three days by comparison. It worked wonders for me and I'm grateful to God that I can see beyond big company marketing ploys to sell it only to smokers.
>
> On hearing of my symptoms of CRI – sudden dizzy spells, joint pain, twitching eyelids and extreme fatigue following chemtrail spraying down Vancouver Island's west coast – a nearby naturopath wrote to say that a doctor who has been

> treating chemsickness for the past year in humans and animals "thinks the brain fog, fatigue, lethargicness, hits the go-getters, high energy people." These were my worst symptoms, not the respiratory stuff."

I didn't get anywhere fast until I used this detox formula.

Then she "came across a wonderful detox for taking toxins and metals out of the system. It is called Herbal D-Tox from Wild Rose. It is a liver cleanse, intestinal cleanse, blood, muscle and lymphatic cleanse. It was recommended to me by a doctor. I have my whole family doing this cleanse and I believe it is good for anyone who feels they have been affected by the chemtrails."

This healer would also "recommend Nettle, Marshmallow and Fenugreek. They are for joint pains, low energy, convalescence, balances sugar/insulin, dryness and inflammation. Then, of course, we know that this stuff has bacteria, etc. – so are you doing Colloidal Silver?"

COLLOIDAL SILVER

The best colloidal silver is freshly made at home. This correspondent believes that the best available machine is the CS Pro HVAC:

> I made a batch that day and started taking it, 1 oz. about every 4 hours. It cleared up the stomach in the first 4 hours, I gargled about a half oz. every 3 hours to clear up the hacking cough, that took all day, the nose I sprayed some in three times, it cleared up. The headache and weakness took another two days to clear up. The cat came home sneezing and make strange sounds the same day. I put 1 oz. in his water bowl and he drank the whole bowl, he had never done that before. He was well the next day.

Another person sick with CRI advises a Colloidal Silver dosage of:

> One tablespoon, 3 times a day for three days, and then one a day the last day and then stop. We did. My husband still has the cough but this stuff worked miracles on me. After the first day, my sinus was completely cleared up.

Herb writes, "After weeks of antibiotics I was still sick, had to have emergency ventilation twice. Then I remembered colloidal silver. I used 4 oz of 500ppm over a 5-day period; I killed whatever this stuff was. I continued taking a maintenance dose."

ZAPPERS

Science has shown that direct-current electricity delivered to the skin by small battery-powered "zappers" kill bacteria and disable viruses from being able to reproduce. (See Hulda Clark's classic book, *The Cure For All Cancers*.)

TEA TREE OIL AND COLLOIDAL SILVER

Advising that her daughter has suffered Chemtrail-Related Illness for months now, a mother named Judy commends colloidal silver water made at home with a $30 kit. "She takes it internally and puts it on the sores."

Her daughter:

> uses tea tree oil on the skin and puts drops of it in her shampoo, plus uses the tea tree oil soap and toothpaste. She also uses it in a spray bottle along with some aloe vera, colloidal silver water and distilled water to mist the skin. She has put a little [food grade] hydrogen peroxide in the mixture, too. Should try and stay away from sugars because they [fungi] like it. She mixes borax and vinegar and puts it into her bath water. She also puts some vinegar into her shampoo and some tea tree oil.

OXYGEN

It is virtually impossible for disease-causing organisms to survive and proliferate in fully oxygenated blood. The 2nd International Symposium on Ozone Applications, held in Havana in March, 1997 heard how ozone inactivates Pseudomonas Aeruginosa and E- Coli.

Ozone is a potent germicidal agent. Though Pseudomonas Aeruginosa is the most resistant pseudomonas strain, ingestion of extremely diluted food-grade hydrogen peroxide or other liquid oxygen preparations can completely knock out pseudomonas bacteria. It can also knock you out! See your local health food store for instructions on proper dilution.

Manuel wrote from Tampa:

> Now the 4th week, I have been suffering from upper respiratory problems. I have been experiencing flu like symptoms, specifically a sore throat. The symptoms seem to go away when I take mega-doses of vitamins and supplements – Echinacea, Ester C, Vitamin C, Golden Seal Root, and Magnesium. Plus gargle with food grade (35%) Hydrogen Peroxide diluted to a 10% solution in clean bottled water.

BREATHE DEEP

Most of us sip shallow breaths of often-polluted air. Breathing deeply of fresh foliage exhalations is exaltation for our entire being. Because as Horowitz hints, big cities are running low on oxygen:

> When this planet was first created, there was a 38 percent oxygen level, and that's one of the reasons why people were living so long. Now, in cities there's about an 18, 19 percent level. Before World War II there was about a 28 percent level.

There are simple ways to get more oxygen delivered into your body. Like exercise. Like breathing…

It is virtually impossible for disease-causing organisms to survive and proliferate in fully oxygenated blood.

MORE HOMEOPATHIC REMEDIES

A homeopathic healer in heavily sprayed Bakersfield says that the herb Pulsatilla is coming up often as "the remedy" for cases he's seeing there. "Likewise," Jeff adds, "MSM (methylsulfonylmethane) seems likely to assist. It's said to kill many micro critters and to facilitate detox as well. Widely available now in health food stores; note that a first effect of taking it may be diarrhea. Lacidophilus might be a suitable adjunct to this." [*www.wellnow.com*]

A GLYCIRRHIZIC VICTORY

Jan reports:

> As you may recall, I had a very serious bout with extreme respiratory problems, extreme fatigue, extreme joint pain, etc., etc., etc. I took 3 cc of Glycirrhizic Acid and found almost complete respiratory relief within hours. I know it saved my life. It comes from Unique Pharmaceuticals in Temple, Texas. This wonderful gift works on 64 different viruses, is an anti-inflammatory, works on pneumonia, bronchitis, tuberculosis, asthma, counteracts the use of prednisone *and* has almost cured a friend of mine of Hepatitis C. For the first time in five years, her liver titers are almost normal. This is a woman who was on her deathbed.

LYCENE

Another CRI-patient writes of the "Best treatment I have found – no side affects":

> 1000mg Lycene daily
> 1000mg Panithetic acid daily
> 100mg chelated Zinc and
> C every 4 hours

This chemtrail-afflicted observer adds: "When I was well enough to sleep five to six hours straight without major bronchial congestion, I started taking Melatonin to stabilize normal sleep patterns. Local hospitals [Hoquiam WA] have been at capacity all during January, February '99 with this stuff."

ESSENTIAL OILS

"They are going at it big time here in PA," Judi wrote in May 2001. "Now they paint the skies with the trails so they create their clouds and skyline. This is crazy and the fungus is extremely hard to get rid of. I am using capsicum, geranium and lavender oil externally and finally getting results."

An email from Inetex explained another therapy using essential oils and flower essences to combat Chemtrails Related Illnesses. Brad and Joanne write how during our recent trip to Florida, we were directly exposed to chemtrails on at least five occasions. We observed many extremely ill people – especially in the Miami metro area. The oils and essences are extremely effective, especially when used every day. We purposely withheld treatment to ourselves in order to test the effectiveness of this treatment, and the results were immediate and lasting.

Ken's chiropractor recommends an essential oil formulation called "Thieves". Simply put some on your fingertips and place your fingers under the nose, inhaling deeply.

MALIC ACID

This correspondent recommends:

> Add a daily dose of malic acid to your immune system cure treatment program, 1200 to 2000 mg, as it is a powerful detoxifier of aluminum and has been shown to reduce the pain associated with FM. Along with coenzyme Q10 (300 mg per day) and L-carnitine (500 mg per day) both are important for energy production.

ORIGINAL OREGANO

"Oil of Oregano rivals modern antibiotic drugs," writes health journalist Bill Sardi.

> Oil pressed from oregano leaves that contain the active ingredient carvacrol may be an effective treatment against some-

> times drug-resistant bacterial infection. Georgetown University researchers have found that oil of oregano appears to reduce infection "as effectively as traditional antibiotics."

Considering the Staph outbreaks in the wake of low-level "gel" drops...

> Oil of oregano at relatively low doses was found to be efficacious against Staphylococcus bacteria and was comparable in its germ-killing properties to antibiotic drugs such as streptomycin, penicillin and vancomycin. [*Science Daily* 10/11/2001] The oregano oil was obtained from North American Herb and Spice Company, a Waukegan, Illinois company that sponsored the study and markets their non-prescription products in retail stores under the trade names Oregamax and Oregacyn.
>
> Earlier this year researchers at the Department of Food Science at the University of Tennessee reported that, among various plant oils, oil of oregano exhibited the greatest antibacterial action against common pathogenic germs such as Staph, E. coli and Listeria. [*Journal Food Protection*, July 2001] Last year British researchers reported oregano oil had antibacterial activity against 25 different bacteria. [*Journal Applied Microbiology*, February 2000]

"Oil of oregano appears to reduce infection "as effectively as traditional antibiotics."

- Georgetown University

Increasingly hard to treat strains of pseudomonas can be neutralized with oregano:

> The body of positive evidence for oregano oil as a major antibiotic is growing. Among 52 plant oils tested, oregano was considered to have "pharmacologic" action against common bugs such as Candida albicans (yeast), E. coli, Salmonella enterica and Pseudomonas aeruginosa. [*Journal Applied Microbiology*, June 1999]

The carvacrol in oil of oregano also kills anthrax spores. [*Archives Microbiology*, October 2000; *Quarterly Review Biology*, March 1998]

But Sardi says it's crucial to note, "Oil of oregano is not to be confused with common oregano in the kitchen spice cupboard, which is usually marjoram...rather than true oregano (Origanum vulgare).

COME CLEAN WITH CILANTRO

Our bodies know best. My trips to the pesticide-free section of my grocery's veggie section have me reaching for cilantro. I learned later that Dr. Yoshiaki Omura discovered that the leaves of the coriander plant can accelerate the excretion of mercury, lead and aluminum from the body.

While treating patients for Chlamydia, Herpes and Cytomegalovirus infections, Omura found that their symptoms would clear up after an initial course of antibiotics – only to recur within a few months.

Taking a closer look, Omura found these infectious organisms flourishing in bodily concentrations of heavy metals such as mercury, lead and aluminum. Somehow the organisms appeared to be using the toxic metals to fend off antibiotics.

Cilantro eliminates aluminum from the body.

But mercury levels in the urine increased after patients consumed a Vietnamese soup containing cilantro (or coriander). Further testing revealed that eating cilantro increased the urinary excretion of lead and aluminum. When cilantro was used with natural antiviral agents and "good" fatty acids, infections could be eliminated for good.

While awaiting further tests to confirm the presence of aluminum in chemtrails, James and Phyllis Balch write in *Prescription For Nutritional healing* that aluminum accumulated in body tissues can be offset and eliminated by taking apple pectin, calcium/magnesium, garlic and kelp to detox. Also recommended is lecithin to heal brain and cell membranes, as well as minerals and multivitamins "high in vitamin-B". (Given the current controversy surrounding soy products, a good source of lecithin is organic eggs.)

RAISING LOW PLATELET COUNTS

When the immune system attacks the body's platelets, bright purple and red bruise-like spots can appear on the skin. Some chemtrail sickness sufferers will immediately recognize this symptom. Low platelet counts are also associated with lupus and mononucleosis (Epstein-Barr) – often reported in the wake of heavy spraying.

Cytomegalo "stealth" viruses – as well as the spontaneous nosebleeds, bruising and rashes reported by many chemtrail eyewitnesses – are also marked by abnormally low platelet production.

Anyone lab-tested and found to have a low platelet count can consider the advice of Naturopathic Doctor Bradley Bongiovanni. The Director of the Naturopathic Medicine Center recommends: "There is one cell salt that is renowned for its ability to raise platelet levels. It's called Ferrum phosphorous. It comes as a 6X potency. Typical dose would be 5 pellets, twice per day, away from food." Remember, aspirin interferes with platelet function.

TREATING MYCOPLASMA INFECTIONS

Powerful antibiotics attack beneficial bacteria and severely suppress the immune system. Before contemplating their use, be *certain* that you test positive for mycoplasma. *All subsequent treatment should be under a physician's guidance.* Blood samples can be sent to the Institute for Molecular Medicine for mycoplasma and other testing. Ph: 714-903-2900 Fax: 714-379-2082 [www.immed.org]

Garth Nicolson, who along with his wife Nancy pioneered mycoplasma detection and treatment, states:

> The recommended treatments for mycoplasmal blood infections require long-term antibiotic therapy – usually multiple 6-week cycles of doxycycline (200-300 mg/day), ciprofloxacin or Cipro (1,500 mg/day.

These drug doses are effective. They are also extremely hard on an already-challenged immune system, liver and kidneys. As Nicolson notes, "These patients are often depleted in vitamins B, C and E and certain minerals."

> High doses of some vitamins must be used. General vitamins plus extra C, E, CoQ-10, beta-carotene, folic acid, bioflavoids

> and biotin are best. L-cysteine, L-tyrosine, L-carnitine and malic acid are reported by some to be useful. Certain minerals are also often depleted in GWI/CFS/FMS patients, such as zinc, magnesium, chromium and selenium. Antibiotic use that depletes normal gut bacteria can result in over-growth of less desirable bacteria. Yogurt and especially Lactobacillus acidophillus tablets are recommended.

Before taking antibiotics or other drugs with "side-effects" often as bad as the original disease, Ken writes to recommend a product called, "Primal Defense."

He also notes that a good all organic "greens" drink such as "Perfect Food" or Dr. Richard Schulze's "Superfood" [1-800-HERBDOC] is the best way to get naturally chelated minerals and true vitamins into the body. The synthetic formulations found in most over-the-counter supplements are next to useless, and may do harm.

Anyone diagnosed with a mycoplasma infection ought to consider natural treatments before opting for extremely harsh antibiotic regimes. According to Ken, an excellent "probiotic" formulation called "Primal Defense" is "extremely beneficial" in eliminating of parasites, protozoa and fungal infections. [www.gardenoflifeusa.com]

Ken also recommends the Master's Miracle Soap and Master's Miracle Neutralizer to assist in removing toxins in or on the body. [http://sci.TheMastersMiracle.com]. When it comes to pharmaceuticals, he warns:

> The same "elite" who own and/or control the same corporations that both produce (manufacture) and profit from the chemicals they are spraying on us, *also* are the owners and/or controllers (and shareholders) of the major pharmaceutical industries/companies that make doxycycline, ciprofloxacin and Cipro (to treat those infections that they *caused* in the first place.
>
> This is the same old same old that they have been doing all along to the populations - they poison them, create the problem of ill health, then milk the sick people for their money by giving them their patented toxins to take to "manage" the illness, while at the same time breaking down their bodies even more

so they can milk them for more money dealing with those "side-effects". Then, if the people happen to just die off, their partners in government now don't have to pay Social Security.

How convenient.

Chapter 14

DIAL 911 FOR CHEMTRAILS

Santa Fe Sept. 13, 2001 – all flights grounded

The quiet splash of a kayak's double-paddle carried clearly over waters calm enough to mirror the sky. It was one of those magical afternoons, with a small wooden boat and its master suspended in time and space. As *Chimera*'s long wooden prow drew a "V" toward the snow-capped mountains of Vancouver Island, I looked up and cursed the telltale X's stretching from horizon to horizon across the Channel-like Strait of Georgia.

Would the meddling Weather Force Specialists from that other country to the south never stop stealing our sovereignty – and skies?

Across the strait, chemtrail-watcher and webmaster Richard Vizzutti was enduring the same assault. "Rick," I wrote, "more than 27 continuous hours here – biggest chemtrails assault I have ever seen in this area."

"Major attack yesterday! No storm front moving in though, according to the weather report," Vizzutti agreed. "The attack we had was a typical heavy attack day for us. Just have not seen a heavy attack for a while. I noticed that they preceded the cumulous clouds that came in today. I was outside when they began to lay one trail over the other. I counted seven lines before I blacked out and almost hit the deck. I spent the rest of the night in bed."

DESECRATION

Spraying chemtrails over the holy ground of Mt. Shasta is a special desecration of land, tradition and spiritual power. As a sacrilege, and sad commentary on the unconsciousness of greed, it's right up there with the chemtrails laid over the ruins of the Twin Towers:

Tammy:

> We live in Mt. Shasta, California, close to the Oregon border. I observed a very strange black jet that was spraying a black substance all above the town. He made several swipes, not just one fly-by. This was just before the 9-11 episode. I told my husband about it and he thought I was crazy. We see these chemtrails ALL the time in our area. I knew instinctively that we were being sprayed by something unhealthy just by the way the trees and bushes have been dying everywhere. They look burned! PS. A lot of people are getting asthma that never had it before - including me.

Then came the thunderbolts of Sept. 11.

As I later wrote in *All Fall Down: The Politics of Terror and Mass Persuasion*:

> We came to this moment in ways and places we will never forget, holding our TV clickers as gingerly as betraying wands summoning evil jinn. We watched slack-jawed, silent or silently cursing, unable to grasp what we were seeing.

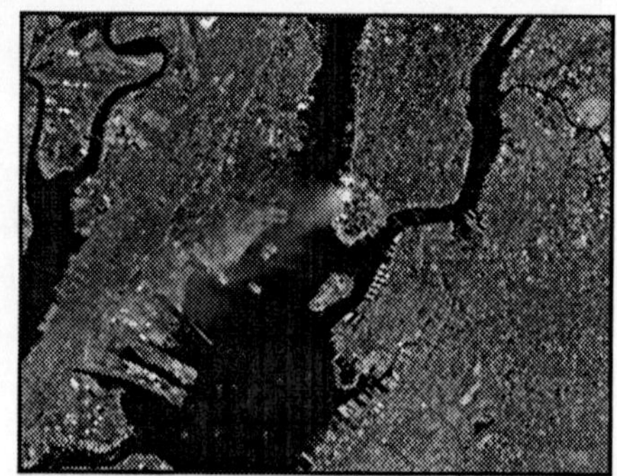

WTC from the shuttle

> The images were grotesque, impossible, preposterous. Assailed

> by revulsion and vertigo, unable to look away, we watched hypnotized by horror as endless replays relentlessly revealed huge airliners floating through the air – *too low! too low!* – before banking like fighters to harpoon twin skyscrapers taller than three *Titanic*s stood on-end.
>
> Staring like passengers assured of the absolute impossibility of the disaster now unfolding, we discovered that big buildings are just as vulnerable as big ships to the inexorable laws of mass, inertia, and gravity. Not since the funeral of a princess did an entire grieving world gape so grimly at the same event. From sunny fishing villages in Honshu, to sleepy European capitals, a bungalow in Maine, a hideout fitted with life-support for a Saudi millionaire...voices in a babble of dialects were shouting the same four words: "Turn on your TV!"
>
> One billion of us did.
>
> And in the glow that replaced archaic campfires with flickering images watched by a global tribe, something in us died as suddenly and irrevocably as those kindred lives before our stricken eyes. Gone in a heartbeat, gone forever was the illusion of our pampered invulnerability.

Urged in a plan called PNAC put together by the Bush Gang as a catalyst to rally knee-jerk Americans around their country's "defensive" dominance of the entire planet, the 911 attack was facilitated by the same men who rigged the Florida 2000 vote in an "selection" that state's Supreme Court later ruled "fraudulent".

This time, the hijackers of America, its Constitution and its future blocked FBI investigations and interrogations that would have nailed the airplane hijackers long before they mounted their attacks. They issued no security alerts despite repeated specific warnings. Then they refused to launch a pair of armed "ready alert" birds, holding the fighters all day on the Andrews runway - just 12 miles away from the White House.

All this is well documented. But there is no impeachment, no courts martial, not even an investigation as a propaganda press continues to censor unpleasant facts, never asking the next question, or putting anything together.

It would take me months of investigation to learn these things. And, unhappily, much more. But on Sept. 11, 2001 I knew only that indeed the world had changed – and not in ways that bode well.

Seeking my bearings, and wanting to fill my trimaran's water tanks for whatever came next, I sailed to Deep Bay – only to be assailed by chemtrails crisscrossing the sky.

Given the circumstances, it seemed especially obscene. But those telltale 'trails definitely did not come from commercial aircraft. All were grounded - except for the bizjets whisking bin Laden family members away from FBI agents wanting to talk to them. (The Bush-bin Laden partnership goes back a long ways. See *All Fall Down*)

Was the climate crisis really so dire? Was something else going on? What was deemed critical enough to continue chemtrail operations in the midst of global grief and shock?

Chemtrails over jagged ruins of the WTC

On Sept. 11 - after commercial aircraft were grounded across Canada and the United States, and no suspects apprehended from the other aircraft aborted from their intended attacks – heavy chemtrail activity was reported over Vancouver, Canada as well as Chicago and Columbus, Ohio, among other locations.

That dark day, Caroline voiced the sentiments of many chemtrail watchers when she wrote to say, "with all this national state of security business going on right now, you'd think, they wouldn't have the time or the resources to continue to chem up the skies with that muck, but they're right on track and still at it, spraying their chemtrails all over the place, right here in Vancouver anyways."

Caroline had just returned from northern Saskatchewan after 11days, to find "they've got 'em just like we do. I don't think you can find a corner or crevice in North America that doesn't have this crap dumped on them. Anyways it really puzzles me with all of the air traffic today supposedly at standstill, yet we're still getting chemtrailed to bits."

Also on Black Tuesday, still reeling from images of a massacre in Manhattan, Rosalie wrote from Chicago:

> A lot of planes today, I noticed about 4 pm, some planes lower than others, the low ones you could see that the emission was from the rear of the plane. They were in two's and three's, seemed to be centering overhead, some were circling back. We are 40 miles south of the quad-cities at the river, and about 100 miles southwest of Chicago.
>
> I had not noticed contrails lately. I am wondering why the trails would be overhead here today, to my knowledge there is nothing military here except for the National Guard, it is rural agricultural here, just a few factories where they make rubber goods, Maytag, Carhartt, etc.

Also from Chicago: "Last night between 1:15-1:30 a.m. I saw no less than 10 chemtrails overhead in the classic grid pattern 2 of which were parallel heading south and then hard banked to the east. These were big big trails. Biologicals perhaps? God forbid."

The following day, Bonnie wrote from Maidstone to report, "On September 12, 2001, when all air traffic was supposed to be grounded, they were right over my house in Maidstone, Ontario spraying those chemtrails."

Reporting for Chemtrail Tracking USA in Houston, Lorie Kramer disclosed that on Sept. 12, with the grounding order still in effect, chemtrails were observed over Maidstone, Ontario as well as Indianapolis and Fort Wayne, Indiana; Lexington, Kentucky; southern Illinois; Detroit, Baltimore, Maryland; Eugene, Oregon and Houston, Texas:

> Between 4-6 am skies became filled with wispy chemtrails could not see planes during this time. Planes sighted about 25,000 ft up making CT's at 5:57 am: two X's made over skies in northwestern suburbs. One plane made one X and two planes made the second X. They then turned off the sprays and increased altitude and flew out of area going west. X's remained in skies till at least 7:45 am.
>
> At 8:30 – 9 am two planes spotted over Livonia area making a chemtrail in shape of a circle. 10:30 am: Feather like trails and lines present in the southern skies.
>
> Northern skies have lines that have spread out into chemclouds going east and west. Chemdome in place from Westland area to Troy and all areas in between.

In Houston, Texas: "Heavy grid spraying north of Houston. I could easily hear these planes fly directly overhead. What's wrong with this picture? There are trails being laid in semi-circle patterns to the south-west of town. Call into area officials. "I saw the plane! No, this is *not* normal air traffic, because there is not supposed to *be* any air traffic."

In Los Angeles:

> As you all know, the airport here is shut down as well as a lot of other stuff. When the marine layer broke this morning there was an immense HAARP cloud canopy above it from horizon to horizon. Apparently offshore spraying was going on big time all night and probably right up until the attacks took place…It's my under-standing that the ban only applies to commercial air traffic, and this definitely appeared to be a military jet, going N to S directly over Santa Monica at 7:10 pm.

In Eugene, Oregon: "After watching the horrors on TV yesterday, I at least thought that our skies would be clear here in Eugene, Oregon. Not so. Although I saw no direct overflights, the sky was *filled, all day* with long clouds that moved in from upwind. The clouds early today look highly suspect."

In Indianapolis, Don went outside to go to work Wednesday morning:

> I look up as I usually do, but this time thinking there would be no Chemtrails because for the first time none of the 4,000 daily flights would be up there. I was absolutely floored when most of the sky was covered with Chemtrails. I know the characteristic tendrils and patterns of Chemtrails, and these were them! They also were about 3-4 hours old for the most part because I also know how long Chemtrails take to reach certain stages of spreading.
>
> If you ever needed proof for government planes causing the Chemtrails, this is it! It was impossible for these to be contrails from commercial planes, because there were zero commercial planes. They must have felt the need to spray during the night, because people would have been alarmed if they saw aircraft flying when all flights were grounded. People might think they are terrorists (not far from true) and bring much attention to them.
>
> It's ironic that bin Laden would be the one to provide positive proof of spraying for you and put an end to it through your efforts armed with this absolute truth. So, please hurry to close this chapter out!

On Sept. 11, Lexington, Kentucky basked under a perfect clear blue sky, "for the first time in years" Laura reported. "I guessed that with the airports shut down the chemical-spraying tankers were also grounded. Unfortunately, Wednesday afternoon spraying resumed."

> I was wondering why, with America preparing for war, these planes were still spraying us instead of being used by the military for refueling, etc. It wasn't until tonight that I realized what I believe they are doing.
>
> I've got the old familiar symptoms: scratchy throat, dry cough, low fever, burning eyes, and a hum in my ears. I also tasted a nasty metallic taste on my lips after being outside for a while.

> I honestly believe that we are being sprayed with either the anthrax vaccine, something similar, or possibly several things in the event of chemical and/or biological warfare. Whoever is doing this may believe this will help and is for our own good, but even so I wish they would tell us! It may be necessary, but in the past this has caused serious illness and death to many people. What do you think?

I think that there is not enough of any vaccine to fill a single tanker ... that vaccines are not effective if sprayed in the air at 37,000 feet where tankers emitting trails visible on radar have been tracked ... and that the best defense against anthrax (according to the medical literature) is vitamin C and garlic.

Not dangerous drugs responsible for Gulf War Illness.

MINNIS' MISCUE

Suddenly, Patrick Minnis was back in the news. In fact, NASA's contrail expert was achieving national prominence. It seemed he had "seized the moment" for his studies of jet plumes during the emergency grounding order issued on Sept. 11, 2001.

On Sept. 12, the chemtrails debunker was cited in the Louisville *Courier Journal* and the *New York Times* for collecting "valuable data" on contrails during a period, Minnis mentioned, when the only planes in the air were nine military flights crossing the skies from Ohio to Virginia.

This was exciting! At last, a reputable scientist would silence the chemtrail heretics!

On Mar. 16, 2002 Minnis had told the Akron, Ohio *Beacon Journal* that the artificial clouds conspiracy theorists find so ominous are "perfectly natural." Despite NASA studies *he had participated in* showing a sharp decrease in contrail activity since Nov. 2001, Minnis told the *Journal* that people were noticing contrails more often because of increased aircraft traffic.

Speaking the previous March 7 from NASA's Langley Research Center in Hampton, Virginia, the atmospheric scientist had complained to *USA Today* that it's impossible to argue with "conspiratorialists". "If you try to pin these people down and refute things, it's, 'Well, you're just part of the conspiracy,'" Minnis muttered. "Logic is not exactly a real selling point for most of them."

"Them" as we have seen, being airline pilots, air traffic controllers, military members, police officers and news staff.

Like other NASA, EPA, Air Force and airport officials across the USA, Minnis was exasperated by incessant insistence that something very unusual is going on in once familiar skies. Nothing is "out there" contrail experts told USA Today, except water vapor and ice crystals. And a lot of hot air.

Deserted skies seemed a curious time to study contrail formation. But the grounding of all non-military aircraft offered prime time to track chemtrail lay downs without any "noise" from commercial contrails to distort the observations.

On Sept. 12, the *New York Times* ran a story slugged, "Empty Sky Aids Study". In the text, Dr. Patrick Minnis exulted in how the most valuable data on contrails were collected as only nine military flights crossed the skies from Ohio to Virginia. The NASA research scientist explained how his team was able to chart "precisely how these contrails fanned out over five hours to form a shield of cirrus clouds covering over 24,000 square miles."

It seemed a curious contradiction to NASA's official Internet-posted contrail analysis, which "assumes the *contrails persist for one hour only*." Using NOAA's own numbers, NASA scientists further estimate that a rare persistent contrail "spreads to 2 km wide and has a length of 60 km."

Minnis did not say whether he was watching the emissions of nine select military tanker planes, perhaps laying a barium electromagnetic conductor across America's northern defenses in the first days following "Black Tuesday" treachery eerily reminiscent of what really went down at the first Pearl Harbor. [*Day of Deceit*]

Instead, Minnis' miscue actually appeared to demonstrate the difference between military aircraft emissions and the civilian variety by recording long-lingering 'trails behind military aircraft on a day when all commercial flights were grounded.

COLUMBUS REVISITED

Long a hotbed of chemtrail activity – and chemtrail protests –

Columbus, Ohio finally achieved national prominence for in-depth chemtrails coverage with a December 6, 2001 article in *Columbus Alive* by Bob Fitrakis and Fritz Chess.

"Stormy Weather" observed "the grounding of virtually all civilian air flights in the immediate aftermath of the September 11 terrorist attacks" heightened "bizarre speculation about what's happening in North American airspace."

Columbus, Ohio

The newspaper was receiving "numerous citizen reports concerning airplanes 'spraying' or leaving behind mysterious 'chemtrails' or 'contrail grids' in the skies over Columbus.

Fitrakiz and Chess reported, "Some feared we were under biochemical attack while others postulated we were being inoculated against anthrax or some other biochemical hazard."

> During a flight to Phoenix in early October, a *Columbus Alive* reporter noted that air traffic was like a nest of hornets over southwest Ohio and Indiana, with jets spraying everywhere.
>
> One plane appeared to be a Boeing KC-135 Stratotanker, a refueling plane. Typically, contrails can only form at temperatures below negative-76 degrees Fahrenheit and at humidity levels of 70 percent or more at high altitudes, according to National Oceanic and Atmospheric Administration meteorologist Thomas Schlattes. Even in most ideal conditions, a jet contrail lasts no more than 30 minutes.
>
> Yet, in the month after the attack on the World Trade Center, there was very little commercial airline traffic and virtually no private civilian air flights. Still, white jets billowing lingering plumes frequently appeared in the skies over Columbus.
>
> An *Alive* reporter, using high-quality binoculars, could see that some of the white planes had orange markings. In addition to

> Stratotankers, KC-10 Extenders, another refueling plane, appeared to be used for spraying.
>
> One scientist familiar with chemtrail experiments even agreed to speak with *Columbus Alive* (though he refused to allow his name to be used), saying that public disclosure of the experiments is inevitable and maybe imminent.

That did not happen.

But while watching the news on CNN, Fitrakis and his wife were watching an interview with the day after Catherine Whitman resigned as head of the EPA. Whitman had come under heavy fire from chemtrail activists for refusing to accept and analyze samples they claimed came from high-altitude aerial spraying by US Air Force tankers over the United States, Canada, Britain and at least nine other allied countries.

Now Fitrakis and his wife turned and looked at each other with raised eyebrows when Whitman blurted, "People criticize the President for not doing anything about global warming. But he's doing a lot of things about global warming that people don't know about."

Bob Fitrakis now believes that HAARP can move "zonal winds" around – just as the Soviets once shifted the jetstream to increase their growing jetstream, using seven similar energy transmitters arrayed around a place called Chernobyl.

With the Test Command confirming that HAARP is for weather mod, Fitrakis feels that an Arctic air mass was moved south from Canada last winter. Like opening the door of a deep freeze – and moving it into the bedroom –temperatures plummeted as Columbus shivered in its coldest winter since the '60's.

Fitrakis told me that massive spraying observed over Columbus that fall could have "created a vacuum" or low pressure area, drawing cold air out of Canada to help cool the rapidly warming continental USA.

MORE DEEP SKIES

Less than three months after the traumatic events of Sept. 11, the senior Air Traffic Control manager known to S.T. Brendt and me as Deep Sky became increasingly worried. His entire family, who unlike himself did not work in the air-filtered confines of a windowless building, were still having health problems. His wife, who had never suffered from allergies, still suffered from episodes of Sudden Onset Acute Asthma that may or may not be linked with the increased aerial activity he was seeing on his scopes.

So Deep Sky began calling his colleagues at FAA flight centers across the United States to ask them if they were seeing what he was degrading his own radarscopes. Had they seen it? And what were they being told?

Controllers at Chicago's O'Hare (still the busiest airport in America), as well as all three New York airports, LA's LAX, San Francisco, Jacksonville, Cleveland, San Diego, Dulles, Washington DC and "the big one" (Atlanta: biggest airport in the nation) responded. All were seeing formations of air force tankers on their scopes.

So were controllers at smaller airports like Westchester County in Armonk, New York and Manchester, New Hampshire.

Every controllers contacted by Deep Sky said they were being told to divert commercial traffic below formations of tankers flying strange patterns they were told were "routine". Instead of enhancing radar coverage, initial explanations from their superiors warned controllers that unspecified "experiments with radar" could degrade their own displays. The controllers confirmed to Deep Sky that they had never seen so much "clutter" or artificial "cloudiness" obscuring their radars.

By then, a growing number of informally networked Air Traffic Controllers were aware of the "chemtrails" controversy. Some cited the short-lived House Resolution 2977 sponsored by Ohio Representative Dennis Kucinich, which sought to ban space warfare and other exotic weapons, including "chemtrails".

Concerned controllers across America told Brendt that while not jeopardized, flight safety was a consideration. Even more worrisome was the fallout they were seeing on their scopes. They knew from their professional meteorology studies that "this stuff falls to the ground." And they wondered about what they termed, potential health hazards.

As federal employees, the FAA radar operators were afraid to come forward with their concerns. But at least one controller working in America's heartland visited a local hospital after heavy tanker activity – to find the emergency room jammed with acute respiratory cases.

"They want to know what the heck is in there," Brendt relayed. "One of them said – al or barium – that's not something you want to be breathing." ("Al" = aluminum)

One controller working in America's heartland became concerned enough about possible health effects after particularly heavy tanker activity to visit a local hospital – only to find the emergency room jammed with acute respiratory cases.

In their talks with Deep Sky and Brendt, concerned controllers across the country independently confirmed that the only further explanation from their superiors was that there are some "experiments". More than five Air Traffic Controllers were told that the tankers were engaged in "climate experiments".

One concerned Air Traffic Controller found the local Emergency Room jammed with acute respiratory cases.

CANADIAN MEDIA MENTIONS CHEMTRAILS

On May 16 that year, the Canadian newspaper, *Ottawa Citizen* reported "fervor: "What one sees here reflects sightings across North America," the *Citizen* reported. "*West Quebec Post* publisher Fred Ryan reports that his readers have been photographing and comparing them [pictures of chemtrails], and such manifestations are listed on the web."

The story was bound to leak through. According to information obtained by a concerned Canadian's Freedom of Information request, from October 2000 to September 2002 nearly 1,000 written Canadian complaints concerning chemtrails filled some 206 pages of correspondence. Another 615 pages of Canadian chemtrails inquiries were released on Mar22, 2003.

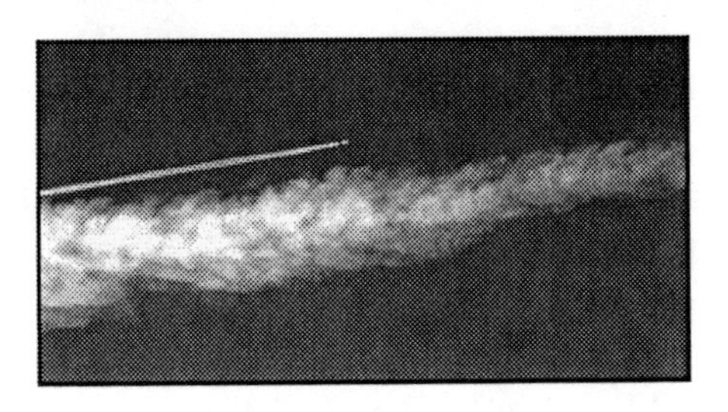

CALDEIRA WARNS OF "SUNSCREEN" HEALTH HAZARDS

Ken Caldeira, the Lawrence Livermore scientist who ran Teller's computer simulations to predict the effectiveness of a planetary sunscreen, told *Columbus Alive*, "We originally did this study to show that this program shouldn't be done." Why not? Because of *negative health effects*, Caldeira replied to Bob Fitrakis.

Caldeira told me that the sunscreen project had never gotten underway – and that he should know because as the man who did the modeling his expertise would be needed. He also insisted that no scientist from LANL was involved in such a project.

CHEMTRAILS OVER AFGHANISTAN

In their rush to explain a phenomenon that for three years had not gone away, American newspaper and broadcast media prominently displayed photos and video clips of "contrails" left by U.S. bombers over Afghanistan.

The Oregonian

a forces get ultimatum

None of those editors and producers stopped to ask how ice-crystal condensation trails could form in the warm dry air over the Afghan desert.

The photographs reminded me of similar satellite shots showing the telltale scrawl of circular chemtrails over another desert around Iraq and Kuwait.

In both cases of modern, hi-tech "war" that was really an indefensible bombardment of civilian populations from the air, the aim was not climate modification.

CHEMTRAILS SCIENTISTS TALK

A LANL scientist working on advanced experiments at Wright-Patterson Air Force Base told *Columbus Alive* that two separate secret "chemtrails" projects are being conducted by the air force. One centers on creating cloud cover to reduce global warming. The other project reflects radiation off artificial chemclouds in order to enhance the effectiveness of military radars and HAARP.

The scientist also revealed that HAARP is used to guide low-pressure systems. These systems are often "picked up" over Canada, and guided south over the Midwestern United States.

But Fitrakis told me that the weather modification "specialists" couldn't accurately forecast the results of such extreme atmospheric meddling. The HAARP-shifted low-pressure systems can bring severe storms in their wake.

As the Columbus, Ohio newspaper learned:

> The scientist claims that the two most common substances being sprayed into chemtrails are aluminum oxide and barium stearate. When you see planes flying back and forth marking parallel lines, X-patterns and grids in a clear sky, that's aluminum oxide, according to the scientist. The goal is to create an artificial sunscreen to reflect solar radiation back into space to alleviate global warming.
>
> In some cases, barium may be sprayed in a similar manner for the purpose of "high-tech 3-D radar imaging.
>
> [William] Thomas, writing in the Nov.-Dec. 2001 issue of *NEXUS New Times* magazine, essentially confirmed this assessment of the activities at the Dayton air base. "The barium spread in exercises conducted out of Wright-Patterson Air Force Base acts as an electrolyte, enhancing conductivity of radar and radio waves," Thomas reported. "Wright-Pat has also long been deeply engaged in HAARP's electromagnetic warfare program."
>
> Throughout the Cold War, both the United States and the Soviet Union actively investigated the military use of weather modification. In 1958, Captain Howard T. Orville served as the White House's chief advisor on weather modification. He publicly admitted that the military was studying "ways to manipu-

late the charges of the earth and sky and so affect the weather through electronic beams to ionize and de-ionize the atmosphere."

The U.S. Air Force admitted to CNN in July that it had broken up a storm over the Atlantic using products made by a company called Dyn-O-Mat. The company's website, dynomat.com, lists "environmental absorbent products" such as Dyn-O-Drought and Dyn-O-Storm. As recently as November 13, another patent was filed outlining a "method of modifying weather."

The abstract reads: "The polymer is dispersed into the cloud and the wind of the storm agitates the mixture causing the polymer to absorb the rain. This reaction forms a gelatinous substance which precipitate to the surface below. Thus, diminishing the cloud's ability to rain."

Sunbury resident Dan King remembers a stormy day in July when he was driving on a newly resurfaced section of I-71 and "the rainwater looked like dish soap water on the highway. I thought it was just from the resurfacing," he said, "but when I got out in the country I saw the same thing. Piles of suds at the side of the road."

The scientist who works at Wright-Patterson told *Alive* that barium stearate is basically soap bonded to a metal and could have produced the soapy rain. It's impossible to know which chemicals are being sprayed or for what reason since, according to the government, chemtrails don't exist. But, increasingly, government skeptics and other watchdogs are demanding to know if chemtrail spraying poses any health risks.

In his *NEXUS* article, William Thomas wrote, "Chemtrails can cause drought by soaking up all available moisture, and drooping chemical curtains fall through vast colonies of UV-mutated bacteria, viruses and fungi living in the upper atmosphere.

> Could these malevolent micro-organisms be piggy-backing on the plumes?"
>
> Thomas suggests that the spraying following September 11 has nothing to do with a deliberate biological attack or the inoculation of the American public. Rather, it's simply an ongoing attempt by humans to fool with Mother Nature.

Fitrakis identified the two contract chemtrails scientists interviewed at Wright-Pat as coming from Lawrence Livermore National Labs.

BETTER LIVING THROUGH BARIUM?

A similar highly secret project is the United States Navy's Radio Frequency Mission Planner. These RFMP computer programs include a subprogram called the Variable Terrain Radio Parabolic Equation. The VTRPE is a 3-D computer program for propagating radio waves in ways that allow battlefield seascapes and terrain to be viewed in three-dimensions on a screen.

The RFMP system depends on satellite imagery to produce 3-D images used for "virtual" war-gaming. Various "battle scenarios" can be modeled in RFMP computers, allowing rapid decision-making during attacks on Third World nations that are lucky to have a handful of PCs in the entire country.

Unhappily, the VTRPE computer program only works well over water. Over land, radar requires an atmospheric condition called "ducting" to conduct its radiating beams across varying terrain.

Releasing barium into the atmosphere acts as an electrolyte to conduct radar waves by causing moisture to remain in clouds. Certain "electroactive" polymer fibers also produced in Ohio can be pre-tuned to conduct specific radio and radar frequencies, and dropped along with the barium mix. As a result, "over the horizon" high-frequency radio and radar transmissions can bend with the barium over the curvature of the Earth. Enemy high frequency communications can also be monitored through barium ducting.

Meteorologists of the 88th Weather Flight claim that their Variable Terrain Radio Parabolic Equation can allow pilots to see what enemy radars can and cannot see under difficult terrain and atmospheric conditions.

A VTRPE system small enough to be fitted into cockpits could also allow pilots to hide behind signal-curtaining inversion layers just as submarines cloak themselves from probing sonar beams in underwater inversion layers.

According to a team of investigators:

> It is believed that barium salt, polymer fibers, aluminum and other chemicals, in the atmosphere are the physical irritants that are either directly or indirectly responsible, for the recent nationwide epidemic increase in cases of nose bleeds, asthma, allergies, pneumonia, upper respiratory symptoms and a noticeable increase in arthritis symptoms, recently reported nationwide.
>
> Chemicals illegally sprayed into the atmosphere are producing atmospheric and ground conditions detrimental to human and animal health but favorable to the growth of harmful molds and fungus. These conditions are not conducive to good health. The soluble salts of barium, an earth metal, are toxic in mammalian systems. They are absorbed rapidly from the gastrointestinal tract and are deposited in the muscles, lungs, and bone. No case data is available from the medical community on the long-term effects of barium in the human body.

On Dec. 31, 2000 *The Idaho Observer* highlighted the work of chemtrail researcher Clifford Carnicom, who found high levels of metallic alkaline salts in rainfall samples collected across the United States. According to Carnicom, "pH test data from across the nation" shows that atmospheric chemistry has been altered by a *20-times increase* in hydroxide ion concentration *within a single year* since chemtrail spraying began.

Three months later, in November 2000, Carnicom commented,

> The identification of barium in the atmosphere as a result of aircraft aerosol criminal activities continues to be confirmed. Studies with a diffraction grating spectrometer have repeatedly identified important signature high-intensity spectral lines at approximately 712 and 728 nanometers in the visible portion

> of the spectrum. All research conducted thus far continues to indicate a unique match to the element of barium.

The scale of acidity and alkalinity ranges from 1 to 14, with 1.0 being extremely acidic and 14.0 being extremely alkaline. Pure water has a pH value of 7.0 – but rainwater falling over much of North America in 1999 was typically an acid of 5.6 or less. As Carnicom points out, "Human biology is sensitive to pH blood changes as low as 0.1."

As reporter Amy Worthington learned, "Barium facilitates weather mod projects because it can create cloud formations at extremely low humidity, when natural clouds cannot form. Barium oxide (a salt) is a desiccant (drying agent) and can be used by the military to de-humidify clouds and dry up unwanted precipitation. Have your skin, mucus membranes and eyes been very dry lately?"

> We know that America's military-industrial complex has been spewing various forms of barium into our atmosphere for years. The University of Alaska has propelled barium into space in order to study the earth's magnetic field lines. The military used barium salts over enemy territory in Libya, Panama and Iraq, reportedly to make the population sick. A recent report from Wright-Patterson Air Force Base confirms that the Air Force has been spraying barium titanate across the United States to facilitate advanced radar studies.

Worthington added: "When barium reacts with water to form barium hydroxide, as it would in the moist atmosphere, it liberates much heat. This could explain why, on heavy spray days in warm weather, people complain about the abnormal, almost microwave-type heat they feel."

Releasing large clouds of barium in the atmosphere also contributes to the biggest source of barium contamination in animals, including humans. According to the "Barium Material Safety Data Sheet" released by the University of Utah, barium exposure outside the workplace occurs mostly from drinking contaminated water.

Highly reflective, silvery-white barium is nearly double the refractive index of water, higher in its ability to reflect sunlight than glass.

Ingesting high levels of barium "can cause problems with the heart, stomach, liver, kidneys, and other organs."

In fact, ingesting high levels of barium compounds that dissolve well in water over the short term has resulted in:

* Difficulties in breathing

* Increased blood pressure

* Changes in heart rhythm

* Stomach irritation

* Brain swelling

* Muscle weakness

* Damage to the liver, kidney, heart, and spleen.

University researchers also warn, "We don't know the effects in people of ingesting low levels of barium over the long term. Animal studies have found increased blood pressure and changes in the heart from ingesting barium over a long time."

Refusing to delete barium from its toxic watch list, the U.S. Environmental Protection Agency requires that all releases of barium compounds be reported under section 313 of the Emergency Planning and Community Right-to-Know Act, and section 6607 of the Pollution Prevention Act of 1990. The EPA allows only 2 parts of barium per million parts of drinking water (2 ppm). All discharges into the environment of 10 pounds or more of barium cyanide must be reported.

SCANNERS

As 2002 drew to a close, chemtrails continue to be reported across Canada, the USA, UK and Europe. Lou Aubuchont reports from Maine, "We have had spraying on and off all this month, some days heavy, some with just a few chemjets showing up, but they are still quite active here in the northeast. I've noticed that on heavy spray days the chemjets are usually accompanied at some point into the spraying by a P-3 Orion weather bird out of the Brunswick Naval Air Station."

Aubuchont was listening in on his radio scanner. But he was only hearing airborne fragments of conversations that hopped around frequencies faster than Aubuchont's scanner could follow.

Still, the transmissions were tantalizing.

In late Sept. 2002, Lou Aubuchont explained, "My scanner seems to be able to pick up the chatter when they are really close but not both ends of the transmissions. What I get is coming directly from the aircraft, I get nothing from a ground source/control."

He had concluded, "They are using a computer controlled system that changes frequencies rapidly and my scanner only captures a frequency from the aircraft when they are very close, like right overhead."

A year after we went to the media with the Deep Sky tapes, the spraying had not let up over Maine. "We have been getting sprayed on average of three times per week and the spraying has been on a huge scale covering hundreds of thousands of square miles by the time the spraying stops," Lou Aubuchont wrote on Sept. 27, 2002.

On Oct. 9, he notified me of "Heavy spraying over Maine and New Hampshire": At 10:00 am, I saw the first plumes being spread across the sky here in Parsonsfield, Maine and from that point on it was just tanker after tanker laying down a massive grid that extended well over into New Hampshire.

> They came from the northeast, northwest and east to west, it was quite a show and by 3:30PM the sky was a complete whiteout. We had some high thin cirrus clouds overhead when the spraying started here. The tankers were below the clouds and as the "Chemtrails" spread out it became hard to tell the cloud cover from the "Chemcloud". But we ended up with a sick looking yellow-white overcast. You know, if it is just a *hoax* as the U.S.A.F. portrays it as being, it's one *hell* of a *hoax*.

MORE SKEPTICS BITE THE CHEMDUST

Less than a month after the horror and cover-up of 911, it was chemtrails-as-usual over the land of the free and its northern neighbor. In Hamilton, Ontario, the spraying was so heavy, family members

Lysander, Stephanie and Arthur Zimmerman began making connections between their health and the skies overhead.

As Lysander relates:

> I started becoming aware of a chronic bronchial congestion that still persists today. After submitting sputum samples to my doctor on two occasions and receiving negative results for typical bronchial microorganisms, I began to question the cause of my persistent illness. During the weeks to follow my father and I also began noticing bizarre cloud formations and we recalled an article that we had previously read about mysterious "chemtrails".

Initially, Stephanie Holliday and the Zimmermans "were skeptical of the chemtrail theories."

But Lysander Zimmerman relates how "that all changed one afternoon in late January when I emerged from my grandparents' home to see a perfectly linear cloud formation stretching across the entire sky."

As he scanned the sky for the aircraft responsible, Lysander "was astounded to see an aerial spraying operation taking place with some six or seven jets in participation. Each plane was leaving a long thin dense white trail behind that would not dissipate."

Lysander was familiar with the existence of jet condensation trails. But he had never witnessed anything like this before:

> Over a period of an hour or so, the trails slowly widened before transforming into cirrus-like cloud formations. After several hours, the sky was blanketed with a thin haze, accompanied by cirrocumulus-like waves, a cirrostratus-like blanket and cirrus-like wisps. Although these cloud types are perfectly natural, I was amazed that I had just witnessed a cloud manufacturing operation.

So far, Lysander Zimmerman has accumulated over two hours of chemtrails video clips over his Ontario city. The intruders are coming up from the 'States, he says:

> Most of these large high-flying white jet planes we witness making "chemtrails" appear to originate from the United States, flying north and northwest from over Lake Ontario. Multiple jets take part in these operations forming all sorts of cloud patterns

> including grids, X-shapes, multiple parallel lines, and curved trails (including U-shapes). However, the majority of sprayings randomly blanket the sky without any set formations.
>
> The planes can be observed making lasting chemtrails in the same sky as other [planes] simply leaving behind rapidly dissipating contrails. The heaviest spraying operations appear to take place in the early morning just before and after sunrise and continue all day. Other heavy sprayings take place above naturally existing cloud covers. The "chemtrails" and "chemclouds" can be seen in breaks in the natural cloud cover.
>
> Some operations take place at night or during the early morning hours. The planes are much lower and can be heard passing over repeatedly. On at least four occasions, my family has been kept awake as planes passed over our house every five to 10 minutes for about an hour.
>
> One night in May at about midnight, my father and I watched as two "chemjets" flew overhead in perfect tandem, leaving behind the long trails barely visible in the glow of the urban lights below. A couple of weeks ago, my father and grandparents witnessed a plane leave a chemtrail underneath the full moon on a cloudless night. Later on, the jets could be heard flying back and forth across the sky.
>
> The haze produced by the chemtrails refracts light, occasionally producing rainbow-like rings around the sun and moon. The "chemclouds" seem much more reflective than natural clouds at night.
>
> The skies have recently been covered by this white haze. Is this the same white haze that Teller says will remain in the sky for five years at a time as it is compounded by continuous aerial scattering operations?

The Zimmermans collected samples of chemtrail fallout on three occasions. (Arthur Zimmerman holds a PhD in Engineering.) Each sample came from rainwater falling through chemtrail-laden air. But they could have combed it out of their hair. As Lysander Zimmerman relates, "a heavy cover of silver-brown powder – sometimes a very fine fibrous deposit – is most visible on neighbourhood automobiles. Could these strange particles be the cause of my congestion?"

SPRING IN SEDONA

Sedona used to be a special place renowned for spiritual healing and cosmic connection. That vibe is still present. But this alleged "vortex center" has been getting hammered with chemtrails since at least early 1999.

"So many good things have changed for the worse since then, helped along by a faceless oligarchy carving up what's left of the Earth pie and drooling down their chins. And too much – like chemtrails – has remained the same," one resident wrote.

On March 23, 2002 Carol wrote a brief update: "I live in Sedona, AZ which is a very beautiful place with relatively little air pollution. But we have frequent and sometimes very heavy chemtrails."

And then it was summer.

For much of the USA and Canada, a parching drought continued. Crops failed. Major herds of cattle were sold off. And vast forest fires burned in Australia and the USA. Were the sky pirates trying to ruin farmers in some kind of bizarre domination trip? It made no sense to spray megatons of desiccants into air already almost wrung out of moisture.

On June 24, a "Chem 11" Internet message board message read:

> I was just watching NBC coverage of the 50-mile wide fire front that is raging through Arizona. Three years of drought have basically turned surrounding forests in the area into kindling. Wanna take a wild guess what I saw in the skies above Heber during the on-location interviews? If you said "fulminating artificial clouds of hydroscopic aerosols dispensed by jet aircraft, sucking the moisture out of the atmosphere; thereby preventing natural cloud formation and precipitation" you win an official Clifford Carnicom Drought Inducement hyperlink!

Dec. 16, 2002:

I live in western Montana in Hamilton and everyday for a long time I have seen dozens of chemtrails over this part of Montana and I visited Sun Valley Idaho a large ski area about 300 miles south of Hamilton and on every clear day there is chemtrail activity every where to the point of looking like cloud cover Shouldn't we be worried about all this? -Susan

Jan. 8, 2003

I have witnessed chemtrails in Whitby and Oshawa, Ontario for at least two summers in a row, perhaps even three summers now. I searched online for "weird clouds", "greasy clouds" - and was surprised to find a whole lot of links, website and people talking about "chemtrails". I don't know if this is related or not, but since 1998 I have developed asthma, fibromyalgia and eczema! I used to joke and say there is "something in the air" when I first started getting sick, but now I *know* there is. My friend also got very sick and now she has bad arthritis the past couple of years. I am going to start carrying my digital camera around with me and get photos of this happening in my area here because we get heavy spraying going on from Toronto all along the lake to at least Oshawa, that I know of, and possibly even further. -Anne-Marie

Jan. 10, 2003:

A friend of ours here has a four-year-old daughter who came down with some of the classic CT symptoms late Tues night. It got so bad that she was taken to an emergency room and admitted to the hospital, and was released on Thurs, I believe. Vomiting became so often and so extreme that the mother started keeping score: 30 times. We have the "Norwalk" flu virus going around here which hangs on for days or weeks. I have never heard of a flu victim becoming dehydrated, eyes sunken in and yellowish, and a general shriveled up look and in need of IV.

The dehydration and need for IV tells me, a layman with no medical experience, that this wasn't ordinary flu. The most critical timespan of the illness was about 48 hours in length.

> That seems speedy to me for flu. When I had my illness three years ago I waited longer to finally go to a hospital. We share some commonalities, such as the need for IV and the improvement after having it.
>
> She went into a hospital late Tues night around 1130 or midnight. Was released about 48 hours later. During this timespan the whole pediatric wing of the hospital was filled up with more kids with the same problem. Now isn't that interesting? And, they were released the same day as her too - the length of the illness as well as the time it hit was virtually the same for all these youngsters.

On Feb. 22, 2003, Ginger wrote from Niles, Michigan to report that as she was getting into her truck, she looked up in the sky and saw what she thought were two vapor trails.

But … "They were not evaporating as they should. I've lived on a Naval Air Base, so I know very well how vapor trails are supposed to behave."

Then Ginger started getting sick. Despite a trip to the ER, it got worse. Then her fingers started peeling. With her son, ex-husband and his girlfriend all sick, Ginger was concerned for her pregnant daughter.

On March 15, 2003, Lou Aubuchont sent an update:
Exactly one week ago on Saturday we had a big day of Chemtrails here. Today was a repeat of last Saturday, lots of Chem spraying in all directions. We had a partially cloudy sky here this morning, puffy cumulus clouds at about three thousand to four thousand feet and moving fast to the east, as a high-pressure front was moving in from the southwest.

> At 2:20 PM, Tiff and I went out to run some errands. The scattered cumulus clouds had cleared away exposing the heavy chemtrail spraying that was going on all around us, nothing directly over us but as we looked around while driving we could see chemtrails in every direction clear to the horizon - exactly seven days from one big spray day to the next big spray day.
>
> Saturday's are not high air traffic days over the north east, what

we have seen now for two Saturday's in a row is anything but normal air traffic. There must have been hundreds of aircraft involved in today's spraying, as the area affected was huge, taking in all of what we could see of Maine and New Hampshire in every direction.

At sunset the sky was covered with a milky white sick looking overcast, the sun looked like an orange ball with blue and greenish fingers of prismatic colors all around it - the horizon full of dark criss-crossing chemtrails.

KC-135 NEARLY CRASHES

Three weeks later, what could have been a chemplane nearly augured into a Northern California hillside:

> Our county is the home of a large natural lake, surrounded by several communities. There is a large mountain, 4200' above sea level, sitting on the south shore. I live on the north shore and my brother lives on the south shore on the lower slope of the mountain, facing the lake.
>
> Tuesday he was in the shower when he began to hear a high pitched whine, like a screaming turbine. The noise grew in intensity and the house began to shake or vibrate slightly. He jumped out of the shower and went to the deck that looks across the lake. Out from the right side, at just above the level of the mountain came a large four-engine jet, he said, that looked like a 747 or similar. Silver with no markings that he could see.
>
> He said the jet heeled slightly to it's right and started a shallow dive towards the lake – *below* the level of the mountain!
>
> He and the neighbors were stunned, thinking it was going to crash into the water. As the plane passed his deck, the sound was deafening, the house shaking. It sounded like the pilot was giving the engines all they had. The plane pulled up slightly, leveled it wings and proceeded towards the west, just clearing

> the hills west of the main city. Hot on it's tail was another plane of similar size with four-engines and also silver, but at a higher altitude, going in the same direction.
>
> I also talked to a friend living near there and he said he heard it, looked out the kitchen window and seen the plane coming right at his house at very low level. He thought it was going to crash into the house and ran for his life. Nothing on the local news or paper so far.
>
> My brother is a pilot, private license; has flown overseas on large aircraft and knows what he sees. Many witnessed this incident and all have very similar stories, and all say they were very large planes.

AN UNUSUAL WEATHER REPORT

People sometimes ask if chemtrails are ever picked up on TV weather radar. The answer is: sometimes.

A Twin Cities correspondent described a plume "about 50 miles wide and 300 miles long, going from eastern North Dakota, southeast to the Twin Cities picked up on radar."

That's mostly the direction local spray planes seem to use – NW to SE – "so that fits. What blew me away was that [weather jockey] Paul Douglas even made a comment about HAARP or the government related to this, and may have also said something about aluminum. I about fell out of my chair."

WEATHER (REPORTING) WARS

While Californians were dodging hedge-hopping KC-135s, a San Antonio TV weatherman's attempt to cover-up a weather modification operation gone awry pitted two 'papers against each other.

It seems that a "well-known local weatherman" named Albert Flores was fired after losing his cool when questioned by the *San Antonio Lightning* about a cloud-seeding story he'd written for rival *San Antonio Express-News*.

"Cloud Seeding Didn't Cause The Recent Flooding" was written by Flores to silence persistent rumors about weather mod programs in the San Antonio and south Texas area – and their possible link to recent record flooding in the "target area" of 3.1 million acres.

As Flores helpfully pointed out, "The last seeding took place on June 28, a few days before the recent downpours began." Flores quoted the Edwards Aquifer Authority general manager, Greg Ellis, who declared, "We had nothing to do with that. We stopped seeding clouds on the 28th of June."

But "locals" unused to swimming to work were a mite touchy about what happened next.

According to the July 29, 2002 edition of the *Express-News,* downpours during the first week of July dropped "more than 35 inches" north of San Antonio:

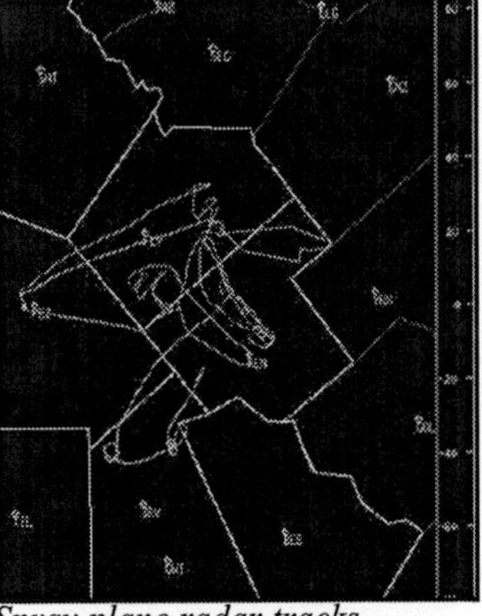

Spray plane radar tracks, San Antonio June 20/02

"The best estimates are that our cloud-seeding operations put 175,000 acre-feet of water on the ground over the three-year period," Ellis said. An acre-foot is 325,851 gallons – enough to supply two families of four for a year.

> "The rain we got in this event – during the three days of the heaviest rain – is estimated to be from three million acre-feet to five million acre-feet," Ellis said. "Even if we had planes flying, we couldn't have produced that kind of rain."

The good news was the severe flooding jumped the level of the Edwards Aquifer, which supplies water to more than 1.5 million people in South Central Texas, "more than 40 feet after the rains, pulling the city of San Antonio out of its drought restrictions."

But the furor flew when the *Lightning* reported light aircraft "seeding clouds just south of Bexar County on June 30th – the very day the record rainstorms began. Charts provided by Todd Flanagan, the chief meteorologist involved in the cloud seeding operation, showed the light cloud seeding plane had been active the day of the record rains."

After learning that "the Edwards Aquifer Authority weather modification seeding program, which was designed to bring more rain to the area, was in full operation on June 30th, the *Lightning* editors wondered if a "Man Made Flood" had turned San Antonio into an aquarium." The storms that have battered San Antonio and large portions of South Central Texas began that same day."

Cloud-seeding meteorologist Todd Flanagan confirmed that he had seeded clouds on the day the deluge began. Saying he was "fairly certain" there was no connection, Flanagan did not reassure chemtrail critics when he added that cloud seeding and meteorology are "an inexact science."

If this tempest in a Texas-size teapot is a typical response to geoengineering mishaps, when chemtrails finally go mainstream, liability claims by the inhabitants of entire regions struck by twisters, drought or flooding will be "bigger than big" – perhaps even big enough to end this ill-begotten meddling.

U.S. MILITARY RECEIVES LICENSE TO POLLUTE

Or maybe not. As Erminia Cassani reported on her Moonbow website, on April 25, 2002 Congress held a special session to hear the U.S. military establishment insist on "special exemptions" from environmental laws while carrying out "national security" missions.

The brass did not explain how further wrecking our space colony's closed recirculating life-support systems might "improve" national security. Not exactly known for Earth-friendly practices, the brass hats whined that new emission limits under a "Clean Air Act" their Tom Clancy Commander In Chief hadn't got around to gutting yet could put most military machines in serious violation of current pollution laws.

Cassani considered the military request, then responded: "Would that mean that all those aluminum oxide and barium-laden Chemtrails that certain military jets exude are *currently* in violation of the Clean Air Act?"

Or perhaps…"all that high-carbon soot particulate in military jet fuel that spews out into the environment, while making those Chemtrails, is *currently* in violation of the Clean Air Act?"

Cassani's conclusion in both cases: "You bet your precious lungs they are."

A "counter-panel" drawn from many environmental activist groups protested the Pentagon's request to poison Americans just like they bomb foreign families – with impunity.

"Gees, where have these people been for the last seven years?" asked Cassani. "Haven't they noticed those big fluffy trails in the sky that hang and drip there for hours on end and all those black carbon soot lines surrounding them that *no one* has claimed accountability for so far?"

> Uh, excuse me.... but irreparable harm has *already* been done to the public. I suggest they go take a look at some pulmonary, cardio-respiratory and skin clinical medical journals and survey the damage to the public that has already been visited upon us. In this bill, the DoD is seeking exemption from the Clean Air Act, the Endangered Species Act, the Superfund Law and other environmental protection laws. Figures. May as well hit 'em all just in case...

CAUGHT IN THE ACT

Why don't we have more good photographs of spray planes on the ground? The quick answer is that few people carry cameras, telephoto lenses and the tripods necessary for sharp images – especially video camcorders.

Another startling answer came on Mar. 16, 2001 in a letter to former "Coast To Coast" radio host, Art Bell:

> Every day, white private aircraft fly over the small town where I reside and release/spray substances on the population. Several of my neighbors with chemical sensitivities get gravely ill from this - particularly in the summer when the heat is rather unbearable.
>
> At first, we thought this was pesticides to handle the mosquitoes in the area but then they began spraying through the winter months. I have checked with the city, etc. and found only a blank wall...asked around and no one knew anything about it. So an associate and I decided to follow one of these aircraft to see where they landed. We discovered a small airport to the north with a couple of strips and some warehouses.
>
> When we got out there (we were using binoculars to survey the

area and to try to get a registration number, camera in hand) the plane was just landing and we were on the road right next to the strips.

Next thing we know the plane revs up and begins immediately taxiing for a take off, the pilot looking at us. At the same time the plane takes off, makes a sharp turn towards us and buzzes the car (not more than a 100 ft. over our heads), a security car tears down this road after us. We decide it best to quickly move on and take another tack...

To make this short, I finally spotted one of these aircraft actually releasing a spray and this one had an Army insignia on its side...All pretty frightening taken in context of all the other suppression of civil liberties (overtly and covertly) taking place here and in Europe. -Brenda Livingston Living-Tracer Enterprises [www.*tracers.8m.com*]

FOX IN THE HENHOUSE

With the notable exception of an ABC News affiliate in Memphis, which presented balanced coverage to the sky trails photographed by their own news team; televised chemtrails coverage follows a predictable pattern. Mimicking an earlier segment by a FOX affiliate in Houston, Fox News affiliate WSVN Ch 7 in Miami recently ran a 15 second "spot" ad publicizing their upcoming chemtrails story. According to one viewer, the clip started out showing a red sky emblazoned with the words "Biological Agents".

"Biological Agents sprayed over US Cities?" asked the voice over. "The government says they stopped it decades ago. Or did they?"

Then the ad said: "WSVN's Beatriz Canals investigates these strange streaks in the sky!"...before switching to a shot of a man aiming a video camera at the sky, saying, "The evidence is out there."

Cut to fake red sky facetiously captioned: "Clouds of Secrecy". *Woo woo!*

DISINFORMATION FROM DURANGO

On Nov. 19, 2002, the *Durango Herald*'s contemptuous chemtrails commentary appeared in a "story" by Jennifer Kostka helpfully headlined: "Scientists Dismiss 'Chemtrail' Theories".

In the tradition of *USA Today* and similar chemtrail "coverage" by mainstream media mesmerizers, Kostka immediately confused chemtrails with contrails – then belabored the obvious point that contrails are harmless. (Though jet exhaust is not.)

Plenty of experts are always happy to discuss water vapor while taking potshots at those contrary conspiratorialists. "I have looked at those (chemtrail) Websites a couple of times, and they're right up there with the UFO folks," Paul Newman, a physicist with the Atmospheric Chemistry and Dynamics Branch of NASA, told Kostka.

The Durango drivel was prompted by a local talk on chemtrails:

> Clifford Carnicom, a geophysicist and mathematician from Santa Fe, spoke at Storehouse Baptist Church south of Durango on Saturday night. Carnicom told about 50 residents that he believes a national or global organization is placing harmful particulates in jet emissions, which he calls "aerosol trails."

Carnicom said none of the statements refute his theory or address the evidence he presented Saturday night. Carnicom presented videos and photographs he said showed suspicious aerosol trails that stayed suspended in the sky longer than normal. However, Charles Knight, a senior scientist at the National Center for Atmospheric Research in Boulder, said that under certain weather conditions contrails could stay suspended in the sky for days.

Kostka did not report that in regards to the "certain weather conditions" necessary for contrail formation, Carnicom has produced plenty of high altitude temperature and humidity data on days of heavy aerosol spraying over Santa Fe. His official weather soundings showed conclusively that contrails *could not have formed* under the atmospheric conditions existing at the times of heavy sky gridding.

Nor did the reporter refer to Steadham's documented discrepancies between contrail and chemtrail longevity over Houston.

Kostka did not report the Espanola lab findings. Nor did the newspaper quote the Air Traffic Controllers who described the climate mod missions by US Air Force tankers to radio reporter S.T. Brendt and myself. The Wright-Patterson scientists who described their work on chemtrails projects at Wright-Patterson to *Columbus Alive* reporter Bob Fitrakis also went unmentioned in a story that carefully overlooked irrefutable evidence of massive, ongoing chemtrail activity. Instead, Kostka quoted FAA spokesman Allen Kenitzer mouthing the standard denials: "A couple of years ago we were getting swamped with calls about this. All of these reports turned out to be nothing."

But Clifford Carnicom got the last word. "This is a very standard reply to receive, that everything's normal," the long-time chemtrails researcher told Kostka. "It is not normal. Contrails are composed of water vapor. What I'm speaking of is not emissions of water vapor. What I'm speaking of is the emissions of aerosol trails."

I LEFT MY CHEMTRAILS IN SAN FRANCISCO

Santa Cruz, CA Nov. 2002

Even as Kostka was describing contrails, chemtrails were still regularly banding the sky above the Golden Gate.

"All this week grids and big blankets of perfectly straight and very wide lines have appeared over San Francisco," wrote a November 2002 correspondent.

"I was downtown on Thursday. While walking from the top of a hill (Sutter St) and heading down towards Market St and it looked like the entire area was filled with smoke.

When I got home, there were X's and grids all around my neighborhood. Friday there were more. My husband, who's having a hard time accepting this stuff, even commented about the "pretty" sunset, the chemtrails were bubble gum pink!"

> Saturday morning I zipped over to the market at 7:30 am and there was a huge blanket of perfectly straight "clouds" going from Pac Bell Park (the new baseball stadium near the Bay Bridge) going south towards Candlestick Park (the old one, near the airport.) Occasionally another wide stripe crossed over the large blanket.
>
> Last night as the moon rose it looked like she was behind a big fuzzy blanket. Definitely *not* fog! Today, Sunday we have pretty much normal clouds.
>
> Interestingly, my favorite cat has been suffering from asthma and a cough all year. Its been assumed that it was an allergic reaction to her cat litter and to one of our rabbit's fur. Wednesday her cough suddenly came back. I noticed my husband reaching for his inhaler a lot more than usual and my lungs have been tight and my eyes slightly red. Getting back to my cat, the cough persisted and the light bulb in my head went off! She began coughing with the chem trails! Another friend of mine who lives just outside of the wine country about 1 1/2 hours north of SF reports that she's finding a yellow powder everywhere. But this sounds like another issue…an even scarier one.

On Dec. 9, 2002, Kathleen reported "an outbreak of a flu-like illness in huge numbers in the SF Bay Area: mild fever, congestion, sore throat, weakness, chills. One doctor's office in SF had 40 calls in three days!"

Residents in Santa Rosa and Ukiah, two to three hours' drive to the north, as well as someone near Seattle, a person in Milwaukee, and a guy in upstate NY – all told Kathleen there were no flu outbreaks in their area. The CDC website reported no flu in the USA.

But in the Bay Area… "It's been several days and my husband and I can't shake it," Kathleen wrote. "One friend has relapsed after a week, another has relapsed after two weeks. Of course, we get our fair share of chemtrails, and I'm very suspicious. A big anti-war rally in SF is scheduled for 12/28."

That same day, in north central Arizona, as the chemplanes passed over, Jackie passed out! "I became instantly dizzy, staggered with delirium, felt nauseated, whole body went limp, hair standing on end as if in an electromagnetic field. Tried going outside several times in two hours; same thing each time. Relief instantly upon going inside and closing the door." Three hours later, the artificial overcast left by the tankers still covered the sky.

DUSTED IN DIXIE

While U.S. media attention remained focused on crushing U.S. military attacks on destitute families in mud hut villages, Americans continued to face attacks from their own air force in their own skies.

On Dec. 3, 2002, Rose Marie reported a disturbing incident in Jackson, MS:

> My sister had a very sudden onset of an illness with very severe untreatable dry cough, and sudden imbalance of her body where she could not sit up without falling over, could not walk, she fell four times, also she became confused with mild hallucinations. When checked at the hospital she was found to have low sodium and potassium in her electrolytes. The doctors could not account for her sudden drop in electrolytes. She is still weak, shaky and depressed.

The doctors should look up! "We have heavy contrail activity all days including holidays and weekends." Rose Marie stated. "We start out with clear skies and end up with strange cloud coverage, and we have overnight rain showers that make sure the chemicals are brought to earth."

Rose Marie feared for outdoor vegetables, waterways and animals eating chemtrail-contaminated grass, our waterways are being contaminated. In addition, "Most of the people living around me are having strange illness taking for ever to get over and the people with depressions are severely depressed and not always responding to meds."

In Alabama last New Year's, Rose Marie saw heavy chemtrail activity. "I believe it has gotten worse over the last few months," she now says. Concerned that the former Land of the Free could soon become a completely controlled nation of people living "in fear and despair", Rose Marie declared, "We have got to educate the public and elect people for the government that will save us, not destroy us. Unfortunately with 9-11 our leaders seem to be heroes and many of our citizens believe them. If our leaders did anything to orchestrate the entire event, I pray the public will know the truth."

UNMERRY CHRISTMAS FROM A SERGEANT-MAJOR

The day after Christmas 2002, a retired Canadian Army sergeant major named Phil wrote from Teulon, a town approximately 30 minutes drive due north of Winnipeg:

> This summer on a couple of different occasions I observed these aircraft flying back and forth emitting these chemtrails for about an hour each time. On one of these occasions I watched with my neighbor who expressed extreme surprise and wonder at this activity. These aircraft emitted what I thought at first was their normal exhaust, after a few minutes it was obvious that the exhaust was not dissipating, but was just spreading, and forming into a light cloud which covered a great amount of area in the sky. Like the people in Espanola, we found that quite a few people suffered from the same illnesses, however my efforts in bringing attention to this activity was met with a bit of skepticism and just a cursory interest.

HEAVY CHEMTRAILS OVER MAINE AND NEW HAMPSHIRE

As 2002 came to a close, Lou Aubuchont decided to write a "Good Wishes" letter to his local New Hampshire paper. But on the morning of Dec. 30, he looked out the kitchen window where S.T. had seen her first chemtrail and saw "trail after trail…a whole sky full of them, and the jet tankers making them."

Aubuchont cursed with naval fluency as he watched "eleven jets in under ten minutes leave the white plumes behind them – the kind that do not dissipate like normal contrail's do; the kind that hang in the sky and spread out unlike normal contrails do; the kind that turn a crystal clear blue sky into an overcast mass of manmade *Gack*!"

That was just the start.

At 9:30, "I went out for a while and in my travels I counted forty-seven separate aircraft making Chemtrails before I actually lost count."

By 11:30 am, "most of central and southern New Hampshire was being covered by a thick gray/white mass of Chemtrails…We do not get this much air traffic in a month let alone one day."

December 30th "was almost as bad" as March, 12, 2001 "when over three hundred and seventy aircraft were counted by a group of people in Gilford, NH in only five hours."

Aubuchont saw a single jet "leaving a short *normal* contrail that dissipated quickly as the aircraft moved across the sky." But the rest "were leaving Chemtrails that stretched across the sky for miles, lingered and spread out."

The arrival and departure numbers for Maine and New Hampshire for December 30th, 2002, Aubuchont saw, "do not even come close to the amount of aircraft that I saw in the sky that day."

SCIENTISTS CONDEMN CHEMTRAILS

Some people think that a benevolent government is protecting them from climate change disaster with chemtrails. In fact, the only cure for this planet's terminal lung disease is, as Jay Michaelson said, to stop smoking – and switch *in this moment* to an energy conservation, clean fuels mentality.

Spraying a sunscreen into the atmosphere and maintaining it with repeated applications of chemicals that haze the sky before raining down on wild and domestic lives below could be disastrous.

As the Abrupt Climate Change Committee of the National Academy of Scientists wrote in their 900-page "Impacts" study, a sunscreen could block enough sunlight to slow global warming, but… "The benefits of aerosol 'cooling' would not be uniform and could allow some regions to be heated to excess and others to deficit."

There's another problem with chemtrails: Triggering violent rainstorms by spraying ahead of approaching storm fronts deprives "downwind" regions of that moisture. Spraying much drier air with chemtrails absorbs the last available moisture – also depriving wide regions of badly needed rainfall.

The NCAR atmospheric wizards in Boulder discovered another big bummer in blasting the sky with chemtrails: "Stratospheric aerosols of airborne particulates left by high-flying aircraft *react with chlorine compounds to release ozone-destroying chlorine molecules.*"

Besides, it's not working.

In their report, issued just before the chemtrails program cranked up in the fall of 1998, the NAS looked at America's sky-high sulphur-dioxide emissions and found them to be *double* the amount of SO2 they were considering deliberately adding to the atmosphere to abort run-away global warming.

In fact, they found the average concentration of cloud-condensing nuclei over the northern Atlantic to be about five-times higher than at remote locations in the southern Pacific.

With all this cloud-forming nuclei belching from smoke stacks and automobile exhaust pipes, the scientists said, "there should already be some cloud-enhancing effects evident in the northern hemisphere."

Not surprisingly, "several studies have examined trends in cloudiness in the northern hemisphere and have all come to the same conclusion: The total cloud amount has been increasing in the northern hemisphere (study areas include United States, North America, the North Atlantic, and Europe) since the early 1900s."

The first period corresponds to a time of rapid growth of Made In The USA. SO2 emissions after the Depression and extends to the end of World War II. The second sulphur spike marks the proliferation of tall stacks from 1965 to 1980, which *doubled* the loft and lifetime of SO2 pollution – primarily from coal-fired power plants.

As expected, "Between 1900 and 1980 the mean cloud cover over the conterminous United States has increased about 10 percent."

Artificial cirrus overcasts created by zooming jet traffic added another 5% permanent cloud cover over the United States. This, say America's top atmospheric experts, "should be more than sufficient to compensate for an equivalent doubling of CO2."

Actually, "because CO2 increased only about 12 percent during the same period, the net effect should have been a cooling."

OOPS!

"However, analyses of temperature data in the northern hemisphere over the same periods consistently indicate that the mean temperature has risen about 0.5° to 0.7°C overall." In other words, more than a blistering 1-degree Fahrenheit in the last 100 years!

Based on this reality check, chemtrails deployed as a sunshade are not going to cut it.

CHEMTRAIL CONCLUSIONS

Nearly four years into my chemtrails investigation, this reporter can say with certainty that at least three clandestine aerial operations are being conducted over North America today.

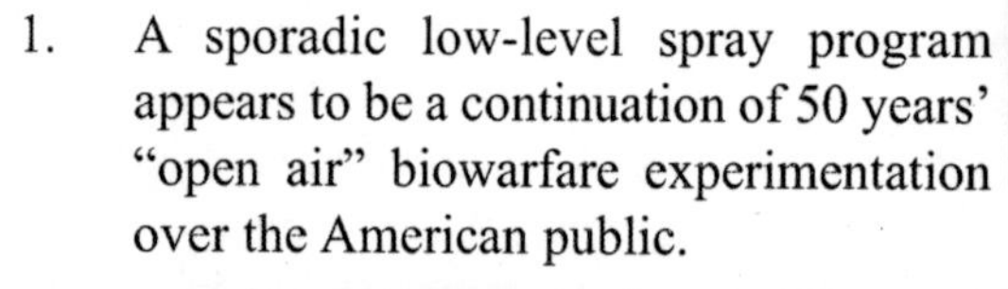

1. A sporadic low-level spray program appears to be a continuation of 50 years' "open air" biowarfare experimentation over the American public.

2. A much more extensive operation under-way since 1996 (and very possibly longer), at "greenhouse" altitudes is aimed at reflecting enough incoming sunlight to slow runaway global warming and permit petroleum pollution and profits as usual.

3. A related higher-altitude operation continues to see barium chemtrails spread over much of North America – as well as more active war zones – in order to conduct military radar and radio beams "over the horizon" for enhanced communications, 3D radar imaging, robot drone control – and we can only wonder – possible psychotronic experiments.

STAY CALM, WE'RE SINKING

Some suggest that chemtrails are being spiked with "calmatives" and similar psychoactive substances to dull minds already zoned into near coma by Prozac and similar "inhibitors", illicit drugs, alcohol, aspartame, fluoride and teevee.

"Psycho" is the key word. US military mind control efforts dating back to the infamous and well-documented MK Ultra program of the 'Sixties and 'Seventies are ongoing. As CNN reported on Sept. 26, 2002: "The U.S. military is exploring ways to use drugs such as Valium to calm people without killing them during riots or other crowd control situations where lethal weapons are inappropriate."

Wired weighed in on a month later, describing "calmatives, better known as psychotropic, central nervous system depressants" containing "fentanyls (an ultra-potent, heroin-like synthetic) and rohypnol, aka 'roofies,' the so-called date-rape drug – as crowd-control mechanisms."

Edward Hammond of the Sunshine Project, an international network of activists against biotech weapons, is no fan of mind rape. "It's a rotten idea" to drug large crowds of civilians, Hammond said. "It is sick and repugnant. It is illegal."

Category 1 Calmatives can trigger sudden unconsciousness, slowed breathing, mental confusion, elevated blood pressure, vomiting, paralysis – and, as the Russian Special Forces demonstrated in Moscow later that month – death. International laws prohibiting torture and protecting Human Rights outlaw the use of mind-altering drugs against populations – no matter how benign the Orwellian term for "calmatives".

The Sunshine Project's reviews of the Pentagon's non-lethal program confirmed that calmatives – including aerosol-sprayed Valium, Prozac and Zoloft – "can effectively act on central nervous system tissues and produce a less anxious, less aggressive, more tranquil-like behavior."

"Drugging large crowds is a rotten idea.
It is sick and repugnant. It is illegal."

A report prepared for Marine Corps researchers on "The Advantages and Limitations of Calmatives for Use as a Non-Lethal Technique" is not good news for freedom-loving folks upset over the continuing chemtrails cover-up and Washington's complicity in the events of 911. "At times," says the Sunshine review, "the report veers very close to defining dissent as a psychological disorder."

Could opium-derived "calmatives" be mixed into chemtrails to promote a more docile, tranquil populace? Not in their present form. Even if enough Prozac could be found to fill one tanker plane, supplying a squadron of KC-135s or KC-10s with enough mood-altering pharmaceuticals for a single mission is out of the question.

Even if it could be done, spray planes would have to come in over crowds at rooftop level to ensure effective coverage. Dispersing tranquilizers – or biologicals – from high altitudes results in too much dilution through dispersion to achieve "effective" concentrations at ground level.

Instead, the Pentagon's "Non-Lethal" weaponeers are filling mortar shells with Category One "Calmatives" for use against Americans and other uppity folks. The mind controllers have no comment on the non-lethality of a mortar round landing on someone's head.

The world was treated to a demonstration of "non-lethal" weaponry in Nov. 2002, when at least 120 people were killed after Russian security forces pumped heroin-derived fentanyl gas into a theatre taken over by Chechen terrorists seeking an end to Russian terror-bombing of Chechnya neighborhoods. The gas knocked out many of the more than 800 hostages held in the theatre, as well as most of their captors. We will never know whether other police tactics would have resulted in more – or fewer – casualties.

Meanwhile, any chemical constituents of chemtrails capable of crossing the blood-brain barrier would almost certainly have neurological effects – that is, disrupt the firing of neurons in the brain, altering perceptions and cognitive capacity.

UNHOLY ALLIANCE

Is the US government capable of spraying bad things out of airplanes on the American people? You bet.

A corporate-controlled government that according to a detailed inventory sold chemical, biological and nuclear arms-making capability to Saddam Hussein is certainly capable of attacking its own citizens to further its geopolitical ambitions.

The anthrax attacks following the facilitated Sept. 11 attacks led the FBI to a corporation named Battelle. The world's biggest weapons maker was soon implicated FBI as the only company in the United

States with the motive, ability and expertise needed to engineer the electrostatic-charged Ames strain of anthrax that was distributed through the mail to Democratic opponents of the Bushwhackers, and major media figures.

It turns out that a joint Battelle-CIA venture cynically dubbed "Project Jefferson" looked at placing a static charge on anthrax in order to float spores from an opened envelope around an entire room. In 2001, Battelle hired US bioweaponeer expert William Patrick to write a report describing how anthrax could be sent to targeted individuals through the mail.

Aimed at sparking panic without widespread fatalities, the risky rush to nationally stockpiled anthrax vaccines netted a multi-million dollar windfall for Battelle's corporate partner, Bioport.

The only company licensed to produce anthrax vaccine in the United States, Bioport landed an exclusive $29 million contract with the Department of Defense to "manufacture, test, bottle and store the anthrax vaccine" – less than a month after acquiring exclusive manufacturing and distribution of anthrax vaccine in 1998

Bioport was founded by a financier of the bin Laden family through the Carlyle Group. This wealthy warmaking investment firm has made hundreds of millions of dollars in recent years thanks to insider tips and influence from company "consultants" – including former President George Bush, James Baker and other key members of the Gulf War administration. In December 2001, FBI Director Robert Mueller announced that the FBI had no further plans to investigate anyone with, or formerly with, Battelle.

Battelle Corp. works with the CIA and the US Air Force developing "aerosols" to spread bioweapons – including anthrax, and possible mind-altering agents.

Reporter Bob Fitrakis refers to Battelle as "a CIA front". Along with its illegal and extremely hazardous biowarfare work, Battelle works closely with Wright Patterson Air Force Base. In ongoing secret experiments involving Alaska's high-energy transmitter, HAARP and over-the-horizon radar imaging, Wright-Pat is currently flying USAF tankers to spread barium-iron "antennas" over the United States – and more distant war zones, such as Kosovo and Afghanistan.

Besides its recently opened office at the Dugway "open air" biowarfare testing facilities, Battelle operates an office near Wright-Pat devoted to testing *aerosol dispersion* of bioagents.

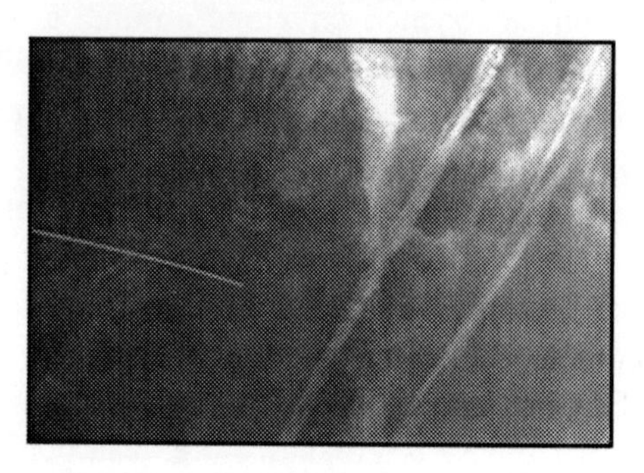

Presumably from low altitudes and at night, which has been common biowar practice.

But you never know about "black" projects whose originators keep coming up with "add-ons" to test on a trusting populace.

Such improvised experiments tend to go sideways.

"Conspiratorialists" who have long suspected a biowar component to the massive aerial spraying of the United States over the past four-and-a-half years will no doubt wonder what a CIA–contracted corporation involved in biowarfare and implicated in anthrax attacks on American citizens is doing as a partner in a secret US Air Force project that sprays various chemicals over American cities?

New Hampshire

CLOUDY DAYS

Deteriorating weather conditions are often observed in the wake of an activity referred to by the US Air Force as "aerial obscuration". These unpredicted weather changes include sudden temperature drops, high winds, unusually heavy or unseasonable precipitation, and murky overcasts on days forecast for "sunny weather".

Is it possible for fleets of spray aircraft to alter the heat balance of weather systems containing more energy that all atomic arsenals combined?

As a self-proclaimed high-level military source involved in atmospheric research emailed me:

> From the basic theorems of the '60's and '70's, the modeling of the '80's and '90's, we probably have a basis for some large-scale experiments and might be glimpsing the results. Being an old 'weather mod' person, I've been accustomed to the adage that a little goes a long way. With proper conditions (most of the time in January and February) the striking of a match, pre-laced with Iodine, on a silver coin would turn a serene valley into a blinding snow storm in a short time."

Concurrent with this toxic sky spraying, in timing and location too drastic and too often occurring to be coincidence, epidemics of sudden, acute and sometimes fatal illness continue to occur among populations exposed to chemical clouds.

Widespread accounts of a "metallic taste" in the mouth, odors of petroleum, difficulty in breathing and other acute allergic reactions by observers on the ground suggest that the rapid fall-rate of highly allergenic JP-8 jet fuel, as well as other toxic chemicals present in varying spray mixes, may be major factors in adverse health reactions among residents of heavily sprayed areas.

The prevalence of fungal infections in 99% of surveyed sufferers from Chemtrail-Related Illness, and the growing belief among prominent health researchers that novel forms of fungi are responsible for many mystery ailments, lends credence to this author's theory that rapidly descending particulates in chemtrail fallout are bringing airborne bacteria, viruses and fungi "down to Earth" – and into lungs unprepared to confront these unfamiliar life-forms.

Even more disturbing are independent lab tests of samples obtained from deliberate low-level drops of cobweb-like and gel material that reveal a mix of pathogenic bacilli and molds capable of killing children, the elderly or those with weakened immune systems.

Weather modification and atmospheric amelioration can in no way be attributed to these low-level releases of biological "cocktails". The mix and concentration of these airdropped pathogens – along with telltale "bio-markers" and genetic engineering enzymes – are rarely if ever seen together in nature.

ANECDOTES, NOT ANTIDOTES

There is no indication that either the low-level or higher altitude spraying is an inoculation or antidote. But work is being done by the U.S. military to produce aerosolized vaccines intended not to be sprayed from aircraft but "misted" up the nose.

Filed June 5, 1995 by the Department of Defense, U.S. Patent 5756104 describes a "whole pathogen" intranasal/inhalation vaccine formulation. This highly experimental delivery method uses a "live" virus or bacteria versus the injection method that delivers an attenuated (killed) virus or bacteria. Whole pathogen inoculations, the patent notes, "may have undesirable side effects."

Besides working to invent intranasal inoculations, Maxygen Corporation has also developed air-deliverable anti-biological foam consisting of an enzyme commonly found in laundry detergents. This handy subtilisin is highly effective in breaking down bacterial cellular walls, causing the bacteria to literally explode into a harmless mass. Spraying subtilisin foam from tanker trucks or low-flying aircraft on affected areas or individuals would decontaminate them without using toxic substances like formaldehyde.

Chemtrails are not such a foam.

Chapter 15

WHAT YOU CAN DO

The people of this planet, as well as all other living creatures, urgently need to be informed and consulted on the chemtrail campaign taking place over homes, schools, burrows, nests and neighborhoods. Those responsible for clandestine chemtrail spraying must be held accountable.

It is urgent and essential that someone of conscience come forward with supporting documentation and the credentials necessary to expose and explain the chemtrail conundrum. While penalties for violating "national security" may include imprisonment, a growing chemtrail community is prepared to assist and defend any "whistle-blower" who comes forward with the answers so desperately needed by so many sick and anxious people.

Commensurate with the hearings that uncovered the truth behind the Gulf Biowar and resulting Gulf War Illness, a full congressional investigation must be called to question key FAA, CIA, CDC, EPA, USDA, and other administrative officials under oath.

The questions are simple:

1: "What is the purpose and who is behind the sudden concentrations of unmarked tanker-type aircraft emitting lingering white plumes in criss-crossing stripes, X's and grids over American towns and cities?"

2: "What is the purpose and who is responsible for low-level spraying by C-130 Hercules transports, military helicopters and other aircraft over Pegosa Springs and Fort Collins, Colorado; Burnet, Texas; Espanola, Ontario – and other towns across North America?

Accountability is crucial. Everyone concerned by chemtrails and biowarfare microbes must demand a full disclosure of *all* military weather modification experiments, as well as a publicly accessible monthly accounting of *all* experiments undertaken at *all* Level-4 and Level-5 bio-labs.

GREENPEACE BLINKS

Why doesn't an organization concerned with climate change and global warming grapple with a major climate modification experiment taking place directly overhead? There's an excellent chemtrail photo above their photovoltaic headquarters on the GP website.

> Aug. 16, 2000
>
> Hi, could you please let me know about all this UFO aircraft spraying out all these trails that plume out to large thin clouds, after-effects stinging eyes, congestion. Unmarked dark white aircraft with pluming exhaust coming out and expanding outward, Aug. 16, 2000 Vancouver BC completely bombarded – seen aircraft myself normal clouds going one way contrail/chemtrails going the other...I would like your explanation. Search a search engine or check out the page I gave you.
>
> - Jim

Dear Jim,

It does seem rather unusual and alarming. Greenpeace is aware of this issue, but unfortunately it is not one of our current campaigns. Greenpeace's worldwide campaigns are as follows: Climate, Oceans, Forests, Toxics, Nuclear and Genetic Engineering. Greenpeace Canada focuses on Climate, Forests, Nuclear and GMO.
Peace, Kathy

Hillary Clinton was a guest on the David Letterman show. "Does the government control the weather?" Letterman asked. Without hesitation she replied, "Yes."

A CHEMTRAILS COMMERCIAL

As a constant aerial advertisement of government duplicity, chemtrails can become a powerful catalyst for change. The quickest way to clue people into chemtrails is to show them photographs and videotape of these plume patterns.

Seeing is disbelieving official denials. Since what is happening right outside our windows isn't real until it's on TV, the best way to spread the word is to put chemtrails on big brother's brainwashing box. But don't wait for the big networks.

After receiving funding from a concerned businessman, I illustrated a short script with local and long-distance chemtrail photos and took the package to a major cable TV company. The resulting "Chemtrails 101" advertisement ran around the clock for a month on the "menu" channel of TV listings in the British Columbia capitol, as well as the viewing area surrounding the Comox air base.

The results were astonishing. As cable watchers began calling mainstream media, I began getting calls from newsrooms that had ignored a story taking place over their heads for the past two years. "Our phones are ringing off the hook, Mr. Thomas. We have to interview you."

Local newspapers were pulled into the story. Providing even more prominent and in-depth coverage than television, the weeklies interviewed local residents on all sides of the issue. The Comox brass went ballistic, angrily denouncing the "hoax".

But this move backfired when the Vancouver *Courier* ran a story featuring whistle-blower Terry Stewart. In this latest interview, Stewart revealed that his information of a "military operation" being conducted by USAF planes in local skies came from the Comox airbase.

OOPS!

Try treating yourself to the power of television. Contact you local media – radio, TV, newspapers. Insist on coverage of chemtrails in light of recent FAA revelations. Bring in your own chemtrails video and photos (or a copy of the "Chemtrails: Mystery Lines In The Sky" video), and have TV producers contact me for permission to rebroadcast. Give them websites such as *www.lifeboatnews.com*, www.*homestead.ca/chemtrails* and www.*chemtrailcentral.com*.

Organize a phone and fax campaign. *Persist* until this subject is covered completely and objectively.

Grab your best chemtrail photos and videotape and head immediately to your local cable TV station. Many cable TV managers will be happy to produce a 4-5 minute "public service" announcement on chemtrails - for free. Syndicated cable networks are reach large audiences keenly interested in local issues. Chemtrails communicators can access this grassroots outreach cheaply, or at no cost at all.

CALL THE COPS

Report blatant chemtrail activity to the Highway Patrol, sheriff or RCMP. Ask for a report to be filed. Then check with your local newspaper to make sure that it runs in their section displaying daily or weekly police reports.

As one American reports:

> We had beautiful weather here, and they began spraying nonstop. The first day it was so sunny, after spraying it became real cloudy, no sunset, and a repeat of the same the next day. I called the police last week, and they offered to send someone out for a report. I said you don't have to come out, just stick your head out the door and you can see for yourself. They are only six miles away - and certainly can be seen from City Hall.

> Don's muscles hurt all over his body, he's lethargic - sleeping a lot, and numbness in his extremities. He's outside quite a lot, and I think it's bothering him. He refuses to go to the hospital, or doctor. My cats are still sick, and I keep giving them medicine, they get a little better, and get sick again.

Contact the EPA, Environment Canada, and state, federal and provincial health officials. With an FAA official now on record revealing this climate-modification project involving squadrons of USAF tanker planes, do not accept "harmless contrails" bafflegab.

AIR POWER

Call your nearest air force base. Ask to speak to liaison person coordinating with the U.S. Air Force weather modification for your region.

Call your nearest Air Traffic Control center during stepped up chemtrail activity. Ask to speak to the ATC manager. Ask what is going on. ATC managers have now been instructed to tell concerned callers on the U.S. east coast that they are seeing "a military operation". Insist on details of this military operation, it's objectives and duration.

JUST SAY NOPE

Fill out and submit the electronic petitions available on (USA) and through (Canada) for chemtrail cessation and disclosure.

Demand from your political representative civilian oversight - and complete monthly accounting - of *all* experiments at *all* level 4 and level 5 biolabs.

Protect your family against the new microbes by strengthening immune systems through healthy food and habits. Never underestimate the power of prayer. Celebrate every victory. Give thanks always for the gift of life, and the chance to make the better differences our children will inherit.

GETTING SAMPLES TESTED

Short of running a chemtrail-sniffing Learjet up the back end of a KC-135, sampling rain or snow falling through chemtrails-saturated skies is the best way to zero in on emissions that violate environmental, FAA and international regulations.

Collecting soil samples is tricky because of its contamination by naturally occurring organisms and human-produced metals and toxins. Instead, collect chemtrail rain or snow in sterile glass trays arrayed on a table in your back yard. Then carefully decant your samples into smaller sterile glass jars and take them to the nearest water-testing company, listed in the yellow pages.

While testing for microorganisms costs hundreds of dollars, simple tests for aluminum, barium and quartz typically cost $35 or less.

Do not mention "chemtrails". Instead, when you pick up the results, ask if the levels of aluminum, barium and/or quartz found in the samples appear to be elevated above levels the lab has been used to seeing. If so – and especially if lab technicians express surprise at the readings – check with university geology departments or your state's agricultural department for baseline readings of regional soil analysis going back three decades or longer. The resulting trend lines will show if your lab tests represent an unusual "spike" in these readings.

If so, your next stop is to local health officials with your evidence. Do not mention "chemtrails". Instead, ask if the levels of aluminum and barium (for example) represent a health threat. Both are toxic if ingested by humans.

If any official concerned with agriculture and/or human health expresses concern, you have a media story. Take your air-and-soil pollution story – with contact phone numbers – to your local radio, TV and newspaper(s). Do not mention chemtrails.

Once coverage begins, the next step is to start asking where these contaminants might be coming from. If no new industrial sources are a factor, it's time to start asking about overflights of large aircraft observed emitting lingering plumes over the region. What you're after are radar tapes from the nearest Air Traffic Control facility for the dates/times of observed chemtrail spraying. Contact Greenpeace, Sierra Legal Defense or social advocacy groups for instruction on how to file a Freedom of Information Act (FOIA) request for tower logs and radar tapes.

If your FOIA application is blocked, go back to the media and shout the words "cover-up". Loudly. If your request is approved, check the tower records and radar tapes for military tankers making circuits in "commanded" airspace that excludes all other aircraft. If the tankers show up, their radar "returns" should show lengthy, comet-like trails of particulates. Other commercial jets on the same segment of tape will show normal contrails, or no contrails at all. As long as you refrain from making unsubstantiated allegations, plenty of aviation buffs will be willing to lend their expertise in solving this aerial "mystery".

CHEMTRAILS OR CONTRAILS?

Don't be conned by contrails. To settle the debate concerning whether or not particular plumes are contrails or chemtrails, call your local airport or weather office and ask for temperature and dew point (humidity) for 35,000 feet at the date, time and location of your photographed or videotaped sighting. Ask what scheduled flights were in the area. Ask a weather expert if those conditions permit normal contrail formation.

Chances are, it will be "Gotcha!" time! You now have enough documented evidence to insist on detailed answers concerning any laws broken and hazards posed by large aircraft spraying observable contaminants into the skies over people, crops, water reservoirs and wildlife.

Next step is to contact any surviving member of the recently gutted Environmental Protection Agency. Remember, it is your right to demand a public environmental assessment of these spraying activities. Armed with enough evidence, aggrieved citizens may eventually proceed with a class-action lawsuit to force full disclosure of these aerial operations. And compensation for loss of the enjoyment of peace and serenity, and exposure to possible health hazards from chemtrail fallout.

Good luck! Check out my website: www.willthomas.net. And please keep me posted at: rwt@telus.net

BRINGING HAARP TO HEEL

In February 1998, the European Parliament's Committee on Foreign

Affairs, Security and Defense Policy held public hearings in Brussels on the HAARP program. A "Motion for Resolution" submitted by the committee to the European Parliament:

> Considers HAARP by virtue of its far-reaching impact on the environment to be a global concern and calls for its legal, ecological and ethical implications to be examined by an international independent body; [the Committee] regrets the repeated refusal of the United States Administration to give evidence to the public hearing into the environmental and public risks [of] the HAARP program.

The parliamentary committee went on to produce a "Green Paper" on "the environmental impacts of military activities".

CLOUD BUSTERS

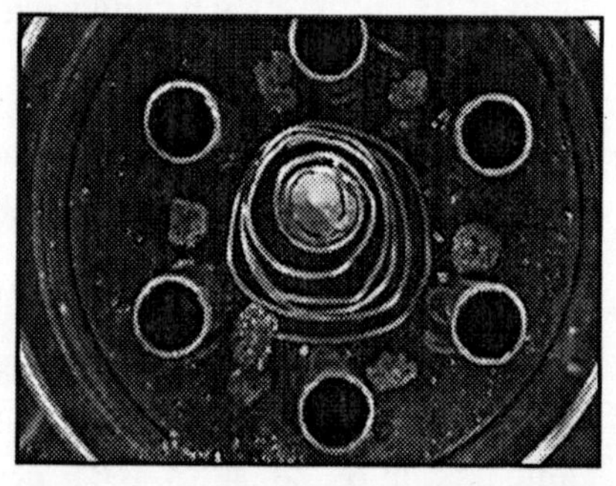

Sticking six crystal-tipped copper pipes in a pair of buckets, dowsers Don Croft and his wife Carol constructed a modified Wilhelm Reich "orgone generator" which they claim drains harmful energy from the atmosphere. Including chemtrails.

A Canadian chemtrail watcher wrote to say he had finished assembling a Chemtrail Buster that uses the principles Wilhelm Reich developed in his "cloudbuster":

He described how:

> A guy named Don Croft and his wife came up with this design. It's a good one, as it poses no threat to the operator or the environment. There is one in Victoria, another either on its way or operating in Vancouver and more in Spokane and Seattle. Each unit has an effective range of about 50 miles, but when more are in vicinity there appears to be a field effect that increases the distance. Apparently the 300 miles between Seattle and Spokane is covered by two units.

> I'd like to see one on the Sunshine Coast and a few more around Vancouver. This is spreading over the Internet. There are CBs in seven countries now. It is refreshing to know that we can do something this proactive. I'm looking forward to clearer skies!
> [www.metatech.org/cloudbuster_&_orgone_generator.html]

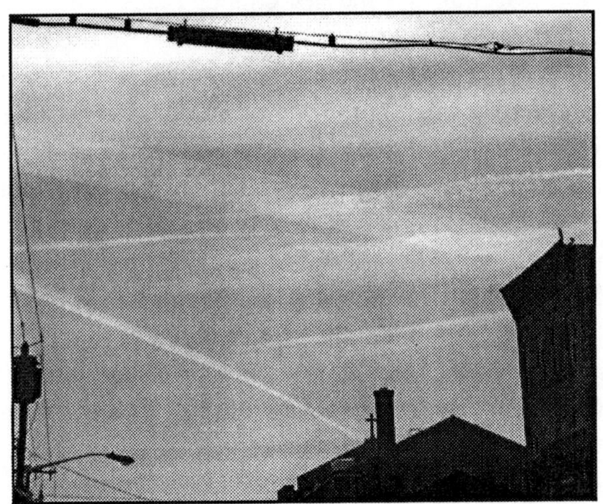

Virginia March 7, 2002

His sister and brother in Virginia will be building their own air defense system in Virginia. "They really get bombarded up there, near Plattsburgh Air Force Base."

Originally invented by orgone-energy guru Wilhelm Reich to coax rain out of dry skies, this improved model is said to be as safe and effective as any detergent.

Croft's daughter confirms that the aura produced by the magical machine is a "healthy blue orgone" energy. As the co-inventor explains:

> Making an orgone generator in a two gallon bucket and sticking copper pipes straight up out of it draws harmful orgone into the generator from many miles around and it goes out as healthy orgone in all directions...This gradual effect may explain why it sometimes takes a cloudbuster up to a week to get enough good stuff up to the 20,000' + altitude to disappear the chemtrails. The average radius for effective chemtrail

> destruction by a cloudbuster seems to be about thirty miles. It's not necessary to point this model to remove the chemtrails. It will do that for up to a fifty-mile radius if it's just left standing in the garden or on the deck.

The idea is to draw deleterious orgone energy down into the chembuster's resin base through the six copper pipes. This DOR is then transmuted into positive orgone energy!

Proponents of crystal-powered "chembusters" insist they work without dangerously disrupting atmospheric energy like Reichian "Orgone Generators" tend to do if overused.

One innovator "angled the pipes/bucket out the front window of my car on the nine-hour trip home yesterday and watched the sky clear all around me as I drove south. Now *that* was simply unbelievable, to see how much of the cloud cover was actually chemtrails! This is sooooo much fun! For less than $200, you can change the world!"

Another man relates how, after he and his sister built a "chemtrail buster" one Sunday in northern New York: "When the resin in the bucket, embedded with six short copper pipes (each containing a quartz crystal) had dried/cured, we added the six long copper pipes and Voila! The chemtrails started disappearing! Absolutely incredible!"

You can buy a six-foot "chembuster" on the Internet for $200 plus shipping.

Ken Adachi is another enthusiast. Finally, after all the emails, chatrooms, photographs and video footage, we can *do something* about chemtrails, he says.

There are other benefits to being around clean "orgone" energy: "Anyone who has been in the presence of a chembuster knows that the local environment becomes less heavy, the sky looks bluer, the air feels clearer, and there seems to be a 'lifting' of mood," Adachi writes.

"Birds will come around singing and a light breeze will kick up. Hundreds of people have experienced this first hand. This is exactly what you notice from a clear mountain top environment, an environment rich in OR atmospheric orgone energy."

He adds, "Many people who have set up a chembuster on their patio or in their garden have had the fun experience of seeing a black helicopter visit them and hover 150 feet over their house, usually at 2 AM in the morning. (Gee, are they trying to send a message?)"

Adachi recommends checking weather radar screens on the Internet after activating your own pipes. "You will see a circular blue ball on the radar map that's just about centered over your chem-buster." If you have a Kirlian photograph taken of your chembuster, "you will see an immense 'aura' of blue surrounding it."

Frederick from Spokane: "When we observed chemtrails overhead we directed the cloudbuster at them and saw them breakup. The same was repeated the following day. This simple technology is affecting our environment in a very positive manner. It is truly grass roots and I feel blessed to be a part of it."

All I know from first-hand experience is that during an exceptionally chemtrail assault, I called a man on a neighboring island who had his "chembuster" aimed at the crosshatched sky. "Why are those chemtrails still there?" I asked.

He didn't know.

LA Rick's chembuster in action...

10 minutes later...

[Plans on the Web] [See also: www.there4iam.com/CBusters.html+; www.there4iam.com/itsworking.html]

CONGRESSIONAL FUROR OVER CHEMTRAILS

More down-to-Earth chemtrail combatants are taking a legislative approach. On October 2, 2001, Democratic Representative Dennis Kucinich brought a bill to ban chemtrails before Congress.

Kucinich's "Space Preservation Act of 2001" was intended "To preserve the cooperative, peaceful uses of space for the benefit of all human-kind by permanently prohibiting the basing of weapons in space by the United States, and to require the President to take action to adopt and implement a world treaty banning space-based weapons."

En route to the Committee on Science, and the Committees on Armed Services and International Relations, House Resolution 2977 reaffirmed the National Aeronautics and

Space Act of 1958, which states that it "is the policy of the United States that activities in space should be devoted to peaceful purposes for the benefit of all mankind."

While permitting peaceful space exploration, Section 3of the new bill calls for a "Permanent Ban On Basing Of Weapons In Space". The President shall—

(1) Implement a permanent ban on space-based weapons of the United States and remove from space any existing space-based weapons of the United States; and

(2) Immediately order the permanent termination of research and development, testing, manufacturing, production, and deployment of all space-based weapons of the United States and their components.

The "Definitions" Section 7 of the bill seeks to ban "exotic weapons" – including "psychotronic" mind-control, plasma and particle beams, or electromagnetic weapons such as HAARP. According to HR2977: "The term 'exotic weapons systems' includes weapons designed to damage space or natural ecosystems (such as the ionosphere and upper atmosphere) or climate, weather, and tectonic systems with the purpose of inducing damage or destruction upon a target population or region on earth or in space."

Section 7 also prohibits "expelling chemical or biological agents in the vicinity of a person" – including "chemtrails".

As Kucinich told reporter Bob Fitrakis, "The truth is there's an entire program in the Department of Defense, 'Vision for 2020,' that's developing these weapons."

Released by the U.S. Space Command in 1998, "Vision for 2020" calls for "Full Spectrum Dominance" of space, land, sea and air superiority. Total military control of Planet Earth and near-Earth orbit by the world's sole superpower is the final step in achieving the Bush "National Security Strategy", which authorizes "first-strike" use of nuclear weapons in order to assure "global domination" by the United States.

As the news of HR2977 lit up the chemtrails community like a thunderbolt, the furor in the Science Committee threatened to scuttle a bill aimed primarily at keeping weapons out of space. HR3616 was quickly substituted. Submitted on Jan. 23, 2002, this new "Space Preservation Act of 2002" omitted all mention of "chemtrails".

> Section 7 (appendix) of bill HR2977 prohibits…"chemtrails".

As Carol Rosin, President of the Institute for Cooperation in Space, explained to outraged chemtrails activists, the switched bills many saw as a betrayal "simply makes it likely that more congress representatives will sign-on to the bill with less debate and controversy."

As Rosin elaborated, "the 'chemtrail' issue…and other specific weapon systems were becoming a distraction from the intent of the bill. It is time for everyone to rise above the negatives and their differences, and to help get this World Treaty and legislation signed into law before Bush breaks the ABM Treaty – at which time he will deploy space-based weapons under the guise of *merely* testing."

HR2977, the original "Space Preservation Act of 2002", also sought to ban devices for inflicting death or injury on…biological life, bodily health, mental health, or physical and economic well-being of a person...through the use of land-based, sea-based, or space-based systems using radiation, electromagnetic, psychotronic, sonic, laser, or other energies directed at individual persons or targeted populations for the purpose of information war, mood management, or mind control of such persons or populations; or by expelling chemical or biological agents in the vicinity of a person.

After looking at the replacement bill, Len Horowitz protested: "In the new bill, however, all of these protections were removed leaving citizens susceptible to control and attack with such "exotic weapons systems" directed by agencies and organizations" detailed in his extensively documented books.

While a presidential contender, Kucinich reportedly replied to a questioner at a May 2003 public rally in Santa Cruz with the honesty and directness he is known for:

"Chemtrails are real," he said.

But un the political "massaging", triage and horse-trading that invariably takes place around newly introduced legislation – especially controversial House Resolutions, provisions not deemed essential to passage of the bill are jettisoned in order to pass the bill into law with its primary objective intact.

Still, it was unfortunate that after the original bill's sponsors included "chemtrails" and similar "black" weapons projects, they were quick to delete them from what was in effect a substitute resolution. Alienating the international chemtrails community cost the "Peaceful Uses of Space:" movement large numbers of savvy, committed "blue sky" proponents as allies in the same fight to keep the US Aerospace Force from its avowed mission of "global domination".

Dennis Kucinich deserves major kudos for putting "chemtrails" on the Congressional agenda. After years of being called "hoaxters" and "UFO nuts", people who know what they are seeing, smelling, sampling and photographing is real can take heart that chemtrails are finally, officially on the Congressional record.

Remember, *no amendments have been made to the original HR-2977*. Technically, this bill still exists. It is still in the "referral" process before the same Science Committee whose protest led to its hasty withdrawal. HR-2977 can be revived at any time.

Jeremy Rifkin is another courageous public advocate. Rifkin could be running a riff on something as crazy as chemtrails when he says, "There is a certain arrogance in science, especially when a particular science is coming of age."

Vancouver, Canada

This arrogance, which has destroyed every culture that has gotten carried away with its own power, is rooted, he adds, "in the old Baconian science which is based on power."

BACON - AND EGGS IN OUR FACES

Sir Francis Bacon fried all of our bacon when he called nature a "common little harlot. She is wild. We must tame, squeeze, mould and shape her."

Good grief. With such profound ignorance of complementary male-female virtues and perspectives underlying Western science – and yin-yang's ancient imperatives for the complementary cooperation of females and male energies so far out of balance, it's no wonder a few arrogant idiots in command of a dying empire are spreading chemtrails to shroud the skies of our dying planet.

TURNING IT AROUND

It does not have to be this way.

Since we attract the kind of energy we put out, it is important that we calm our fears while we spend a few moments every day imagining how we would like to live and what kind of world we would prefer to live in.

Picture every detail of this scene starring yourself. Smell it. Feel it. Live it. *Be it.* A few minutes every day. (Write it down if you like.)

Do not dwell in fear and negativity unless that is the kind of world you intend to create. Because you will.

Take heart. No matter how dire things seem, remember that for every precipitous action there is an equal, opposing reaction. The Koran and the Bible sternly warn, "You will reap the whirlwind that you sow." These are laws of physics and karma. Even for George Bush and his junta, there are no exceptions.

In crisis, the Chinese say, comes opportunity. Looking at how critical are the breakdowns onboard our foundering space colony, just imagine the opportunities for breakthroughs!

But screaming and shouting and typing in ALL CAPS is not going to get the brakes on in time. Since it is clear that we are soon going to arrive at where we are going, it seems like a good plan to change course right away. "We must not only have a basis for discussion," Rifkin reminds us, "but an alternative vision."

Whatever country we live in, it is time to exercise the rights and freedoms we have left, on a daily basis. "Use it or lose it" is a military maxim that also applies directly to exercising our Constitutional rights, accessing the Worldwide Web, and speaking out individually and in citizens groups.

Remember: The "political will" for elected officials to act comes when enough of their constituents raise enough hell. Stay tuned. And keep phoning and emailing your local media and political representatives. The fight to take back our skies isn't over 'til the first pilot sings.

THE PRICE OF OUR ADDICTION

In early March, 1991 – shortly after the world's biggest oil spill began washing ashore at al Jubail – I was in the Saudi environmental headquarters in Dammam as the first hard numbers listing all known sources of oil washing into the Persian Gulf scrolled across an American scientist's computer screen. The 5.5 million barrel total equaled *25 Exxon Valdez* spills. "One-third of this oil," the American told me, "is the result of allied bombing."

Flying through eerie midday darkness, I made two coastal survey flights with the Royal Saudi Air Force. Shivering in bizarre bitter cold,

the stench of Sweet Kuwaiti crude clogging my nostrils, I aimed a camcorder through the helicopter's hatch at scenes of overwhelming desolation. Hour after hour, the chattering chopper flew at 100 knots over shores blackened by vast slicks extending beyond the horizon. Half of the Saudi coastline was heavily oiled; half of the precious mangrove "nurseries" destroyed. When the helicopter landed, no one could speak.

Fresh horrors awaited in Kuwait, where I joined two other members of Earth Trust shortly after liberation to form an environmental emergency response team.

Skirting sand-drifted mines and spreading lakes of Kuwaiti crude, we ventured daily into a creosoted desert.

Groping for breath and sanity beneath the headlight-snuffing gloom of a perpetual "oilcast", we found ourselves surrounded by a thousand blazing and gushing oil wells –all shrieking in a mad chorus of unearthly torment. Pumping gas into my portable carbon burner a decade later, every cell in my body knows where the hose to that gas pump really leads…

ANOTHER BIG LOSS OF *PRESTIGE*

The price of our addiction again hit the news when the supertanker *Prestige* broke in half and went down in deep water off the northwest coast of Spain. A vessel of varying provenance and pedigree, the ill-fated *Prestige* was transporting *twice the tankage* of the ill-fated *Exxon Valdez*.

Bummer, thought tens of millions of drivers listening to updates while idling in gridlocked herds of supertanker-supplied fossil fuel burners. As every Trekkie knows, fouling the air and turning up the heat inside a closed, recirculating, sunheated atmosphere is no way to run a space colony hurtling through the cold, irradiated vacuum of deep space.

As Extreme Weather Events and the march of microbes into warming northern climes threaten to overwhelm global insurers and the banks that back them, a few more trips down to the 7-11 could crash the global casino.

It might be a good idea to throw a few more cans of beans in the cupboard. As I learned in Kuwait, denial remains the strongest human propensity. Despite daily headlines of freakish lethal weather – and the prospect of rocketing more Middle East cities as a convenient distraction – the most sought after vehicle in the US today is a road-hogging replica of the military "Humvee". This road-hogging masturbatory model of American military prowess in killing "colored" children gets 10 miles to the gallon.

KEEP 'EM HUMMING

It would never play on Star Trek.

Especially when in order to keep all the "Hummers" humming – and all the tanks and bombers ready to blow up every disenfranchised "Two-Thirds Worlder" who complains – we continue to look the other way while raining endless streams of bombs on impoverished and defenseless families - held hostage to tyrants - who have done us no harm.

As I documented in *Scorched Eart*h, and my "Eco War" documentary video…fighting for oil burns a lot of oil.

It takes more than a half-million gallons to fuel a single armored division for one day. The seven carriers steaming to attack Iraq will consume more than *14 million gallons* of fuel to reach the Persian Gulf. And each Tomcat catapulted from their decks devours several hundred gallons of fuel *per minute* at full power. All told, the last 46 day war to ensure cheap prices at the pumps consumed some 20 million gallons of oil *each day* – while releasing another 40 to 60 million tons of globe-girdling, sulfur-laden soot from 1,000 burning and gushing wellheads over a span of 200 apocalyptic days.

PAYING THE PRICE

Is the price of our oil addiction too high? The chief air war planner during Desert Storm, retired Air Force Gen. G. Lee Butler, reminds us that the price we're paying for petroleum products does not reflect its true social and environmental costs.

Multiply what you're currently paying for a gallon of gasoline or a quart of oil by *four*, calculates this former architect of the last Oil War. That's how much you should be paying for filling up your Honda hybrid or SUV.

Americans facing $10 a gallon gas would not doubt grab their guns, form a posse and ride on Washington. But no amount of fury and fire-power can alter the reality of an increasingly rare oil drum. Even if Washington's empire builders get their grips on the planet's last big oil deposits, your corner "gas bar" is a few short decades from running out of cheap gasoline – just as global climate meltdown from pumping all that carbon into the air really kicks in.

Adhering to the new smug slogan NIML – "Not In My Lifetime" - some of us graying warriors and worriers may escape the final ecological reckoning.

But what about our children?

And their children?

And the offspring of all the species not yet driven to extinction by our mad rush to...where exactly? Ah, yes, to more profits for a few.

On Aug. 26, 2002 *The Guardian* headlined "Ecological decline 'far worse' than official estimates." A leaked report by 22 countries allied in an economic organization called the OECD warns that the greenhouse-warming carbon dioxide emissions currently causing erratic climate shifts are expected to more than double over the next 18 years as China, India and much of the teeming Two-Thirds World switch on their own carbon burners – from cars to coal-fired power plants. They don't have much money for filtering emissions. And one in five species of mammals are already extinct.

Are we next?

Mount Kilimanjaro – 1912

Mount Kilimanjaro – today

EXPIRY DATE

Satellites show that we're plundering the place at a pace outstripping our space colony's capacity to support life. With the latest readouts showing more than one-third of the natural world destroyed by humans over the past three decades, the World Wildlife Fund now says that our throwaway planet could "expire" by 2050.

Instead of lending a helping hand to offset all the money hemorrhaging from the impoverished South to the piggish North, the 22 OECD members contribute just .05% of their yearly income to the world's least developed countries. As the "Two-Thirds World" collapses under the press of population, ecological ruin, consumer expectations and debt - and resentment intensifies – the Pentagon will spend nearly $500 billion on weapons of mass destruction this year to keep the billions of people being ripped off in line.

Ensuring the essentials of daily life to everyone on Earth – thereby greatly reducing the likelihood of conflict – would cost about 1/50th as much, the Associated Press reported on May 10, 2002. As for the costs of curbing carbon emissions, it turns out that meeting Kyoto's international reduction targets could be *entirely reimbursed* from the subsidy currently handed to Big Oil. As the OECD report points out, this $57 billion oil handout currently buys a lot of pollution and global warming. Using the same money to cut climate change emissions *would have next to no effect on the global economy.*

RUNNING ON EMPTY

Like any addicts who refuse to admit the folly of their addiction, we insist that Everything Will Be Okay. But the "fill 'er up" fantasy that fueled the American dream - and every wannabe who followed – is about to be rudely interrupted by oil prices beyond the reach of all but the wealthy elite.

International oil expert Colin Campbell points out that per capita oil production has been declining since 1979. "Probable actual physical shortage of all liquid hydrocarbons worldwide won't appear for about 20 years," Campbell calculates.

We're already running on empty, with cheap, easy-to-obtain oil down to a measly one trillion barrels. These reserves include the much-hyped "sea" of Central Asian deposits. As Campbell explains, extensive "dry hole" exploratory wells now disclose separate "reefs" of pooled oil totaling perhaps 1/20th of earlier estimates.

Forget spreading chemtrails to prolong petroleum use. A better bet is to leave that oil in the ground – and expedite a planned, European-style transition to the post-petroleum future that is coming fast. It will take a lot of petroleum to produce the technologies that will take us beyond petroleum. So we'd better not wait to begin that transition until being forced into innovation when cheap oil runs out.

Even if a President-select does not spend America and the world into a fiscal wipe-out by spending *$11,000 a second* on weapons of yet more destruction into, the sudden cessation of "lo-cost" oil will crash the petroleum-addicted American empire as abruptly as their former Soviet rivals collapsed after blundering into the same regions for much the same reasons.

Oil experts agree that even with construction of the blood-drenched UNOCAL pipeline across Afghanistan, and the theft of Iraq's big deposits, we'll be seeing the last cheap oil sometime between 2020 and 2040.

The *World Oil Supply Report* predicts that oil prices "could double and treble within two or three years as the world changes from oil abundance to oil scarcity…which will occur sooner than many people believe."

As a self-appointed Caesar fiddles away his country's last best chances to opt for energies cleaner and cleverer than oil, Japanese automakers will soon be producing only hybrid gas-electric cars. [CBC News Nov. 26, 200] Europeans are already shifting from an Oil-Based Civilization to the Hydrogen Age. (HA!)

Filling up a hydrogen-powered car.

"This historic transition out of carbon-based fossil fuels and into renewable resources and a hydrogen future" comes, Jeremy Rifkin remarks, "when the US is desperately holding on to the past."

While Bush stayed home from last summer's World Environmental Summit, the EU showed up in force and lobbied hard for a worldwide goal of 15% renewable energy by the year 2010. Rifkin reports that the EU "has already set its own internal target of 22% renewable energy for the generation of electricity, and 12% of all energy coming from renewable sources by 2010."

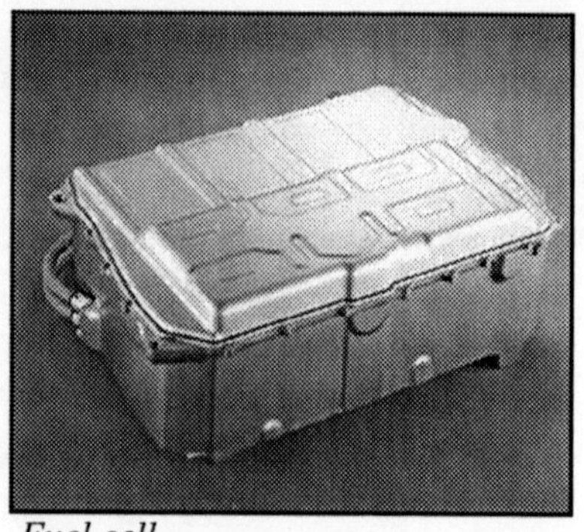

Fuel cell

In a contrast that could prove catastrophic for US competitiveness, while Exxon-Mobil maneuvered to scuttle Kyoto, European energy giant BP had already changed its strategies and its moniker to "Beyond Petroleum".

At Royal Dutch/Shell, chairman Philip Watts told *The Guardian* in the fall of 2002 that his oil company colossus is already making the transition from the hydrocarbon to the hydrogen economy.

Back in a drought and tornado-ravaged USA, all incentives are backwards. Why should Washington's oil administration switch when petroleum remains among the lowest-taxed industries? According to the Institute on Taxation and Economic Policy, had all US oil companies paid the full 35% tax (instead of only 5.7%) on their $735 billion profits from 1996-1998, their federal income taxes would have totaled $257 billion.

That's a lot of electric bicycles.

THOSE AMBER WAVES OF GRAIN

"The simple solution is to use less," Campbell concludes. "We are extremely wasteful energy users. But it involves a fundamental change of attitude and the rejection of classical economic principles, which were built on endless growth in a world of limitless resources. Those days are over."

New days are already dawning. Gen. Butler now heads the Clean Fuels Foundation. Producing ethanol and other biofuels from feed grains and seeds is already big in Brazil, where all cars run on ethanol or transitional blends of 22 percent ethanol/78 percent gasoline or 99 percent ethanol. "They run well and the public is pleased," Butler boasts. "Air quality in Sao Paulo, Brazil, with a population of 14 million, is better than in Los Angeles, New York City or Houston, Texas."

The general's remarks followed an Oct. 2002 article by former CIA director R. James Woolsey, saying, "Replacing gasoline with biomass-derived ethyl alcohol would greatly reduce man-made greenhouse-gas emissions...Over the past 15 years the cost of producing a gallon of alcohol from corn has been cut in half, to about $1 a gallon. If the new technology were to make it possible for costs to fall another 30 to 40 cents, alcohol would become competitive with gasoline when oil reaches around $25 a barrel."

Which will be very soon. What Exxon-Mobil doesn't want you to know is that you can run your jalopy on grass clippings – right past enslaving, ecocidal gas stations.

TURN HERE?

Just follow the signs to the hydrogen exit. As Rifkin riffs: "A change in energy regimes of this magnitude over the course of the next half century is likely to have as profound an impact on human society as the harnessing of coal and steam power more than three centuries ago. The fossil-fuel era forever changed our living patterns, our notion of commerce and governance, and the values we live by. So too will the coming hydrogen economy."

The Manhattan Institute and General Electric are just as jubilant. In a joint press release proclaiming "The Coming Hydrogen Economy", these major manipulators gushed: "The miracle of this new power is the huge amount of energy it will generate, [utilizing] the most abundant element of earth, hydrogen."

"Not so fast!" shouts Lifeboat News editor and oil watcher Paul Grignon, who points out that the smokestack energy required to manufacture "clean" windmills, solar panels, tidal and geothermal plants largely negates any subsequent savings in petroleum and pollution.

As for the hydrogen "miracle", the dirty energy needed to pry enough H loose from its atomic H20 bonds to fuel our widely copied consumer culture is prohibitive.

"Hydrogen cars would indeed leave city air wonderfully clean," Grignon writes, "providing the city is not downwind of the coal-fired plant which burns coal at 40% efficiency to produce the electricity used to produce the hydrogen at 40% efficiency – which is then rebonded with oxygen at 40% efficiency"- delivering through fuel cells an "*end use just 6.4% of the original energy in the coal.*"

So don't burn coal to make hydrogen to power fuel cells. In that case, Grignon continues, "In order to be truly clean and sustainable, it will have to be generated from *present time* solar input, geothermal and gravitational forces, via thermal plants, solar panels, bacterial or enzymatic reaction, wind or ocean-driven mechanical power or hydroelectricity."

The catch is, there aren't enough clean means to "crack" enough water molecules to replace our planetary petroleum addiction with a hydrogen addiction. Even "unlimited" solar energy in the form of wind, tides and photons of sunlight "only arrives at a steady rate, in a very diffuse form," Grignon grouses. "It will be extremely difficult, if not impossible to extract as much usable energy for human use as we have been accustomed to, having had 400 *million years* of *stored* sunlight at our disposal in the form of fossil fuels."

Pointing to GE's real agenda, Grignon concludes: "There is a very real possibility that the only way hydrogen can ever stand any chance of being 'abundant' in the sense of perpetuating our glorious consumer society is if it were made with electricity generated in nuclear power plants. Tens of thousands of them." And General Electric, Grignon points out, "is the only remaining player in the nuclear power plant business."

NOW WHAT?

If the premise behind any "unlimited" energy source is unlimited consumption, forget it. All energy (except nuclear "breeder" reactors) is finite in the sense that it can only be produced – at decreased efficiency – from other forms of energy. "Unlimited consumption" is another name for cancer.

Avoiding the radioactive paradox of using nuke plants to produce "clean" hydrogen fuel in order to power planet-wrecking consumption brings us back to the only sure way to provide a clean energy future – or any future at all. When faced with total systems failure onboard any spaceship, the first step is to immediately Turn Off All Nonessential Machinery.

We must lift our collective feet off the petroleum pedal. Or pray that gasoline is quickly priced at its true value – currently around $100 a barrel, figures the General Accounting Office, once you tot up the environmental and health care costs from pursuing petroleum, and all the lost jobs as the world's sole Superpower keeps writing worthless IOU's on a compounding $7 trillion debt. [*PR Newswire* Dec. 5, 2002]

Park your personal carbon burner. For local self-transportation, put wheels on your feet, use a bicycle or an electric bike, share other carbon burners already in operation. Or celebrate three million years of nomadic exploration by using both feet to walk *away* from convenience stores. There is nothing convenient about the Sixth Great Extinction Event currently underway.

AMERICANS FAVOR ALTERNATIVE ENERGY

It's not that Americans don't want to embrace Sol Power. It's simply that an oil junta has hijacked the world's biggest energy consumers, and the Big Oil backers like Enron and Halliburton who paid big bucks to see them take power.

As this book goes to press, the results of a Gallup survey show that 91% of those polled favor investing in alternative sources of energy – including solar, wind, and fuel cells.

The poll was conducted Nov. 8-11, 2001. Given what *TIME* magazine calls, "The Mess In Iraq", the numbers of war-weary Americans favoring alt. energy independence are probably even higher than 9 out of 10. [*EarthVision Environmental News* Dec. 3, 2001]

ONE-THIRD

Here's what we can do right now to stop the killing and slow the gathering onslaught of climate catastrophe Greenpeace co-founder Robert Hunter calls, "Thermageddon". Aim to cut your personal energy bill by one-third. It's not that tough. Just turning lights and appliances down or off, leaving cars parked and woodstoves unlit can buy some time to make more changes.

Curtailing torrents of wasted energy will reduce the overloads on our space colony's failing life-support systems, allowing these living webs to begin reconnecting and regenerating. As we pare down our personal and industrial energy needs, as our machines shrink and grow "smarter" in their power usage, energy efficiency guru

Amory Lovins told me that eliminating one-third of wasted energy would negate the need to drill in the fragile Arctic. Or go to war over imported Middle Eastern oil.

Hunter and Amory Lovins

Ending our oil addiction is more about changing our minds than changing technologies. Questioning our daily habits and assumptions leads naturally to reducing consumption.

The most effective way to deal with the oil, warmaking and nuclear mafias is to simply walk away.

CREATE A CHEMTRAIL "NO FLY ZONE" OVER YOUR HOMETOWN

Angry over constant chemtrailing, and determined not to take it any more, two brothers have turned the city of Victoria into a No-Fly Zone for chemtrail aircraft. On Friday April 17th, Ben called the Victoria International Airport to complain about large aircraft flying in close proximity to each other over this busy capitol. He told the airport manager, "You've got a bunch of hot dog pilots crisscrossing all over the place. It looks like the Snowbirds." (The Canadian Air Force eight-plane aerobatic team).

The official told him he had no proof.

"We've got five hours of tape," Ben corrected him. "We've got four jets on tape flying within ten seconds of each other. They are billowing out exhaust all over the place, and they are endangering public safety."

The official then said, "I don't know whose planes those are."

"You guys should know who's flying over Victoria airport," Ben chastised. "That means you have no control of the planes."

"That's not true," the official said, a bit more heatedly.

"I thought you just said that you don't know who's planes those are," Ben reminded him. "It's a circus. If this keeps occurring to go to have a class action lawsuit on your hands.'

"That scared them," Ben told me.

His brother James confirmed that no spray planes have overflown Victoria since their conversation with the airport authority.

But the brothers didn't stop there.

During the spraying, a freak hailstorm turned to rain. James a rinsed out his plastic cup and collected some rainwater pouring off the roof of his van. Holding the cup under a light, the brothers saw the bottom of the cup covered in shiny silver particles.

When they took it to a water-testing lab for analysis, two lab technicians took a quick look and said, "That amount shouldn't be there."

Both lab technicians were aware of – and angry about – chemtrails. They gave Ben and James proper lab containers, along with instructions on how to take two separate samples for analysis at a bigger lab in Vancouver.

The brothers strongly recommend that when placing a call to local airport officials, don't use the word "chemtrails".

"I acted like I didn't know what was going on," Ben told me. His complaint centered solely on "public endangerment" from aircraft flying to close together. This is illegal over populated areas. And their videotape evidence was the clincher. "They didn't like to hear about a class action lawsuit," Ben said.

The brothers also complained about what appeared to be "heavy pollution" coming from the tightly spaced jets.

The videotape evidence of four large aircraft flying within ten seconds of each other is enough to take to court.

Controllers say that airliners at cruising altitude are not allowed to fly to within twenty minutes of each other. Except for landings and takeoffs, airliners at cruising altitudes cannot fly close together in time or space. Military aircraft are also prohibited from discharging fuel or other pollutants over populated areas. Nor are they allowed to endanger people on the ground.

At least not over North America.

When all else fails – get together and sue the bums! This time, we will win.

William Thomas
Gulf Islands, Canada
May 2004

SOME AREAS REPORTING CHEMTRAIL ACTIVITY

Albuquerque, Amsterdam (**Netherlands**), Asheville, Aspen, Athens (**Greece**), Atlanta, Austin, Baltimore, Barcelona (**Spain**), Birmingham **(England**), Bakersfield, Bangor, Belgium, Boise, Bozeman, Brooklyn, Buffalo, Buford, Byron Bay (**Australia**), Calgary (**Canada**), Canberra (**Australia**), Charlotte, Cheyenne, Chicago, Cincinnati, Clayton, Cleveland, Columbus, Dallas, Denver, Espanola (**Canada**), **Falmouth** (UK), **Fargo** Flagstaff, Flint, Galesburg, Glasgow (**Scotland**), Gresham, Harrison, Heemskerk (**Holland**), **Henån** (Sweden), Houston, Hundred Mile House (**Canada**), Huntsville, Isle of Man (**UK**), Istanbul (**Turkey**) Jonesboro, Kansas City, Karoo (South Africa), Knoxville, Lancaster (**UK**), Lansing, Las Vegas, Lexington, Little Rock, London, Los Angeles, Mallorca (**Spain**), Mannheim (**Germany**), Memphis, Miami, Moab, Moose Jaw (**Canada**), Naples (**Italy**), Nashville, Nelson (**Canada**), Oakville, Omaha, Orust (**Croatia**), Parhump, Paris (**France**), Penticton (**Canada**), Peoria, Philadelphia, Pingelly (**Australia**), Phoenix, Pittsburgh, Portland, Quirindi (**Australia**), Reno, Rijeka (**Croatia**), Richmond, Rockford, Sacramento, Salem, Sallisaw, Salt Lake, San Antonio, San Francisco, Santa Fe, Sarasota, Seattle, Scotland (**UK**), Sonora, South Wales (**UK**), Spokane, Springfield, Stuttgart (**Germany**), **Switzerland**, Tampa, Times Square, Toronto **(Canada),** Tucson, Valdez, Vancouver **(Canada),** Venice **(Italy), Versailles** (France), Victoria **(Canada)**, Walnut Creek, Waukesha, Wilmette, Wuerzburg **(Germany).**

Ancient Chinese proverb:
"You can call a chicken a donkey. But it is still a chicken."

Modern Western proverb:
"You can call a chemtrail a contrail. But it is still a chemtrail."

Printed in the United States
41610LVS00003B/43-90

9 781893 157101